Gerald Holowaty
24238 Cottage Lane
Warren, Michigan 48089

R. C. SMITH

Southern Alberta
Institute of Technology

MATERIALS OF
CONSTRUCTION

McGRAW-HILL

BOOK COMPANY

New York

St. Louis

San Francisco

London

Toronto

Sydney

MATERIALS OF CONSTRUCTION

58476

456789 HDBP 754321069

PREFACE

The construction industry is growing and evolving, constantly seeking new and better materials for building and more efficient uses for old ones. The list of construction materials is constantly growing and a basic knowledge of the important ones is essential to anyone engaged in the designing and planning, estimating, or actual construction of a building.

Manufacturers of building materials publish excellent descriptions of specific products. A great many books have been written on particular materials or allied groups of materials. Others have been written covering basic construction materials.

One purpose of this book is to present, for students or others who are not particularly familiar with building construction the fundamental aspects of all the important materials used in modern construction. It will not take the place of those books or brochures dealing exhaustively with one particular material.

The second purpose is to give a brief description of how some of these materials can be used to the best advantage. Again, manufacturers publish descriptions and detailed drawings on the recommended methods of using a specific product, and interested persons should avail themselves of this technical information whenever necessary.

It is the author's hope that this book will serve to introduce many materials to the reader and that this introduction may be instrumental in promoting a search for more detailed information on specific materials.

The information available in this book has been made possible through the kind cooperation of a great many organizations and manufacturers, to whom I wish to acknowledge a deep appreciation. They have all been most helpful to me and I am sure that they will continue to be equally as helpful to anyone who seeks further information on any of the materials discussed in these pages. A list of contributing companies and organizations follows.

R. C. SMITH

LIST OF
CONTRIBUTORS

Aluminum Company of Canada, Limited
Alliance Wall Corp.
American Concrete Institute
Anaconda Company
The Arborite Company, Division of Domtar
 Construction Materials, Ltd.
British Columbia Lumber Manufacturers'
 Association
Bethlehem Steel Co.
Better Finishes & Coatings Co.
Besser Technical Center
Building Products of Canada Limited
Building Stone Institute
Canadian Institute of Steel Construction
Canadian Sheet Steel Building Institute
Canadian Pulp and Paper Association
Canadian Industries Limited
Canadian Wood Development Council
Canadian Lumbermen's Association
Canadian Johns-Manville Co., Limited
Canadian Standards Association
Celotex Corp.
Chambers Brothers Company
Chisholm, Boyd & White Co.
CIBA Products Company
Ciment Fondu Lafarge Corp.
Columbia Acoustics & Fireproofing Co.
Consolidated Concrete Limited
Crown Zellerbach Corporation
Dominion Foundries and Steel, Limited
Domtar Construction Materials Ltd.
Dow Chemical Co.
Expanded Shale, Clay and Slate Institute
Evertex Co. Ltd.
Fiberglas Canada, Limited
The Flintkote Company of Canada Limited

Harris Mfg. Co.
Hewitt-Robins, Inc.
Industrial Development Office, Saskatchewan
International Panel Boards Limited
Indiana Limestone Co.
The Jeffrey Manufacturing Co.
Libby-Owens-Ford Glass Co.
The Master Builders Co., Limited
McCready Products Ltd.
Minnesota Mining & Mfg. Co.
Mississippi Glass Co.
National Concrete Masonry Association
National Research Council
Pilkington Bros. Ltd.
Pittsburgh Plate Glass Co.
Pittsburgh Corning Corporation
Plywood Manufacturers' Association of British
 Columbia
Posey Iron Works, Inc.
Portland Cement Association
Red Cedar Shingle & Handsplit Shake Bureau
Sonoco Products Co.
Southern Pine Inspection Bureau
Southern Pine Association
The Steel Co. of Canada, Limited
Stramit Corporation Ltd.
Structural Clay Products Institute
Thiokol Chemical Corp.
Tremco Mfg. Co.
United States Steel Corporation
United States Ceramic Tile Co.
Vermiculite Institute
Western Gypsum Products, Limited
Western Perlite Co. Ltd.
W. R. Grace & Co. of Canada Ltd.

CONTENTS

Exam on: 1, 2, 3, 4,
6, 7, 8, 9, 10,
17, 19, 21.

TABLES

MATERIALS OF CONSTRUCTION

1

WOOD

Throughout the ages man has used wood for a variety of purposes—as a fuel, as a building material, in weapons, and in transportation. With the development of science and engineering, wood has been replaced by other materials in many instances, but at the same time there has been a tremendous increase in the number and variety of products made either directly or indirectly from wood.

Wood has always been a prominent material in the construction industry for many reasons. It is one of the traditional building materials. It is easily worked, has durability and beauty. It has great ability to absorb shocks from sudden loads. In addition, wood has freedom from rust and corrosion, is comparatively light in weight, and is adaptable to a countless variety of purposes.

It is only within comparatively recent times that men have begun to realize that the accessible supply of wood for lumber was not inexhaustible. Sound conservation techniques must be applied to the sources of supply if it is to continue as a competitive material in the field of construction. This need for conservation has resulted in a great deal of work and study on forest care and management, reforestation, identification and control of tree pests and diseases, and prevention and control of forest fires.

STRUCTURE OF WOOD

Wood is useful as a building material because of the manner in which a tree forms its fibers, growing by the addition of new material to the outer layer just under the bark and preserving its old fibers as it adds new ones.

Looking at a cross section of a tree, as illustrated in Fig. 1·1, one can see that the trunk consists of a series of concentric rings covered by a layer of bark. Each ring represents one year of tree growth and is called an *annual ring*. This growth takes place just under the bark, in the *cambium* layer. The cells which are formed there are long, thin tubular fibers composed mainly of *cellulose*. They are bound together by a substance known as *lignin*, which connects them into bundles. These bundles of fibers run the length of the tree and carry food from the roots to the branches and leaves.

1

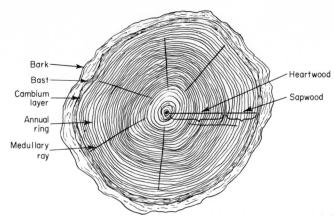

Figure 1 · 1
Cross section of tree.
(British Columbia Lumber Manufacturers'
Association)

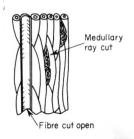

Figure 1 · 2
Magnified view along fibers.

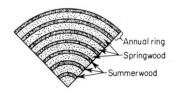

Figure 1 · 3
Section of annual rings.

Running at right angles to these fibers, from the outer layer inward, are other groups of cells known as *medullary rays*. These carry food from the inner bark (*bast*) to the cambium layer and act as storage tanks for food. These rays are more pronounced in some species, such as oak, than others but are present in all trees. Figure 1 · 2 illustrates a group of cells running lengthwise with the cut ends of medullary rays running across them.

As one layer of wood succeeds another, the cells in the inner layers die, cease to function for food storage, and become useful only to give the tree stiffness. This older wood is known as *heartwood* and is usually darker in color, drier, and harder than the living layer, the *sapwood*.

In many kinds of trees each annual ring is divided into two layers, as shown in Fig. 1 · 3. The inner layer consists of cells with relatively large cavities and thin walls, as a result of more rapid spring growth. This is the *springwood*. Later in the year the cells grow more slowly and have thick walls and small cavities; this heavier, harder, stronger material is called the *summerwood*. The amount of summerwood is one measure of the density of the wood; the higher the density the greater the strength.

CLASSIFICATION OF TREES

Trees generally are divided into two groups, *hardwoods* and *softwoods*. Botanists refer to the former as "deciduous," trees that have broad leaves which are normally shed in the fall. Softwoods are called "conifers," trees that have needles rather than leaves and that bear their seeds in cones.

The term hardwood or softwood applied to a particular species does not necessarily indicate the relative hardness of that particular kind of wood. Some trees in the hardwood class, such as basswood or poplar, are softer than the average softwood. Longleaf southern pine and Douglas fir, on the other hand, both in the softwood group, are harder than several of the hardwoods.

PROPERTIES AND USES OF SOME COMMON TREES

(H) = hardwood   (S) = softwood

Ash (H) Heavy, hard, coarse-grained. Reddish-brown heartwood with sapwood almost white. Used for interior trim, plywood, tool handles, some furniture and cabinet work.

Beech (H) Heavy, hard, strong. Works fairly easily, takes good polish. Color, white to brown. Used for furniture, tool handles, plywood.

Birch (H) Heavy, very strong, fine-grained, hard. Takes excellent finish, beautiful polish. Heartwood is brown, sometimes tinged with red; sapwood is a creamy yellow. Used for furniture, flooring, plywood. Birch has a relatively large volume change due to changes in moisture content.

Cedar (western red) (S) The largest cedar native to North America. Heartwood color varies from pinkish-red to deep, warm brown; the thin sapwood layer is light yellow. The wood is soft and light, straight-grained but lacks strength. It has high resistance to changes in moisture content and retains its size and shape exceptionally well after seasoning. Used for shingles, shakes, planking, siding, prefabricated building logs, yard lumber.

Cedar (Tennessee) (S) Soft, very light, close-grained but lacks strength. Heartwood is a light reddish-brown, sapwood almost white. Has strong odor which is an insect repellent. Used for closet and trunk linings.

Cherry (H) Light and close-grained. Works easily and takes good finish. Heartwood is reddish-brown; sapwood is yellowish-white. Used for cabinet work and interior trim.

Chestnut (H) Light, open-grained, works easily. Heartwood is dark tan, sapwood light brown. Used for cabinet work.

Cypress (S) Light, very durable, close-grained, easily worked. Sapwood is light brown, heartwood bright yellow. Used for interior and exterior trim and for cabinet work.

Elm (H) Very heavy and hard. Color is light brown, tinged with red and gray. Used for tool handles and for heavy construction purposes.

Fir (Douglas) (S) Hard, strong, durable. Heartwood color ranges from light red to yellow; sapwood is whitish. Used for all types of construction and in the manufacture of plywood.

Gum (H) Soft-textured, durable, close-grained. Color is similar to walnut, with heartwood a reddish-brown, sapwood yellowish-white. Has a tendency to warp but works easily. Used for furniture, sometimes as a substitute for walnut.

Hemlock (western) (S) Fine textured, straight-grained, easily worked. Free from pitch, possesses exceptionally good

3

gluing properties. Used for general building purposes, often interchanged with fir.

Larch (S) Fairly hard and strong, resembling Douglas fir more closely than any other softwood. Heartwood is deep reddish-brown, the sapwood much lighter. Suitable for construction purposes.

Mahogany (H) Strong, open-pored, durable. Works easily and takes a very good finish. Color is reddish-brown. Inferior-quality mahogany contains small, gray specks. Used for furniture, plywood, interior trim.

Maple (*sugar*) (H) One of the hardest and strongest woods in America. Very close-grained. Takes an excellent finish but is difficult to work. Light yellow to brown in color. Used for flooring and furniture.

Maple (silver) (H) Soft, light, easily worked; not very strong or durable. Used most frequently for wood turning and for interior trim.

Oak (*white*) (H) Very heavy and hard, close-grained with open pores. Takes excellent finish but is difficult to work. Tan heartwood with light sapwood. Used for flooring, furniture, plywood, interior trim.

Oak (*red*) (H) A little softer than white oak, with coarser grain. Color varies from tan to reddish-brown. Used for furniture, plywood, bearing posts, implement parts, interior trim.

Pine (*white*) (S) Soft, light, durable; works very easily. Creamy-white heartwood. Used for furniture.

Pine (*sugar*) (S) Very soft, light, uniform in texture. Works very easily and takes an excellent finish. In the quarter-sawed boards, reddish-brown specks are easily recognized. Heartwood is reddish-brown, sapwood a light yellow. Used for interior trim and inexpensive furniture.

Pine (*ponderosa*) (S) Pale-yellow sapwood, darker heartwood. Fairly soft, strong, uniform in texture. Works easily and smoothly without splintering. Ideal for shopwork.

Pine (*lodgepole*) (S) Light in color, sapwood almost white. Soft, straight-grained, of fine, uniform texture. It seasons easily and uniformly and is of moderate durability. Used for lumber and for mine props.

Pine (*yellow or southern*) (S) Hard, tough, strong. Very difficult to work. Heartwood is orange-red, sapwood is lighter. Used for heavy structural purposes such as floor planks, beams, timbers.

Poplar (H) Light, soft, uniform texture. Works easily. Color varies from yellow to white. Used for crates, plywood, occasional pieces of inexpensive furniture.

Redwood (S) Light, easily worked. Coarse-grained, but lacks strength. Dull red in color. Used for interior and exterior trim, planking, shingles.

Spruce (*white*) (S) Light weight, soft, works very easily. Color varies from white to pale yellow with little contrast between heartwood and sapwood. Is of medium strength among the softwoods but not very durable in situations

4

favorable to decay. Used as light construction material and is of particular value as paper pulp.

Spruce (Engelmann) (S) Wood is light in color, straight-grained. Works easily, takes a good finish. Trees are usually larger than white spruce and produce a larger percentage of lumber clear of defects. Used for oars, paddles, sounding boards for musical instruments, construction work.

Spruce (Sitka) (S) Trees grow very tall with straight grain. Color is creamy white with sometimes a pinkish tinge. Wood is tough, strong, resists splintering and shattering well. Used in airframe construction, masts and spars, scaffolding, general construction.

Walnut (H) Very hard, strong, durable; easily worked, takes an excellent finish. Used in fine cabinet work, furniture, flooring, plywood, interior trim. Reddish-brown to dark brown heartwood with lighter sapwood.

MOISTURE IN WOOD

Moisture in wood is found in two forms, *hygroscopic* and *free*. Hygroscopic moisture is that which is present inside the hollow wood fibers; free moisture is found outside the cell walls, in a fiber bundle. When wood dries, the free moisture evaporates first. When it is gone, but the cells still contain their hygroscopic moisture, the wood is said to be at the "fiber saturation point." This occurs for most species when the wood has reached a moisture content of about 25 percent of the oven-dry weight. The moisture content of green wood may vary from about 35 percent for some species to nearly 200 percent in the sapwood of white pine and hemlock.

The moisture content of wood is usually expressed as a percentage of the oven-dry weight and can be determined by the oven-dry method or by the electric-moisture-meter method. The former is a laboratory method and requires accurate equipment and careful techniques; the latter is used for quick checks which will give reasonably accurate results on wood with from 6 to 25 percent moisture content.

Test pieces are required for the oven-dry method. They should be cut the full width of the board and from ½ to ¾ in. long. The sections should be cut at least 2 ft from the end of the board to eliminate a sample that may have end-dried. The pieces should be weighed immediately and the results recorded as the "original weight." The samples are placed in an oven heated to 212°F and left until all the moisture has been removed. The weights have to be checked several times until it is found that the pieces are no longer losing weight—that the weights are constant. The pieces are removed from the oven and weighed immediately. This result is recorded as the "oven-dry" weight. Then the moisture content, based on oven-dry weight, can be calculated using the following formula:

$$\text{Moisture content (in percent)} = \frac{\text{original weight} - \text{oven-dry weight} \times 100}{\text{oven-dry weight}}$$

The electric moisture meter passes an electric current between two points in a piece of wood. The resistance to the current passing through the wood varies with the moisture content; test results are converted into a moisture-percentage reading on a dial.

WOOD GRAIN

The term "grain" as applied to wood is used very loosely. In general it refers to the appearance of a piece of wood on one of its cut surfaces. It may refer to the appearance of the annual rings on the end or face of a board or to the appearance of the longitudinal fibers on the surface. Thus we hear the terms "edge grain," "flat grain," "angle grain," "close grain," "open grain," "cross grain," "even grain," "medium grain," and "coarse grain."

When a board is cut from the log so that the annual rings run approximately at right angles to the face, the result is *edge-grain* lumber. When the annual rings run more or less parallel to the surface, the lumber is said to have *flat grain,* while if the rings are at about 45° to the face, the piece is said to have *angle grain.*

Close grain refers to a type of wood in which the fiber bundles are closely packed together so that no open pores or spaces are visible on the surface. Poplar and most of the softwoods are common close-grain woods. A wood is *open-grain* when there are visible open pores on the face because fiber bundles are not so closely packed together. Oak is an outstanding example of wood with open grain.

Cross grain refers to wood whose fibers do not run parallel to the length of the board. Somewhere on the surface the ends of fiber bundles that have been cut across appear as a rough spot, very difficult to plane or finish.

Even grain, medium grain, and *coarse grain* refer to the appearance of the annual rings on the surface—their width, spacing, and the resulting texture of wood.

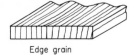
Edge grain

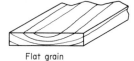
Flat grain

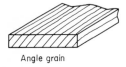
Angle grain

Figure 1 · 4
Wood grain.

THE MANUFACTURE OF LUMBER

The manufacture of lumber begins with the logging operation—converting the standing trees into sawlogs, ready for the sawmill. There are as many methods of logging as there are varieties of timber and topography, but the general prin-

6

ciples of *felling, bucking, skidding,* and *hauling* are fundamental and common to all.

Trees are selected, undercut, and felled with an ax, cross-
cut, or power saw. A crew then sets to work on limbing and
bucking—operations in which the branches are cut off and
the trunk cut into logs 12 to 40 ft long. The logs must then be
moved out of the bush to an assembly point for transportation to a distant mill or to a mill set up in a convenient location
in the forest. In such a mill, the logs are sawed into rough
lumber, which is then trucked to a central point for any
further finishing operations.

The assembly point or *skidway* will be located on the bank
of a river or lake, near the seashore, alongside a railway spur,
or near a truck or sleigh road. Moving the logs to the skidway
is known as skidding and the method will vary with the terrain. In the mountains much of the skidding is done by cable
and *highline* rigged to *spar trees* while in less rugged terrain
it is usually done with crawler tractors.

Logs are *decked* on the skidway, from which they may be
rolled or chuted into the water or loaded onto railway flatcars,
trucks, or logging sleighs for transportation to a mill. Logs
dumped into a river are usually carried downstream by the
current, but logs dumped into a lake or the sea must be surrounded by a *boom chain* and towed by tug to the mill. Here
they are placed in a millpond to be sorted and held ready for
sawing.

On their way to the mill, logs pass through a *barker,* which
removes the bark and leaves the logs clean for the saw. They
go first to a *headsaw,* either a large band saw or a large circu-
lar saw. Here they may be cut up in various ways, depending
on the size of the log, the type of machinery being used beyond the headsaw, and current orders. Logs may be cut
directly into boards and planks of various thicknesses, designated by *quarters:* 1 in. = 4 quarters (4/4), 2 in. = 8
quarters (8/4), 3½ in. = 14 quarters (14/4), etc. The log may
merely have slabs removed from two opposite sides or it may
be cut into squared timbers of various sizes. These last two
are called *cants,* which must go through a *resaw* to be cut
into several boards or planks.

The lumber is edge-trimmed and cut to width by *edgers;*
cut to length on *trimmers;* graded according to quality and
species; sorted by length, thickness, and grade; and taken to
a yard for piling or to a *dry kiln.* Later a considerable portion
of the rough lumber is put through a *planer,* which smooths
the surfaces, reduces it to the finished width and thickness,
and shapes it for a particular use.

Figure 1·5 illustrates how a log might be cut to produce
different thicknesses and types of lumber. Notice the wide 4-
and 6-in. cants that are cut from the log. These will go to a
resaw, which will cut them up in the direction indicated to
produce edge-grain boards. This is quarter-sawed lumber.
Other boards, which are cut directly from the log with no

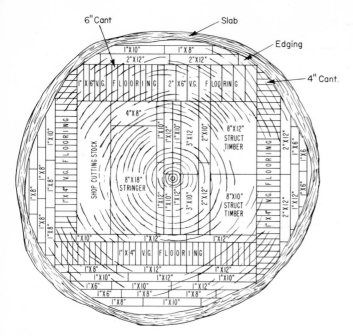

Figure 1 · 5
Log cutting pattern.

attention paid to the direction of the grain, are plain or slash sawed. One piece of shop cutting stock is shown. This is *factory lumber* (see below), which is intended for use in a shop where it will be cut up into relatively small pieces. The large *stick* shown here will go to a resaw to be cut into thinner pieces. Several pieces of *structural lumber* (see below) are also shown. Notice that they are cut from the heartwood of the log.

SOFTWOOD LUMBER TYPES

Three general categories of softwood lumber are cut, depending on the eventual use to which each is to be put. They are yard lumber, factory lumber, and structural lumber.

Yard lumber is made to be used in ordinary light construction and finishing work and consists of 1- and 2-in. material manufactured into common boards, shiplap, shelving, dimension lumber (2×2 in. to 2×12 in.), center match, flooring, roof plank, siding, V joint, trim, and molding of all kinds. Consult a standard pattern book put out by lumbermen's associations for all the patterns made under the yard-lumber category.

Shop lumber is usually left in 1 in. and 2 in. rough thickness, often containing knots or other defects not ordinarily permissible in other categories. It is intended for use in shops or mills making sash, doors, cabinets, etc., where it will be cut into relatively short pieces and the defective material discarded.

Structural lumber is intended for use in heavy construction

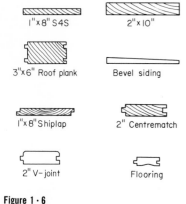

Figure 1 · 6
Yard lumber.

for load-bearing purposes and is cut into timbers of larger size than yard lumber, 3 in. or more thick and 4 in. or more wide. It is made from the heartwood of the log, giving the densest, driest, strongest material possible.

Each of these categories of lumber has its own system of grading rules, which have become fairly standard throughout the lumber manufacturing industry. In general, grades depend on appearance, strength characteristics such as density, and the results of wood diseases or lumber defects.

WOOD DISEASES AND LUMBER DEFECTS

Various types of fungi are considered to be the chief causes of diseases in wood. These are low forms of plant growth, producing thin branching tubes which spread through the wood and use the cellulose, lignin, and other chemical compounds of the cell walls as food. This of course disintegrates the cell walls and reduces the strength of the wood. These fungi require food, air, moisture, and suitable conditions of temperature for development.

Three common wood diseases produced by various types of fungi are *sap stain, mold,* and *wood rot.* Certain fungi appear on green lumber, penetrate the wood with their thread-like roots (*hyphae*), and discolor the wood. They cease to be active after the lumber has been seasoned, and the wood is not appreciably weakened by this discoloration.

Other fungi cause molds which damage the wood mostly at the surface. Their roots pass through spaces between the bundles of fibers and take up the tree's nourishment instead of breaking down the cell walls. Such growths are usually found only near the surface of the sapwood.

Another kind of fungus causes rot, the destruction of the walls of the wood cells, by feeding on the cellulose or the lignin. When the cellulose is destroyed, a brittle, brownish, punky residue is left. When the lignin is dissolved, a soft, white mass of cellulose is left.

There are two stages in the progress of most types of decay; they differ somewhat in their characteristics and effects upon the wood. The first, *incipient decay,* is the result of early growth of the fungus; it usually shows up in the form of discoloration. The cell walls in this first stage are not injured enough to seriously affect the hardness or strength of the wood.

The second stage is *advanced decay;* in this case serious destructive action can easily be seen. "Brown rot" is one common type where the cellulose has been destroyed; "white rot" is the result when the lignin and other colored parts of the cell have been destroyed. Such rot appears in scattered spots, often with black margins.

The solution of the problems of stains and rot in wood is

one of prevention rather than cure. The removal of moisture by kiln-drying or subjecting the lumber to heat and dipping it in certain toxic materials or wood preservatives all help to prevent the growth of fungi.

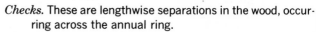

LUMBER DEFECTS

Lumber defects, flaws in the wood which affect either the strength or the appearance or both, can have many causes. One has already been discussed—wood diseases. Another is the action of animal parasites. Defects also can be caused by too-rapid seasoning, faulty manufacturing, or some natural growth of the wood. The most common defects are:

Checks. These are lengthwise separations in the wood, occurring across the annual ring.

Shakes. Lengthwise separations in the wood, occurring between annual rings.

Wane. Bark or other soft material left on the edge of a board.

Knots. Cross sections or longitudinal sections of tree branches that have been cut with the board. There are several kinds of knots, including round, spike, sound, pin, loose, and cluster.

Pitch pocket. An accumulation of tree sap in a well-defined opening between annual rings.

Bark pocket. Bark partially or wholly encased in the wood.

Sap streak. A heavy accumulation of sap in the fibers of the wood, producing a distinctive streak of color.

Splits. A lengthwise separation of the wood, caused by handling.

Torn grain. A condition where part of the surface has been chipped or torn out below the line of cut.

Skips. An area that failed to surface when the piece went through the planer.

Machine burn. An area that has been darkened by overheating due to machine rollers.

Warp. A condition in which the flat, plane surface has been distorted in some manner. An edgewise deviation is called a *crook;* a flat deviation is a *bow;* a deviation across the width is a *cup.*

Check

Shake

Wane

Figure 1·7
Lumber defects.

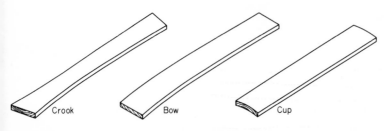
Crook   Bow   Cup

Figure 1·8
Warped lumber.

10

Wormholes. Small holes caused by wood borers.
Sap stain. Described above in wood diseases.
Incipient or *advanced decay.* Described above.

For a complete description of wood diseases, their cause and control, one should consult texts on this subject. Very good ones are published by the various forestry departments and forest-products laboratories across the country.

SEASONING OF LUMBER

As clay is burned and steel is tempered, so lumber must be dried. Water content represents from 30 to 100 percent or more of the dry weight of a board as it comes from the log. Most of this moisture must be eliminated before the lumber can be used for the great majority of purposes. In addition, the shipping weight of lumber is reduced by drying, and there is less danger of rot or stain developing in dry lumber.

Two methods are available for drying lumber: *air-drying* and *kiln-drying.* Most lumber to be used in general construction is air-dried. The moisture content can be reduced to about 15 percent by this method, and this is adequate for most construction lumber. Lumber is strip-piled at a slope on a solid foundation. Strip-piling allows air to circulate around every piece while the sloping allows water to run off quickly.

Lumber which is required for more refined uses such as flooring, furniture, and general interior use must be dried to a moisture content of not more than 5 to 10 percent. This is done in a dry kiln—a large, airtight structure, scientifically heated by steam pipes—in which the lumber is artificially dried to the correct moisture content. Not only are lower moisture contents produced by a dry-kiln but this process, which would take months in a drying yard, is completed in days or weeks in a kiln.

Wood dries by the evaporation of water from the surface. This surface evaporation causes moisture in the interior to migrate toward the drier surface, thus setting up what is called a "moisture gradient" in the wood. Drying continues until the moisture content in the interior is the same as it is on the surface.

Lumber to be kiln-dried is stacked in separated layers in the kiln and preheated before drying commences. Drying then begins in very humid air, which is gradually made drier as the operation continues. Temperature and humidity conditions in the kiln are kept uniform throughout the pile and varied as drying progresses by means of valves that control the heating and humidifying systems. The proper temperature is maintained—high or low depending on the type of lumber being dried—until the required moisture content is obtained throughout the pile.

SOFTWOOD LUMBER GRADES

Yard Lumber

For purposes of grading, yard lumber is divided into a number of classes, depending on use, including vertical (edge) grain and flat or mixed grain finishing materials, boards, light framing, joists, and planks.

Finishing materials are subdivided into several groups—finish, casing and base, flooring and decking, siding and ceiling, stepping, window jamb, sill, door jamb and window stool. In some cases the pieces in one category are separated into edge-grain and flat-grain grades.

In the edge-grain class, the best grade is usually "B and Better," followed by "C" grade and then "D" grade. In the flat-grain class, the best grade is usually "C and Better," followed by "D" grade. In each case specifications state quite clearly just what defects are allowed and how many, how much waste may be present in the lumber, and the purpose for which each grade is recommended. Grading and dressing rules books are available covering each common species of softwood lumber. They should be consulted for details of various grades.

Boards, rough or surfaced, are produced in five grades—select merchantable, construction, standard, utility, and economy. The exact characteristics and limiting provisions of each are given in grading and dressing rules. The top grade in this category is recommended for high-class work and exposed use, both inside and out, and will usually be of the finest appearance. Construction grade is widely used for sub-floors, walls, roof sheathing, and form work. The remaining grades are quite serviceable but have less importance placed on appearance and presence of defects. Manufacturers recommend the best use for each grade.

Light framing, 2 to 4 in. thick and 2 to 4 in. wide, is produced in five grades—select structural, construction, standard, utility, and economy. Select structural is used where a combination of strength and fine appearance is required. Construction grade is primarily used for framing in which the members will not be exposed. Pieces are of good appearance but emphasis is on serviceability. The characteristics and limiting defect provisions of construction grade are listed below to demonstrate the application of grading rules.

Stained wood	Allowed
Splits	Allowed
Checks	Allowed
Pinholes	Limited
Torn grain	Allowed
Skips	Occasional, $\frac{1}{16} \times 2$ in.
Pitch pockets	Medium
Pitch streaks	Allowed

Wane	Approximately one-fourth of any face
Sound, tight knots	For 2-in. face width—1-in. knot
	For 3-in. face width—1¼-in. knot
	For 4-in. face width—1½-in. knot
	Two such are permitted for each 12 ft of length
Spike knots	Permitted if judged to have no more effect than other knots
Unsound knots	Two-thirds the size of allowable sound knots

All or nearly all of the permissible defects for the grade are never present in maximum number or size in any one piece. Any piece with an unusual combination of defects is usually excluded from the grade. Readers are advised to become familiar with the grading standards for all grades by consulting a grading and dressing rules book.

Standard, utility, and economy grades of light framing are used for less important work; suggested uses accompany the grade specifications. Allowable defects increase in number and size in each successive grade, and in economy grade, lumber of more than one species may be included in an order. For example, hemlock and larch could be included with fir although nominally this would be a fir grade.

Joists and planks, 2 to 4 in. thick and 6 in. wide or wider, are classed in the same five grades as light framing. The first three grades in this category are also included in the structural-lumber classification, having stress values given to them, as will be explained later. In general, this class of yard lumber is used for floor and roof framing, beams, posts, trusses, etc. Grading rules must be consulted to determine the specifications regarding defects for each grade and the recommended use of each.

Factory Lumber

Softwood factory lumber is made from several species, including fir, hemlock, spruce, and cedar. Grades are established by the number and length of cuttings that can be obtained from a piece, after which the individual pieces are graded. Four classifications are used, based on "A" grade, consisting of cuttings 9½ in. wide or wider and 18 in. long or longer, which must be clear on both sides but may have bright sapwood, and "B" grade, consisting of cuttings 5 in. wide or wider, 3 ft long or longer, which must have a face equal to "B or Better" grade in vertical grain finish:

1. *Select shop* consists of at least 70 percent A and/or B cuttings.

2. *No. 1 shop* consists of 50 to 70 percent of A and/or B cuttings.

13

3. *No. 2 shop* consists of 33⅓ to 50 percent A and/or B cuttings.

4. *No. 3 shop* admits all factory-lumber-type pieces below the grade of No. 2 shop, if they contain at least 10 percent of mixed A and/or B cuttings. Complete details on grades in this type of lumber can be found in a grading rules book.

STRUCTURAL LUMBER

Classification

Knots, slope of grain, checks and shakes, moisture content, etc., vary in their effect on the strength of timber according to the type of loads which are applied to it. The thickness of the piece causes variations in the effects of seasoning. For these reasons, structural lumber is often classified first according to size and use as follows:

Joists and planks. This is lumber of rectangular cross section, 2 to 4 in. thick and 6 in. or more wide. It is graded with respect to its strength in bending when loaded on the edge as a joist or on the wide face as a plank.

Beams and stringers. This is timber 5 in. or more thick with the width more than 2 in. greater than the thickness. It is graded with respect to its strength in bending when loaded on the narrow face.

Posts and timbers. Timber of square or nearly square cross section, 5 in. or more thick, with the width not more than 2 in. greater than the thickness. It is graded primarily for its strength parallel to the grain but can be adopted for miscellaneous uses in which strength in bending is not especially important.

Grading

Structural lumber is intended for use in engineering construction, with allowable working stresses assigned to each grade. The essential difference between it and construction grades of yard lumber is in the degree of grading for strength. Structural-lumber grading includes:

1. A careful inspection of all four sides of every piece for knots, their size and location. Figures 1·9 to 1·11 illustrate how knots are checked for size in joists and planks, beams and stringers, and posts and timbers. In Fig. 1·9, the *average* dimension indicated by A is measured. When measuring B, measure from the edge of the wide face to a line parallel to the edge. C is measured from the edge of the narrow face to a line parallel to the edge, while D is measured between lines parallel to the edges. In Fig. 1·10, the least dimension is taken as A. B is measured between lines parallel to the edges, while C is measured from the edge of the narrow face

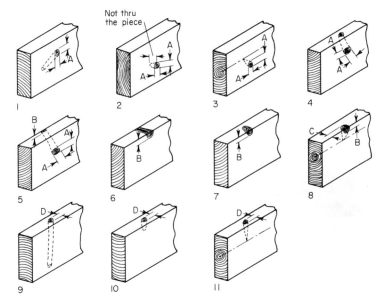

Figure 1 · 9
Measuring knots in
joists and planks.
(British Columbia Lumber Manufacturers'
Association)

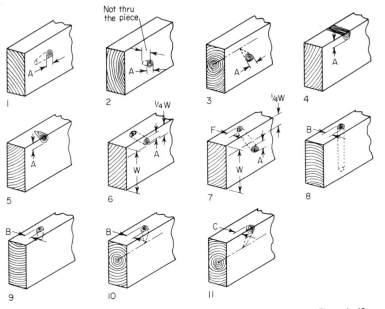

Figure 1 · 10
Measuring knots in
beams and stringers.
(British Columbia Lumber Manufacturers'
Association)

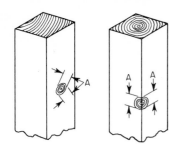

Figure 1 · 11
Measuring knots in
posts and timbers.
(British Columbia Lumber Manufacturers'
Association)

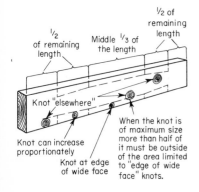

Figure 1 · 12
Checking knots for location.
(British Columbia Lumber Manufacturers'
Association)

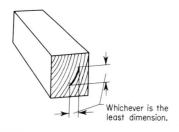

Figure 1 · 13
Measuring shake.
(British Columbia Lumber Manufacturers'
Association)

to a line parallel to the edge. In Fig. 1 · 11, the average dimension is taken as A.

Figure 1 · 12 illustrates how knots are checked for location. In joists and planks, along the edges of the wide face and in the middle third of the length, knots are restricted to a given size. On the edges of the wide face, immediately outside the middle third of the length, knot sizes may be increased proportionately for a distance equal to half of the remaining length, to the size permitted elsewhere on the face. The remaining portion of the length may contain knots equal to the largest knot permitted elsewhere. Knots away from the edges outside of the critical areas may be of the largest size permitted.

2. A careful inspection of sides and ends of each piece for checks, shakes, and splits. Figures 1 · 13 to 1 · 15 illustrate how these measurements are made.

3. Tests which will allow the determination of unit working stresses. The basic stress is derived from the results of tests on small clear specimens of wood; it includes adjustments for variation in material, length of loading period, and a safety factor. This basic stress is then reduced according to the limitations in a specific grade to give the allowable unit working stress.

4. Inspection for slope of grain. This is a deviation in the direction of the wood fibers from a line parallel to the edges of the piece. The slope is expressed as a ratio of the amount of deviation for a given length, e.g., a slope grain of 1 in 8. This means that the fibers deviate from a line parallel to the edges of the piece by 1 in. in 8 in. of length. Figure 1 · 16 illustrates the measurement of the slope of grain.

5. Measuring the rate of growth or density of the piece. Within limits, the number of annual rings per inch is an indication of the amount of wood substance per unit of volume. For some species, particularly Douglas fir, southern pine, larch, and redwood, this factor is taken into account in assigning grades. Rate-of-growth requirements are sometimes a part of a grading rule for reasons of texture as well as for strength. The terms "medium grain" and "close grain" are used to designate texture, and "dense material" is used to signify strength. Medium grain means an average of four or more annual rings per inch at either end of a piece, measured at right angles to the annual rings. Close grain means an average of six but not more than approximately 30 annual rings per inch. Dense material averages six or more annual rings per inch and, in addition, one-third or more summerwood, on either end. Figure 1 · 17 illustrates how rate of growth is measured.

6. Measuring the moisture content. Lumber may be unseasoned, partially seasoned, or seasoned. It is unseasoned if the moisture content is at or above the fiber saturation point; it is seasoned usually if the moisture content ranges from 12 to 15 percent; it is partially seasoned if the moisture

content lies between these two. The allowable working stresses for structural lumber are based on "green" lumber, and since the strength and stiffness increase as the moisture content decreases, this increase offsets any decrease in strength due to shrinkage checking.

Grades

Generally, softwood structural lumber is divided into five grades: dense select structural, select structural, dense construction, construction, and standard. Some species have some grade names which are different, and not all species or classes in a species are given the five different gradings.

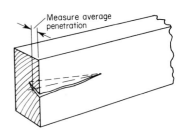

Figure 1 · 14
Measuring a check.
(British Columbia Lumber Manufacturers' Association)

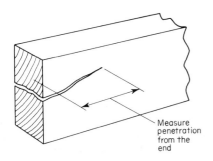

Figure 1 · 15
Measuring a split.
(British Columbia Lumber Manufacturers' Association)

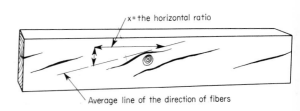

Figure 1 · 16
Measuring slope of grain.
(British Columbia Lumber Manufacturers' Association)

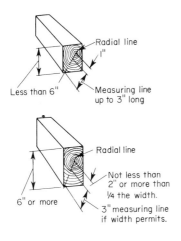

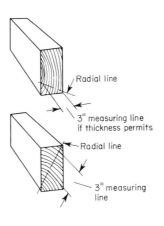

Figure 1 · 17
Measuring rate of growth.
(British Columbia Lumber Manufacturers' Association)

Grades are allotted on the basis of the grading techniques outlined above. For example, dense select structural joists and planks are so graded on the basis of the following characteristics and limiting provisions:

Bending stress	2050f
Stained sapwood	Allowed
Splits	Very short
Checks	Single or opposite each other with a sum total equal to approximately one-fourth the thickness
Torn grain	Medium
Skips	Occasional, small
Grain	Close
Slope of grain	In middle third of length not to exceed 1 in. in 12 in. Rest of piece may be 1 in. in 10 in.
Pitch pockets	Medium
Pitch streaks	Allowed
Wane	Approximately one-eighth of any face

Knots—sound, tight, and well spaced—may be present in the approximate sizes shown in Table 1·1. Spike knots are permitted if judged to have no more effect than other knots. Holes from any cause have no more effect than knots, but for the sake of appearance they are limited to ½ in. for 6-in. widths and to ¾ in. for 8-in. widths and wider.

For specifications on grades of species, consult the appropriate grading rules book. Table 1·2 gives the allowable unit stresses for the various grades in a number of species commonly used for structural purposes.

Table 1·3 compares a number of softwood species used for structural purposes, with regard to various important qualities such as bending strength, stiffness, and toughness.

Table 1·4 gives the weight per cubic foot for a number of common species of softwood in the green and in the approxi-

Table 1·1
Knot sizes and positions allowed.
(British Columbia Lumber Manufacturers' Association)

	ON NARROW FACES	
FACE WIDTH, IN.	IN MIDDLE THIRD OF LENGTH, IN.	AT ENDS, IN.
2	⅝	¾
3	¾	1¼
4	1	1¾

	ON WIDE FACES	
FACE WIDTH, IN.	AT EDGES IN MIDDLE THIRD OF LENGTH, IN.	ELSEWHERE ON FACE, IN.
6	1⅛	1⅝
8	1½	2
10	1⅞	2⅜
12	2¼	2¾
14 and wider	2½	3

Table 1·2
Allowable unit stresses
for various species and
grades of structural lumber.
(Southern Pine Association)

SPECIES AND GRADE	EXTREME FIBER IN BENDING f AND TENSION PARALLEL TO GRAIN, LB/SQ IN.	HORIZONTAL SHEAR, LB/SQ IN.	COMPRESSION PERPENDICULAR TO GRAIN, LB/SQ IN.	COMPRESSION PARALLEL TO GRAIN, LB/SQ IN.	MODULUS OF ELASTICITY
Southern pine					
Dense select structural	2,400	120	455	1,750	1,600,000
Dense structural	2,000	120	455	1,400	1,600,000
Merchantable structural longleaf	1,800	120	455	1,300	1,600,000
Dense No. 1 structural	1,600	120	455	1,150	1,600,000
No. 1 dense 1400f	1,400	140	455	1,400	1,600,000
No. 1 1200f	1,200	120	390	1,200	1,600,000
Douglas fir					
Dense select structural	2,050	120	455	1,650	1,600,000
Select structural	1,900	120	415	1,500	1,600,000
Dense construction	1,750	120	455	1,400	1,600,000
Construction	1,500	120	390	1,200	1,600,000
Standard	1,200	95	390	1,000	1,600,000
West Coast hemlock					
Select structural	1,600	100	365	1,100	1,500,000
Construction	1,500	100	365	1,100	1,500,000
Standard	1,200	80	365	1,000	1,500,000
West Coast cypress					
Select structural	1,500	95	330	1,150	1,200,000
Structural	1,200	95	330	950	1,200,000
Eastern hemlock Lodgepole pine Ponderosa pine					
Select structural	1,300	90	300	900	1,100,000
Structural	1,050	90	300	750	1,100,000
Western red cedar White pine					
Select structural	1,150	80	260	900	1,000,000
Structural	900	80	260	750	1,000,000

mately air-dry state. There is a considerable variation of density within a species so that these figures must be taken as the average weight for the species.

LUMBER TALLYING

In North America practically all lumber is sold by board measure. The unit of measurement is the board foot—a piece

Table 1 · 3
Comparative strength values
for various softwoods.
(Southern Pine Association)

SPECIES	BENDING STRENGTH	STIFFNESS	STRENGTH AS A POST	TOUGHNESS	HARDNESS	NAIL-HOLDING POWER OF SIDE GRAIN
Southern pine	100	100	100	100	100	100
Douglas fir	86	97	84	79	79	80
Western larch	85	81	81	79	84	86
Western hemlock	70	76	66	71	65	77
Eastern hemlock	69	64	62	65	67	64
Balsam fir	65	78	59	68	48	58
Eastern spruce	65	70	58	65	52	61
Western white pine	64	73	58	63	45	69
Ponderosa pine	62	60	54	56	54	64
Sugar pine	60	60	53	53	50	53

Table 1 · 4
Weight of
structural timbers,
lb/cu ft.

SPECIES	GREEN	12% MOISTURE CONTENT
Eastern cedar	34	21
Western red cedar	29	24
West Coast cypress	35	30
Douglas fir (coast region)	40	34
Balsam fir	46	24
Eastern hemlock	61	30
Western hemlock	44	30
Western larch	52	40
Jack pine	40	31
Lodgepole pine	40	29
Western white pine	36	26
Ponderosa pine	47	32
Eastern white pine	46	27
Eastern spruce	38	26
Englemann spruce	37	28
Sitka spruce	31	27

of lumber 12 in. wide, 1 in. thick, and 1 ft long. If a piece of lumber is 12 in. wide, 1 in. thick, and 12 ft long, it contains 12 bd ft. Notice the area of the end of this piece. It is $1 \times 12 = 12$ sq in. Notice that this figure is the number of board feet in the piece if it is 12 ft long. This fact is a clue to a simple method of tallying lumber in any quantity. The product of the end dimensions of any piece of lumber is the number of board feet in the piece if it is 12 feet long. Take, for example, a board 2×12 in. by 12 ft long. The area of the end $= 2 \times 12 = 24$ sq in. Then the board has 24 bd ft in it; 20 pieces 2×12 in. by 12 ft long contain $2 \times 12 \times 20 = 480$ bd ft.

In other words, 12 ft is a standard length as far as tallying is concerned. If the piece is only 10 ft long, it is one-sixth shorter than standard and will have one-sixth fewer board feet in it; if it is 16 ft long, it is one-third longer than standard

20

and will have one-third more board feet in it. Thus a board 2 × 6 in. by 10 ft long contains 2 × 6 − (⅙ of 12) = 10 bd ft, while one 2 × 10 in. by 16 ft long contains 2 × 10 + (⅓ of 20) = 26⅔ bd ft.

EXAMPLE: How many board feet are there in 54 pieces 1 × 10 in. by 14 ft long?

SOLUTION: 1 × 10 × 54 + (⅙ of 540) = 630 bd ft

EXAMPLE: How many board feet are there in 12 structural timbers 6 × 14 in. by 18 ft long?

SOLUTION: 6 × 14 × 12 + (½ of 6 × 14 × 12) = 1,512 bd ft

EXAMPLE: How many board feet are there in a pile of lumber 6 ft wide, 4 ft high, and 10 ft long?

SOLUTION: 72 × 48 − (⅙ of 72 × 48) = 2,880 bd ft

Lumber less than 1 in. thick is usually calculated as being 1 in. thick for tallying and sales purposes. To make up for the fact that the buyer receives less wood content than is indicated by tallying, the unit price is adjusted to reflect the actual wood content.

Lumber is sold at a given price per 1,000 bd ft (M). To calculate the cost of a given quantity of lumber at a given price, multiply the number of board feet by the cost per M and divide by 1,000.

EXAMPLE: Calculate the cost of six pieces 2 × 4 in. by 14 ft long @ $105 per M.

SOLUTION: Number of board feet = 2 × 4 × 6 + (⅙ of 2 × 4 × 6) = 56 bd ft.

$$\text{Cost} = \frac{56 \times 105}{1,000} = \$5.88$$

It often helps to express a quantity of board feet as a number of pieces of given length. To do so, first multiply the board feet by 12 and divide by thickness × width to find the number of lineal feet. Then divide this quantity by the given length to find the number of pieces.

EXAMPLE: How many pieces 2 × 6 in. by 16 ft long are there in 1,200 bd ft of 2 × 6 in. stock?

SOLUTION: $\dfrac{1,200 \times 12}{2 \times 6 \times 16} = 75$ pieces

EXAMPLE: Find the number of pieces in the following order.

1,000 bd ft 2 × 4 in. by 14 ft
1,200 bd ft 2 × 4 in. by 16 ft
1,400 bd ft 2 × 4 in. by 18 ft

21

SOLUTION: No. of pieces 14 ft long $= \dfrac{1,000 \times 12}{2 \times 4 \times 14} = 107$

No. of pieces 16 ft long $= \dfrac{1,200 \times 12}{2 \times 4 \times 16} = 112$

No. of pieces 18 ft long $= \dfrac{1,400 \times 12}{2 \times 4 \times 18} = 117$

Most lumber manufacturing associations prepare and distribute booklets on lumber tallying and shipping. These give complete descriptions of the many facets of lumber tallying and should be studied for a complete explanation of this phase of the lumber industry.

HARDWOOD LUMBER

Sawed hardwood lumber is used for a variety of purposes in construction including flooring, dimension lumber—both solid and laminated—construction and utility boards, finishing lumber, interior trim and molding, wall paneling, stair treads and risers, and structural timbers. A great deal of sawed hardwood is also used in furniture manufacture.

Because of its relative scarcity, hardwood lumber is produced in a great variety of lengths, widths, and thicknesses, including very thin slabs called *flitches,* which are often used to cover less expensive woods.

Standard Hardwood Grades

The standard grades of hardwood lumber are Firsts, Seconds, Selects, No. 1 Common, No. 2 Common, Sound Wormy, No. 3A Common, and No. 3B Common. Firsts and Seconds are usually combined as one grade, with various percentages of Firsts being required, depending on the species, in the combined grade. For example, in Philippine mahogany, 40 percent of the combined grade must be Firsts; in plain oak, 33⅓ percent of the combined grade must be Firsts. For particulars on all species of hardwood, consult a hardwood grading rules book, available from the National Hardwood Lumber Association. Selects and No. 1 Common may be combined as one grade with most species and No. 3A Common and No. 3B Common may be combined as No. 3 Common.

The grading rules covering Firsts and Seconds are generally as follows:

1 Widths may be 6 in. and wider.
2 Lengths may be 8 to 16 ft, admitting 30 percent of 8 to 11 ft of which one-half may be 8 ft and 9 ft.

3 No piece shall be admitted which contains pith exceeding in length in inches the length of the board in feet.

4 Wane exceeding in length one-twelfth of the length of the piece will not be admitted; splits must not exceed in length in inches twice the length of the board in feet.

5 The average diameter of a knot or hole must not exceed in inches one-third of the length of the piece in feet.

6 Warp and cup will not be admitted if sufficient to prevent the board from dressing two sides to standard thickness.

7 The minimum size cutting allowed from a piece will be 4 in. wide by 5 ft long or 3 in. wide by 7 ft long.

A cutting is defined as a portion of a board or plank obtained by cross-cutting or ripping or both. It may be a clear face cutting or a sound cutting. The former must have one face clear while the latter is a cutting free from rot, pith, shake, and wane. Texture is not considered and sound knots, bird pecks, stain, streaks, and small wormholes are admitted.

ROUGH	DRESSED, S1S OR S2S*	ROUGH	DRESSED, S1S OR S2S*
⅜	³⁄₁₆	1½	1⅜
½	⁵⁄₁₆	2	1¹³⁄₁₆
⅝	⁷⁄₁₆	2½	2⁵⁄₁₆
¾	⁹⁄₁₆	3	2¾
1	1³⁄₁₆	4	3¾
1¼	1⅛		

Table 1·5
Standard thicknesses
of hardwood lumber, in.
(Canadian Lumbermen's Association)

* S1S = surfaced one side; S2S = surfaced two sides.

GLUE-LAMINATED TIMBER

The term *laminated timber* is used to describe a wooden member built up of several layers of wood whose grain directions are all substantially parallel. It must not be confused with plywood, in which the layers have grain running at right angles to each other. *Glue laminated* refers to a wooden member whose layers are held together with glue, generally considered as the most satisfactory method of fastening. This type of wood member is in quite common use today for beams and girders; posts and columns; arches; bowstring truss chords; dredge spuds; ships' keels, knees, and masts.

Advantages of Glue-laminated Timbers

1 The size of wooden structural members need not be limited by the size of available trees. They may be built up to any desired size from small components. Transportation facilities and the economy factor are the two main limitations on the size of laminated timbers.

2   Trees which are too small for the production of large
    sawed timbers will produce material which is perfectly
    satisfactory for laminated members. Thus the supply of
    available material is significantly enlarged.

3   Low-grade lumber can be used in sections of laminated
    timbers where compression or tension stresses will be
    low, so reducing the overall cost of the member.

4   Lumber to be used in laminating can be seasoned much
    more quickly and easily while in small units. In addition,
    the development of defects such as checks due to
    seasoning is minimized in small pieces.

5   Laminated members are dry when erected, resulting in
    the minimum amount of deflection due to loading.

6   A camber or crown can be built into laminated timbers
    to take care of deflection due to loading.

7   Curved members such as arch ribs are easily made by
    bending thin sections to the required curvature and
    laminating them.

8   In some cases it is possible to taper certain sections of a
    member in proportion to the diminishing stresses. This
    may save material and also produce a more graceful
    structure.

9   In general, the variation in strength from one timber to
    another will be less than with sawed timbers. The natu-
    ral variability of the species is at least partially overcome
    by laminating a number of pieces.

10 Subject to certain limitations, it is possible to use two or
    more species together. This takes advantage of the
    economy of low-strength species and the superior
    qualities of a high-strength wood.

Disadvantages of Glue-laminated Timbers

1   There is an appreciable waste of material, the amount
    depending on the size and shape of the member. The
    sides and edges of each piece must be planed to finished
    dimensions from the rough size, which is the size to
    which sawed timbers are usually cut.

2   High-quality glue must be purchased in quantity, and
    some kinds require very careful handling.

3   Buildings and equipment must be provided for the fabri-
    cation, handling, and finishing of the laminated timbers.

4   Greater protection must be given the members during
    transportation and erection on the site.

5   In general labor and supervision costs will be higher than
    for certain other forms of timber construction.

Species of Wood Used

The softwood species which are most commonly used for
general construction will, in most cases, be equally suitable

for glue-laminated members. Softwoods are most commonly chosen because of their low cost, lightness, and strength; but for certain types of member such as glue-laminated ships' keels, hardwood is often used. A favorite wood for this job is white oak because of its ability to withstand fresh or salt water.

Preparation of pieces for lamination. Laminations should be dressed to uniform thickness to avoid thick glue lines or unglued areas. If there is to be edge lamination, the edges also must be dressed. Tests have shown that planed-to-planed surfaces develop the strongest glue bond. When end joints have to be made, the ends should be scarfed, as illustrated in Fig. 1·18. End joints should be spaced as shown in Fig. 1·19. If more than one grade in a species or more than one species is to be used in a member, then the pieces should be marked so that the stronger ones can be located in positions which will be subjected to the greatest stress.

Arrangement of laminations. Various arrangements of laminations in a member may be used, as illustrated in Fig. 1·20. Notice that in Fig. 1·20c, the edge joints are staggered in each successive lamination. This is to avoid the occurrence of a cleavage plane running completely through the member. Plywood may be incorporated into laminated members, as shown in Fig. 1·21.

Moisture content of lumber for laminating. Green lumber should not be used for glue-laminated construction. The lumber should be air- or kiln-dried to a suitable moisture content, depending on the use of the member and the type of glue to be used. Moisture content should not vary from piece

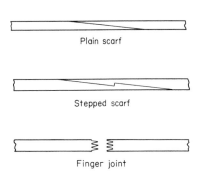

Plain scarf

Stepped scarf

Finger joint

Figure 1 · 18
Scarfed joints.

Figure 1 · 19
Minimum spacing of end joints.

 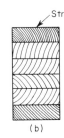 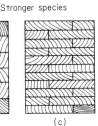 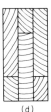 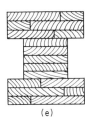

Stronger species

(a)   (b)   (c)   (d)   (e)

Figure 1 · 20
Typical laminated beam sections.

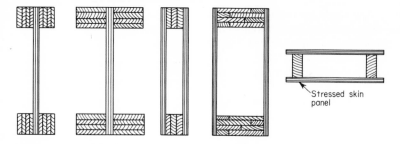

Figure 1 · 21
Typical laminated beams
using plywood.

to piece by more than 2½ percent, and there should not be more than 2½ percent variation from one part of a laminated member to another. Generally speaking, members to be used in the interior of heated buildings should be dried to a moisture content of 8 to 10 percent while those to be used outside may have a moisture content of 12 to 15 percent.

Glues used in laminating. There are many types of adhesive on the market, most of which will develop an adequate bond with softwood if properly used. However, experience has shown that certain glues prove to be most suitable, among them being casein glue, urea-formaldehyde resins, phenol-formaldehyde resins, and resorcinol-phenol-formaldehyde resins.

Casein is inexpensive in first cost and can be used on wood with a fairly wide range of moisture content. It will set well over a considerable range of temperatures and is satisfactory for use in dry locations. It is not recommended where the member will be submerged in water or exposed to the weather for any appreciable length of time.

Urea-formaldehyde resins are relatively cheap and will cure at from 70°F to much higher temperatures. They will withstand soaking in cool water or severe weathering for short periods of time, but prolonged immersion, particularly in salt water, is not recommended.

Phenol-formaldehyde-resin glues are not generally suitable for glue-laminating because of the high temperature needed to cure them. However, they are very water-resistant, mold-resistant, and durable over long periods of time. They are useful in those members combining plywood with timber since the thin plywood sheets present little difficulty in getting heat to the glued surface.

Resorcinol-phenol-formaldehyde-resin glues are expensive but have excellent qualities of durability and water resistance. They can be cured at from room temperature to the temperatures required for phenol-formaldehyde glues.

PLYWOOD

Plywood is made by bonding together thin layers of wood in such a way that the grain of each layer is at right angles to the grain of each adjacent layer (see Fig. 1·22). In most plywood an odd number of layers is used to give a balanced construction and to reduce any tendency to cupping. The outside layers are called the *faces*, the center layer is the *core*, and where more than three piles are used, those between face and core are called *crossbands*.

Each layer of plywood is called a *veneer*; these are produced in several ways including rotary cutting, half-round cutting with the stay log, slicing, and sawing (see Fig. 1·23). Rotary cutting is by far the most important method of manufacturing veneer. Logs which are to be made into rotary-cut veneer are kept in wet storage to prevent end-checking and

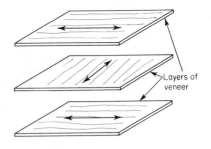

**Figure 1 · 22
Construction of plywood.**

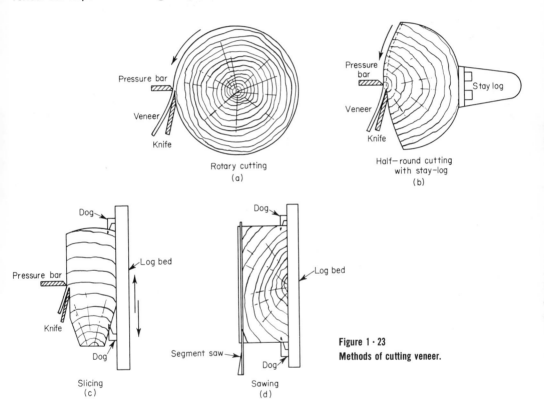

Rotary cutting
(a)

Half—round cutting
with stay-log
(b)

Slicing
(c)

Sawing
(d)

**Figure 1 · 23
Methods of cutting veneer.**

to inhibit the growth of fungi. When required, the logs are removed from storage and cut into *bolts,* slightly longer than the finished veneer sheets. The bolts are softened by heating them with hot water or steam, and the bark is removed. Each bolt is centered in a large lathe (Fig. 1·26), and the cutting mechanism—a pressure bar and knife that run the full length of the bolt—is put in place. As the bolt is turned, the knife peels off a thin layer of veneer while the pressure bar compresses the wood ahead of the knife to reduce splitting and cutting checks.

Figure 1 · 24
Logs for plywood mill.
(Plywood Manufacturers' Association
of British Columbia)

The continuous sheet of veneer is clipped by machine into pieces that have few knots or other defects (Fig. 1·27). The pieces are put through a drier (Fig. 1·28), where the moisture content is reduced to between 3 and 8 percent, depending on the type of glue to be used. A splicer edge-glues pieces into a continuous sheet large enough for face plies, and a patching machine (Fig. 1·29) removes defects still remaining in these sheets and inserts a patch which matches the grain as closely as possible. The core and crossbands are not usually edge-glued.

Figure 1 · 25
Bolts on the way into
plywood plant.
(Plywood Manufacturers' Association
of British Columbia)

Figure 1 · 26
Bolt mounted in lathe.
(Plywood Manufacturers' Association
of British Columbia)

Figure 1 · 27
Clipped pieces of veneer coming from clipper.
(Plywood Manufacturers' Association of British Columbia)

Figure 1 · 28
Veneer drier. (Plywood Manufacturers' Association of British Columbia)

Figure 1 · 29
Plywood patching machine.
(Plywood Manufacturers' Association of British Columbia)

Figure 1 · 30
Applying glue to veneer. (Plywood
Manufacturers' Association
of British Columbia)

Waterproof glue is applied by machine to the face plies,
core, and crossbands (Fig. 1·30). They are assembled into
plywood form and placed in hot presses (Fig. 1·31), which
compress the veneers into solid sheets of approximately the
proper thickness. At the same time the heat cures the glue, a
process which takes from 2 to 20 minutes, depending on the
thickness of the stock, the type of glue, and the temperature
of the press.

Figure 1 · 31
Hot press. (Plywood Manufacturers' Association
of British Columbia)

Figure 1 · 32
Trimming plywood sheets. (Plywood
Manufacturers' Association
of British Columbia)

The plywood sheets are trimmed to dimensions (Fig.
1·32), squared on double cutoff saws, and sanded to thickness (Fig. 1·33). They are again examined for minor flaws,
graded, and packaged for shipment.

Figure 1 · 33
Sanding plywood to thickness. (Plywood
Manufacturers' Association
of British Columbia)

Figure 1 · 34
Plywood packaged for shipment. (Plywood
Manufacturers' Association
of British Columbia)

PROPERTIES OF PLYWOOD

One of the main advantages of plywood is that it has good strength across as well as along the panel. Wood is considerably stronger and stiffer along the grain than across it; in plywood the grain runs in two directions at right angles, so cross-panel strength is improved. The more plies there are in a panel, the more nearly equal the strength in both directions will be. Three-ply panel has approximately twice as much wood with the grain running in one direction as it has in the other. In seven-ply panels strength is essentially equal in both directions.

The movement in wood due to swelling and shrinking as it absorbs and loses moisture is much greater across the grain than along it. Because in plywood approximately half the wood grain runs in one direction and the other half at right angles to it, the tendency to swell and shrink is neutralized to a large extent.

Because of its successive layers at right angles to one another, plywood cannot be split in the plane of the panel. This is of great importance since it means that nails and screws can be driven very close to the edge of the panels without danger of splitting. For the same reason, plywood has a greater impact resistance to blows than ordinary wood.

Plywood can be bent more easily than ordinary wood of the same thickness. The radius of curvature depends on the thickness of the panel and is limited by the strength of the outer plies in tension and by the strength of the inner plies in compression. When plywood is made with waterproof glue, its ability to bend can be increased considerably by soaking and steaming.

Plywood offers innumerable possibilities for decoration because of the great variety of colors and textures that can be produced on the face plies. Some species, particularly hardwoods, offer a great variation in grain figure. Some also show a wide divergence in color. Decorative effects also can be applied to the face ply by sandblasting, by pressure, or by etching with wire brushes.

PLYWOOD GRADES

Softwood Plywood

Although several species of softwood are used in making plywood, by far the most commonly used species is Douglas fir. Douglas fir plywood is manufactured in a number of grades, thicknesses, and panel dimensions, each grade being given a complete grade description according to national standards. Table 1·6 lists the grades of fir plywood, a description of each grade, and the common uses made of each.

GRADE	DESCRIPTION	USES
Good two sides (G2S)	Each face smooth and sound, no knots or open defects; may contain neatly made patches, suitable for highest grade paint or other finish. Waterproof glue.	Where appearance is the prime consideration, with both sides of panel exposed to view, e.g., furniture, cabinet doors.
Good one side solid back (G/Solid)	Face smooth and sound, no knots or open defects; may contain neatly made patches. Back a firm, solid, paintable surface with neatly made patches, plugs, and small sound knots. Waterproof glue.	Where best appearing surface is required on one side with relatively good appearance on the other, e.g., doors, furniture, built-ins, kitchen cabinets, toys.
Good one side (G1S)	Face smooth and sound, no knots or open defects; may contain neatly made patches. Back may have limited size knotholes or other defects which have no material effect on strength or serviceability. Waterproof glue.	Where good appearance of one side only is a prime consideration, e.g., paneling, soffits, sliding doors.
Solid two sides (Solid 2S)	Each face solid, contains neatly made patches, plugs, and small sound knots. Similar to back of G/Solid Grade. Waterproof glue.	Same uses as G2S when finishing requirements are not as exacting, e.g., shelving, concrete forms. Recommended for opaque paint finishes.
Solid one side (Solid 1S)	Face solid, contains neatly made patches, plugs, and sound knots. Back may contain limited size knotholes and other defects which have no material effect on strength or serviceability. Waterproof glue.	Same uses as G1S when finishing requirements are not as exacting, e.g., floor underlay where sanded surface is desired. Suitable for concrete forms.
Marine	Both faces smooth and sound, no knots or open defects, may contain neatly made patches. All interior plies solid, with neatly made patches and small sound knots. Waterproof glue.	Hull planking and all marine uses.

Table 1·6
Fir plywood grades and uses.
(British Columbia Plywood Manufacturers' Association)

Panel width (standard all grades): 48 in.
Panel length (standard all grades): 96 in. (108- and 120-in. lengths available on request).
Panel thickness (standard all grades): ¼ in. (sheathing grade ⁵⁄₁₆ in.), ½ in., ⅝ in., ¾ in. (⅞-, 1-, 1⅛-, and 1¼-in. thicknesses available on request).

GRADE	DESCRIPTION	USES
Unsanded sheathing	Construction grade. Each face may have limited size open defects which have no material effect on strength or serviceability. Waterproof glue.	Where strength and economy are required but smooth finish unnecessary, e.g., structural applications such as roof decking, subflooring, and single finish for farm structures, fences, utility, and industrial buildings.
Underlay sheathing	Similar to unsanded sheathing grade except one face has solid surface suitable for application of flexible floorings. Solid surface face may contain plugs, tight knots, rough grain, and limited number of splits which do not affect panel serviceability. Waterproof glue.	For underlay with tile, linoleum, or other flooring. May be used as underlayment over subflooring or as combined subfloor and underlayment. Suitable for exterior finish where smooth surfaces are not required, e.g., fences.

Panel width (standard all grades): 48 in.

Panel length (standard all grades): 96 in. (108- and 120-in. lengths available on request).

Panel thickness (standard all grades): ¼ in. (sheathing grade ⁵⁄₁₆ in.), ½ in., ⅝ in., ¾ in. (⅞-, 1-, 1⅛-, and 1¼-in. thicknesses available on request).

Hardwood Plywood

Plywood is made from many species of hardwood, including poplar, birch, beech, ash, mahogany, walnut, rosewood, elm, and many others. Except with poplar, the usual procedure is first to grade the veneers and then to use various combinations of veneers to make different grades of plywood.

The veneers are classified into three grades, Red (Good), Blue (Sound), and Black (Backing). The specifications for each grade are as follows:

Red. The veneer shall be tightly and smoothly cut, containing the natural character markings inherent to the species, unselected for uniformity of color if one piece. If not one piece, the joints shall be matched to avoid sharp contrasts in color and grain. Blurs, occasional pin knots, slight mineral streaks, slight natural discolorations, sapwood, and inconspicuous small patches shall be permitted. Knots other than pin knots, wormholes, splits, open joints, sand-throughs, cross breaks, rough and lifting grain, shake, doze, and other forms of decay shall not be permitted. Voids and gaps or other openings under the face plies of Good Grade (G) shall not show through the face in such a way as to result in an unde-

34

Table 1 · 7
Nominal veneer thicknesses
and weights of
Douglas fir plywood.
(Douglas Fir Plywood Association)

NET PLYWOOD THICKNESS, IN.	NO. OF PLIES	VENEER THICKNESS, IN. NOMINAL			WEIGHT PER 1,000 SQ FT
		FACES*	CENTERS	CROSSBAND	
1/8—R	3	1/24	1/24		490
1/8—S	3	1/16	1/16		490
3/16—R	3	1/16	1/16		640
3/16—S	3	1/12	1/12		640
1/4—R	3	1/12	1/12		790
1/4—S	3	1/9	1/9		790
5/16—R	3	1/10*	1/10*		950
5/16—S	3	1/8	1/8		950
3/8—R	3	1/8	1/8		1,125
3/8—S	3	1/8	3/16		1,125
3/8—S	5	1/10	1/12	2 at 1/12	1,125
7/16—R	3	1/8	3/16		1,300
7/16—R	5	1/10	1/12	2 at 1/12	1,300
7/16—S	5	1/10	1/10	2 at 1/10	1,300
1/2—R	5	1/10	1/10	2 at 1/10	1,525
1/2—S	5	1/8	1/8	2 at 1/10	1,525
9/16—R	5	1/8	1/8	2 at 1/10	1,675
9/16—S	5	1/8	1/8	2 at 1/8	1,675
5/8—R	5	1/8	1/8	2 at 1/8	1,825
5/8—S	5	1/8	3/16	2 at 1/8	1,825
11/16—R	5	1/8	3/16	2 at 1/8	2,000
11/16—S	5	1/8	1/8	2 at 3/16	2,000
3/4—R	5	1/8	1/8	2 at 3/16	2,225
3/4—S	5	1/8	3/16	2 at 3/16	2,225
3/4—S	7	1/8	2 at 1/12	3 at 1/8	2,225
13/16—R	5	1/8	3/16	2 at 3/16	2,375
13/16—R	7	1/8	2 at 1/12	3 at 1/8	2,375
13/16—S	7	1/8	2 at 1/8	3 at 1/8	2,375
7/8—R	7	1/8	2 at 1/8	3 at 1/8	2,600
7/8—S	7	1/8	2 at 5/32	3 at 1/8	2,600
15/16—R	7	1/8	2 at 5/32	3 at 1/8	2,800
15/16—S	7	1/8	2 at 3/16	3 at 1/8	2,800
1—R	7	1/8	2 at 3/16	3 at 1/8	3,000
1—S	7	1/8	2 at 1/8	3 at 3/16	3,000
1 1/16—R	7	1/8	2 at 1/8	3 at 3/16	3,175
1 1/16—S	7	1/8	2 at 1/6	3 at 3/16	3,175
1 1/8—R	7	1/8	2 at 1/6	3 at 3/16	3,350
1 1/8—S	7	1/8	2 at 3/16	3 at 3/16	3,350
1 3/16—R	7	1/8	2 at 3/16	3 at 3/16	3,525
1 3/16—S	7	1/8	2 at 7/32	3 at 3/16	3,525

S = sanded.
R = rough.
* For sanded panels, thickness is before sanding.

sirable appearance. Voids in other inner plies shall not exceed in width the thickness of the ply in which they occur.

Blue. The veneer shall be tightly cut but need not be matched in color or for grain at the joints. Mineral streaks, stain discoloration, sapwood, patches, small areas of doze in early stages if sound, wormholes, open joints not exceeding the thickness of the face veneer cross breaks, gum spots, small bark pockets, sound tight knots not exceeding ¾ in. average diameter, open knotholes not exceeding ⅛ in. diameter, small areas of rough and lifting grain are permitted. The foregoing defects generally occur singly and a combination of more than three types of defects is not permitted. *The defects in this grade of panel should be such that minor filling and/or patching will provide a suitable high-quality painting surface.* Veneer containing brashness, shake, sandthroughs, face overlaps, excessive doze, and any other form of decay is not permitted.

Black. The veneer may contain brash wood, shake, sandthroughs, compression failures, doze, loose and rough cuttings, open knotholes up to 1½ in. diameter, splits not exceeding ¼ in. wide, which may extend the full length of the panel. The veneer of this grade is used chiefly as the back ply with Good and Sound Grade veneers.

The grades of plywood commonly made by using various combinations of the above three grades of veneer are: Good Both Sides (G2S), Good One Side Sound One Side (G/So), Good One Side Backing One Side (G1S), Sound Both Sides (So2S), Sound One Side Backing One Side (So1S). The grade is marked on each plywood panel by means of a color code consisting of two parallel colored lines appearing on the *left* side of each panel end. G2S is represented by two red lines, G/So by one red and one blue line, G1S by one red and one black line, So2S by two blue lines and So1S by one blue and one black line (Fig. 1·35). In addition, the type of glue bond is indicated by black lines on the *right* side of each panel end. One black line represents exterior waterproof glue; two black lines indicate interior highly water-resistant glue (Fig. 1·36).

Figures 1·37 to 1·40 illustrate a few of the common uses of plywood in the construction industry.

G2S

Good both sides

G/So

Good one side
Sound one side

G/S

Good one side
Backing one side

So2S

Sound both sides

So/S

Sound one side
Backing one side

Figure 1 · 35
Grades of hardwood plywood.
(Plywood Manufacturers' Association
of British Columbia)

Figure 1 · 36
Example of panel marking. (Plywood
Manufacturers' Association
of British Columbia)

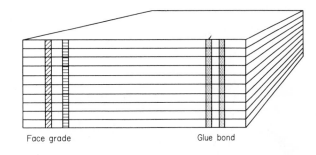

Face grade   Glue bond

Figure 1 · 37
Plywood for exterior use. (Plywood
Manufacturers' Association
of British Columbia)

Figure 1 · 38
Plywood for excavation shoring. (Plywood
Manufacturers' Association
of British Columbia)

Figure 1 · 39
Plywood for sheathing. (Plywood Manufacturers' Association of British Columbia)

Figure 1 · 40
Plywood for formwork. (Plywood Manufacturers' Association of British Columbia)

Normally plywood sheets are made in 8- and 10-ft lengths, but much longer sheets can be made by joining (*scarfing*) two or more sheets end to end. In Fig. 1·41, sheets are being joined in a scarf press.

GLOSSARY

bast	Strong woody fibers found between the outer bark and the cambium layer
bolt	A section of log used to make veneer for plywood

Figure 1 · 41
**Making long sheets by scarfing. (Plywood Manufacturers'
Association of British Columbia)**

boom chain	A long chain made by linking logs to-gether, end to end, with chains or cables
bucking	Cutting a tree trunk into lengths
camber	A light convex curve
cambium layer	Layer of growing cells, just under the bark of a tree
cant	A squared or partially squared log, to be resawed into lumber
cellulose	An inert substance, the chief ingredient of the cell walls of plants
dry kiln	An oven used for removing moisture from lumber
edger	A machine to remove the bark edges of rough sawed boards
flitch	A thin layer of wood, often used as the outer layer of hardwood plywood
highline	A cable running between the tops of two spar trees
lignin	A substance related to cellulose
quarter-sawed	Sawed in such a way as to produce edge-grain lumber
scarf	Tapered end joint in lumber
skidway	A sloping stand on which logs are piled
spar tree	A large standing tree, with the branches removed, used to anchor one end of a cable
structural lumber	Lumber carefully graded for strength and used in structurally designed con-struction
trimmer	A machine to cut boards to length
yard lumber	Lumber commonly used for building purposes

REVIEW QUESTIONS

1 List five properties of wood which have created a demand for it as a building material. Which one of these do you consider to be the most important?

2 Outline briefly some of the steps which are being taken in this country to try to ensure a more constant future supply of wood for lumber.

3 (a) How can one tell the age of a tree by examination?
   (b) List two other facts one could tell about the tree from examination.

4 (a) List three common *hardwoods* whose wood is not hard and three common *softwoods* whose wood is not soft.
   (b) Explain the reason for this apparent contradiction.

5 (a) Explain the difference between *free* and *hygroscopic* moisture in a tree.
   (b) Which type is lost first from a piece of lumber?
   (c) Illustrate by diagram how an electric moisture meter works.

6 (a) In general terms, what does *wood grain* mean?
   (b) Draw a vertical cross section of a piece of *edge-grain* flooring.
   (c) Explain the difference between *cross grain* and *coarse grain* in wood.

7 List seven factors to be considered when grading lumber.

8 (a) Outline briefly the procedure followed in *air-drying* and *kiln-drying* lumber.
   (b) What is the practical lower limit of moisture content achieved in each case?

9 (a) What are the three general use classifications of structural lumber?
   (b) How is each of the three intended to be loaded?
   (c) How does the grading of structural lumber differ from grading of yard or factory lumber?

10 How many board feet of lumber are there in the following order?:

   24 pieces 2 × 4 in., 16 ft long
   15 pieces 2 × 10 in., 12 ft long
   20 pieces 2 × 12 in., 14 ft long
   36 pieces 1 × 8 in., 14 ft long

11 (a) What is laminated timber?
   (b) To what does the term *glue-laminated* refer?
   (c) List six advantages gained in using glue-laminated timbers.
   (d) What factors should be considered when choosing a glue for laminating timber?

12 (a) What are the four most important properties of plywood which give it advantages over sawed lumber?
   (b) What is the major consideration when making plywood in which the core and face plies are made of two different species of wood?

SELECTED SOURCES OF INFORMATION

American Institute of Timber Construction, Washington, D.C.

American Wood Preservers' Association, Washington, D.C.

Canada Dept. of Resources and Development, Forestry Branch, Ottawa, Ont.

Canadian Institute of Timber Construction, Ottawa, Ont.

Canadian Lumbermen's Association, Ottawa, Ont.

Canadian Wood Development Council, Ottawa, Ont.

Douglas Fir Plywood Association, Vancouver, B.C.

National Lumber Manufacturers' Association, Washington, D.C.

Southern Pine Association, New Orleans, La.

U.S. Dept. of Agriculture, Forest Service, Washington, D.C.

West Coast Lumbermen's Association, Portland, Ore.

2

CEMENT, AGGREGATES, AND CONCRETE

Cements have been known and used for at least two thousand years. The Romans used a great deal of this material in their construction projects, many of which still stand. The cements they used were natural and pozzolan cements, made from naturally occurring mixtures of limestone and clay and from a mixture of slaked lime and volcanic ash containing silica.

CEMENTS

PORTLAND CEMENT

It was not until 1824 that the first step was made in producing the type of cement with which we are familiar today. The inventor, Joseph Aspdin, produced a powder made from a calcined mixture of limestone and clay. He called it portland cement because when it hardened it produced a material resembling stone from the quarries near Portland, England.

This method of making cement has been improved upon since that time; but the basic process has remained, and modern portland cement is a properly proportioned mixture of calcareous (containing calcium carbonate) and argillacious (clayey) materials which are heated to the point of incipient fusion and finely pulverized. When this material is mixed with water it hardens into a solid mass through chemical combinations of the ingredients with water.

The calcareous materials are generally found in the form of limestone, chalk, marl, and oyster shells or in the precipitated form obtained as a by-product from the manufacture of alkalis. Argillacious material is obtained from clay, shale, slate, selected blast-furnace slag, iron ore, and sand.

Cement is made in this country from all these materials, each plant using one or more of the calcareous materials in combination with one or more of the argillacious materials, e.g., limestone and clay in proportions of about 4 parts limestone to 1 of clay. Sometimes shale is used in place of clay.

Limestone is quarried, loaded in dump trucks, and fed into large gyratory or jaw crushers. It passes through a hammer mill next where further reduction in size takes place, and from there it goes to rock storage. From storage, the rock is fed to a tube mill, with the clay or crushed shale being added at this point. Water is also added at this point, so that the product of the tube mill is *slurry*, a mixture of very finely ground raw material and water. The slurry is stored in tanks and fed into huge rotary kilns 11 to 12 ft in diameter and from 200 to 455 ft long, with a slope of about ½ in. per ft. The kilns are fired with crushed coal or gas from the discharge end so that the slurry advances against the heat blast as the kilns rotate.

At 800°F, the excess water is driven off and further along the kiln, at 1600°F, the limestone breaks down into calcium oxide and carbon dioxide. Finally at 2700°F, about 30 ft from the discharge end, sintering takes place, the materials reach incipient fusion, and a clinker is formed. The clinker is cooled, crushed, mixed with about 3 percent crushed gypsum, and fed into a tube mill. Here the final grinding takes place so that 75 to 90 percent of the final product will pass a 325-mesh sieve (more than 100,000 openings per sq in.). The cement is finally bagged or loaded in bulk into railway cement cars or cement trucks.

The composition of portland cement is rather complicated but basically it consists of four main ingredients:

Tricalcium silicate, $3CaOSiO_2$ (C_3S)
Dicalcium silicate, $2CaOSiO_2$ (C_2S)
Tricalcium aluminate, $3CaOAl_2O_3$ (C_3A)
Tetracalcium aluminoferrite, $4CaOAl_2O_3Fe_2O_3$ (C_4AF)

The symbols in parentheses are the abbreviations used by the cement association. To these is added about 3 percent gypsum, $CaSO_4$.

The percentage of these four basic ingredients can be varied in order to produce several types of portland cement, each with some unique characteristics. The three most common types are *normal portland cement, high-early-strength portland cement,* and *sulfate-resistant portland cement.* In addition, two other types are made, a *low-heat cement* and a *modified normal portland.*

Normal portland is used for general construction work when the special properties of the other types are not required. It is normally used for reinforced-concrete buildings, bridges, pavements and sidewalks where the soil conditions are normal, most concrete masonry units, and for all uses where the concrete is not subject to special sulfate hazard or where the heat generated by the hydration of the cement is not objectionable.

Modified portland generates heat at a slower rate than normal portland and is used in mass concrete work. It also has better resistance to the action of sulfates.

High-early-strength cement is used where higher strengths are required at early periods. It is particularly useful where it is required to remove forms as soon as possible or to put the concrete into service at an early stage. High-early makes it possible to reduce the period of protection for concrete during cold weather.

Low-heat portland is a special cement for use where the amount and rate of heat generated must be kept to a minimum. Strength is also developed at a slower rate. It is intended for use only in mass concrete construction such as dams where the heat generated during hydration is an important factor.

Sulfate-resistant cement is intended for use in structures subject to attack by waters containing sulfates, such as the water in some manufacturing plants, seawater, and groundwater in some areas.

In the United States normal portland cement is known as Type 1, modified portland as Type 2, high-early-strength as Type 3, low-heat cement as Type 4, and sulfate-resistant cement as Type 5.

The basic ingredients of these five different types is given in Table 2·1.

| TYPE | COMPOUND COMPOSITION, % | | | | FINENESS | |
	C_3S	C_2S	C_3A	C_4AF	SQ CM/ GRAM*	PERCENT PASSING 325-MESH SIEVE
1 Normal	45	27	11	8	1,710	90.7
2 Modified	44	31	5	13	1,990	94.7
3 High early strength	53	19	10	10	2,730	99.5
4 Low heat	28	49	4	12	1,880	93.1
5 Sulfate resistant	38	43	4	8	1,960	93.2

*Surface area as determined by Wagner turbidimeter test.

The rate at which the strength of concrete increases varies according to the type of cement used. Table 2·2 gives the approximate strength values of concrete, using the five types, at three different periods. Concrete made with normal portland cement is the basis of comparison.

Cement is subjected to a considerable number of chemical and physical tests to ensure constant high quality. All of them are outlined in American Standards for Testing Materials. The chemical tests include (1) loss on ignition (4 percent maximum mostly water), (2) insoluble residue (.85 percent maximum), (3) sulfuric anhydride (SO_3) (2 percent maxi-

| TYPE OF PORTLAND CEMENT | COMPRESSIVE STRENGTH—PERCENT OF STRENGTH OF NORMAL PORTLAND-CEMENT CONCRETE | | |
	3 DAYS	28 DAYS	3 MONTHS
1 Normal	100	100	100
2 Modified	80	85	100
3 High early strength	190	130	115
4 Low heat	50	65	90
5 Sulfate resistant	65	65	85

mum), and (4) magnesia (MgO) (4 percent maximum). The physical tests include (1) consistency (Vicat needle) test, (2) soundness test, and (3) tensile test.

ALUMINOUS CEMENT

For many years research has been conducted in an attempt to produce a structural hydraulic cement which would not liberate free lime during and after hydration. Elimination of free lime was desired primarily in order to provide a cement for making concrete which would not be attacked by seawater and injurious groundwaters. It was discovered that a cement with a high content of alumina (Al_2O_3), with approximately equal parts of Al_2O_3 and CaO, would meet this requirement.

This cement is now produced commercially by completely melting a mixture of bauxite (aluminum ore) and a calcareous material (chalk or limestone). The molten material is tapped from the furnace continuously and cast into pigs similar in shape to the iron pigs from a blast furnace. The pigs are crushed and ground to a fine powder (not as fine as portland cement) in a ball mill. The resulting product, without addition of any other materials, is called *Ciment Fondu* (melted cement).

The chemical composition of Ciment Fondu is considerably different from that of portland cement. The Al_2O_3 content is about 40 percent, the content of CaO slightly lower. The SiO_2 content is less than 6 percent. Quite wide variations in these amounts are possible without changing the characteristics of the cement, but the ratio of Al_2O_3 to CaO is not less than 0.85 or greater than 1.3.

The initial set of Ciment Fondu is slower than that of portland cement. The average initial setting times are from two to four hours, and the final set takes place about 30 minutes later. After the final set, the extremely fast hardening process begins, and within 24 hours the concrete has developed the 28-day strength of similar concrete made with portland cement.

Although Ciment Fondu could be used in nearly every situation in which portland cement is used, it is particularly valuable where concrete must be put into service in a short time. Repairs to sewers and concrete water mains, for example, can be made overnight. Machine foundations and floors can be put to use the day after placing. Airport runways can be repaired with little or no disruption of traffic.

The fact that Ciment Fondu generates considerable heat gives it great practical value in cold-weather work. Freezing must be prevented during the first few hours until the concrete begins to generate its own heat. After that, with a normal mix and reasonable bulk, the concrete will generate enough heat to keep the mass from freezing, even at temperatures several degrees below freezing.

Because Ciment Fondu liberates no free lime during hydration, the concrete is highly resistant to attacks by sulfates. It also resists many of the chemicals produced in processing plants better than concrete made with portland cement.

The other important characteristic of Ciment Fondu is its ability to retain binding power when subjected to heat. Thus concrete made with Ciment Fondu and refractory aggregates is useful for flue linings, combustion chambers for domestic furnaces, door linings for annealing furnaces, furnace foundations, etc. Generally it is limited to service below 2500°F.

SPECIAL CEMENTS

WHITE PORTLAND CEMENT

White portland cement is similar in all respects to normal portland except in color. It is made from specially selected materials to produce a pure white, nonstaining cement. Sometimes integral waterproofing is added so that water is repelled at the surface of the concrete and adsorption is reduced.

MASONRY CEMENT

Masonry cement has been specially designed to produce better mortar than that made with normal portland cement or with a lime-cement combination.

It is made by grinding together a carefully proportioned mixture of normal portland cement clinker and high-calcium limestone. To the finely ground product an air-entraining agent, a plasticizing agent, and a set retarder are added.

The mortar made with this cement has particularly good plasticity and workability, good adhesion and bond, and has adequate strength to meet ASTM specifications. It also offers great resistance to efflorescence and has good appearance.

AIR-ENTRAINING PORTLAND CEMENT

Sometimes small amounts of certain air-entraining agents are added to the clinker and ground with it to produce air-entraining cements. Concrete made with them contains millions of minute well-distributed and completely separated air bubbles. The entrained air resulting from the use of these cements should range from about 4 percent for concrete with large-size aggregate to 6 or 7 percent for concrete with ⅜-in. maximum size coarse aggregate.

Concrete containing entrained air has proved to be more resistant to severe frost and to the effects of salt applied to sidewalks and pavements for ice and snow removal.

OIL-WELL CEMENT

This is a special portland cement developed to harden properly at high temperatures found in very deep oil wells.

TYPES OF AGGREGATES USED IN CONCRETE

Concrete can be considered to be an artificial stone made by binding together particles of some inert material with a paste made of cement and water. These inert materials are the *aggregate*. Among the materials used for this purpose are sand, gravel, crushed stone, cinders, crushed furnace slag, burned clay, expanded vermiculite, and perlite. All of these vary in strength and weight; the strength and durability of the concrete depend on the type of aggregate used.

STONE AGGREGATE

Sand, gravel, and crushed stone fall into this category. Because they constitute from 66 to 78 percent of the volume of concrete, they should meet certain requirements if the concrete is to be strong, durable, and economical.

They must be clean, hard, strong, well graded, and of the proper shape, either rounded or of a more or less cubical shape. Sharp, angular, and rough aggregate particles require more fine material and more paste to make good concrete than do rounded ones. Flat, slivery pieces make concrete more difficult to finish and should be limited to not more than 15 percent of the total. Unsound and laminated pieces result in concrete of reduced strength. Particles should be free from coatings of clay or other fine material and free from organic impurities that may affect the setting of the cement paste.

These requirements apply to both fine and coarse aggregate. In the case of coarse aggregate, visual inspection will often disclose these weaknesses, but where doubt exists the aggregate should be tested. However, it is not so easy to inspect fine aggregate in the same way, and normally a series of tests is carried out on these to determine their suitability for concrete.

One test called a *silt test* determines the amount of clay or silt present in sand. It is made as follows:

Place 2 in. of the sand to be tested in a quart jar and then fill the jar three-quarters full with clean water. Place the top on the jar and shake the contents well. Allow the jar to sit for several hours. As the solid material settles out of the water, the very fine material will be deposited last in a layer on top of the sand. When the water is clear again, measure the depth of the silt deposit. If it exceeds ⅛ in., the aggregate contains too much fine material and should not be used for concrete without washing. Figure 2·1 shows a sample of sand with an excessively thick layer of silt on top.

Figure 2·1
A silt test.
(Portland Cement Association)

Figure 2·2
Colorimetric test.
(Portland Cement Association)

A colorimetric test determines whether sand contains injurious amounts of organic matter. Fill an ordinary 12-oz prescription bottle to the 4½-oz mark with the sand to be tested. Fill to the 7-oz mark with a 3 percent solution of sodium hydroxide. Shake the contents well and allow to stand for 24 hours. If the liquid, which was originally clear, is colored, it indicates the presence of some organic matter. A color that ranges from light to dark straw indicates that the amount of organic matter is not serious. If the color ranges from dark straw to chocolate brown, the aggregate is not suitable for concrete unless the organic matter is removed by washing. Figure 2·2 illustrates three samples, in one of which the solution is clear, in one there is slight discoloration, while in the third the solution has turned very dark.

To test the gradation of both fine and coarse aggregates, a set of laboratory sieves are used. They include Nos. 4, 8, 16, 30, 50, and 100 for fine aggregate and 6-in., 3-in., 1½-in., ⅜-in., and No. 4 for coarse aggregate. These sizes are based on square openings; in the case of the numbered sieves, they indicate the number of meshes per lineal inch. For example, a 50-mesh sieve has 50 meshes per linear in. or 2,500 square openings per sq in.

To check the gradation of fine aggregate, weigh out a 1,000-gram sample of dry material and pass it through the fine-aggregate sieves, arranged in order as illustrated in Fig. 2·3(b). Weigh the amount of material retained in each sieve and calculate the percentage of each. The results should correspond to the gradation Table 2·3.

Table 2·3
Gradation range
in fine aggregate.

SIEVE SIZE NO.	PERCENT RETAINED (CUMULATIVE)
4	0-5
8	10-20
16	20-40
30	40-70
50	70-88
100	92-98

To find the cumulative percentage retained on each sieve, add the percentage retained on each one to the total retained on the sieves above. For example, suppose that a 1,000-gram sample yielded the following amounts on each sieve after screening:

SIEVE NO.	AMOUNT RETAINED, GRAMS
4	40
8	121
16	214
30	251
50	209
100	136

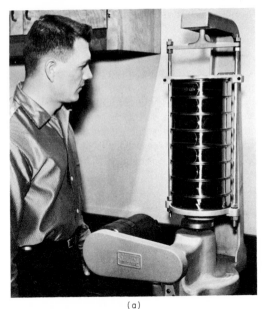

Figure 2·3
(a) Sand screens.
(b) Passing sand through sieves.
(Soiltest, Inc.)

The percentage of the sample retained in each sieve would be:

SIEVE NO.	PERCENT RETAINED
4	4.0
8	12.1
16	21.4
30	25.1
50	20.9
100	13.6

Then the cumulative percentages would be:

SIEVE NO.	PERCENT RETAINED (CUMULATIVE)
4	4.0
8	16.1
16	37.5
30	62.6
50	83.5
100	97.1

Another test made on fine aggregate determines the relative fineness or coarseness of the material, a *fineness modulus test*. A 500-gram sample is taken and screened. The percentage retained on each screen and the cumulative percentages are calculated as above. The cumulative percentages are totaled and divided by 100. The resulting number is the fineness modulus number. Allowable fineness modulus numbers range from 2.20 to 3.20. Numbers from 2.20 to

2.60 indicate a fine sand; those from 2.61 to 2.90, medium sand; and those from 2.91 to 3.20, coarse sand.

The amount of moisture in fine aggregate is determined by a *moisture test*. Again, a 500-gram sample is taken, placed in a shallow pan, and dried by gas jets in an oven or by pouring methyl hydrate over the sample and burning it off. Drying continues until the sample no longer continues to lose weight. Now, loss in weight/dry weight $\times$ 100 = percentage of total moisture. From this total subtract 1 for adsorbed moisture (moisture contained in the surface crevasses of the aggregate particles) and the result is the percentage of free moisture in the sample.

Tests are also carried out on both fine and coarse aggregates to determine their specific gravity. One simple method is to take a 1,000-gram sample, place it in water, and catch and measure the water displaced. The volume of water converted to grams and divided into 1,000 gives the specific gravity of the sample.

Samples of aggregates to be tested should be as representative as possible. To ensure this, a quantity of the material should be taken from a number of locations in the stockpile. The total sample should be thoroughly mixed and then passed through a splitter. This piece of equipment, (Fig. 2·4) divides the whole sample into two equal parts. One half of the sample is then discarded and the other half passed through the splitter again. This procedure is repeated until a final sample of the required size is obtained.

Figure 2·4
Sand splitter.
(Soiltest, Inc.)

LIGHTWEIGHT AGGREGATES

Table 2·4 outlines the results of some tests carried out by the Bureau of Reclamation on a variety of types and sizes of lightweight aggregates used for concrete.

Expanded Shale

This lightweight aggregate, variously known as *herculite* or *haydite,* is produced by passing a crushed shale through a rotary kiln at about 2000°F. Gases within the shale expand, forming millions of tiny air cells within the mass. When the material cools and solidifies, these cells remain, each surrounded by a hard vitreous waterproof membrane. Each piece of material is likewise surrounded by a vitreous shell.

Particles form in various sizes from very fine to ¾ in., and the product is carefully screened into three commercial sizes: Fine: 0 to ³⁄₁₆ in.; Medium: ³⁄₁₆ to ⅜ in.; Coarse: ⅜ to ¾ in. Fine aggregate weighs about 1,600 lb per cu yd, medium about 1,200 lb, and coarse about 1,000 lb.

Herculite is used to a large extent to replace stone aggregates in the production of structural concrete, because it reduces weight by about one-third with no loss of structural strength for comparable cement contents. Because of the light weight and its insulating value, due to its cellular structure, it is also used for plaster stucco and gunite aggregate. It has high resistance to heat and for this reason is used for refractory linings, fireproofing of structural steel, and for the construction of other concrete surfaces exposed to high temperatures. The concrete made from such aggregate also has better sound absorption and acoustical properties than that made with stone aggregate.

Because of their comparative lightness, herculite aggregates have a greater tendency to segregate than stone aggregates. Overvibration of the concrete should be avoided because this causes the coarser particles to rise to the surface and results in a surface which is difficult to finish. A vinsol-resin air-entraining agent is recommended to improve the workability of the concrete and to reduce segregation. Air entrainment should normally range from 4 to 6 percent.

Vermiculite and Perlite Aggregates

Vermiculite and perlite lightweight aggregates are described in Chap. 14. They are not used for making structural concrete, but they are widely used for insulating concrete roof decks and floor slabs and for plaster aggregate.

Expanded Slag

Blast-furnace slag is crushed to appropriate size for use in mass concrete construction, but sometimes it may contain too much sulfur to be used for reinforced concrete. The particles of aggregate are quite porous, but their surfaces provide a good bond for the cement paste. Concrete made from them

Table 2·4
Results of tests carried out by
Bureau of Reclamation.
(Portland Cement Association)

GRADINGS SUBMITTED	SIEVE ANALYSES—AGGREGATE PASSING U.S. STANDARD SIEVES, PERCENT BY WEIGHT								FINE-NESS MODULUS
	¾- IN.	⅜- IN.	NO. 4	NO. 8	NO. 16	NO. 30	NO. 50	NO. 100	
R1. Expanded shale or clay, coated:									
Coarse	99	1	0	—	—	—	—	—	7.00
Medium	100	86	20	1	1	1	1	1	5.89
Fine	—	100	99	98	64	28	8	2	3.01
R2. Expanded shale or clay, crushed	100	74	49	34	22	13	7	4	4.97
R3. Expanded slag:									
Coarse	100	90	28	7	5	4	4	4	5.58
Fine	—	100	99	73	49	29	16	11	2.23
R4. Expanded slag	—	100	90	56	25	9	3	1	4.16
R5. Expanded slag	—	100	96	78	47	20	8	4	3.47
R6. Scoria	—	100	94	74	57	42	25	11	2.97
R7. Treated pumice[g]	100	67	7	1	1	1	1	1	6.21
R8. Pumice:									
Coarse	100	97	44	13	9	8	8	7	5.14
Medium	—	100	99	76	47	26	16	11	3.25
Fine	—	—	100	94	71	50	37	28	2.20
R9. Pumice	96	38	11	9	7	5	5	5	6.24
R10. Pumice	—	100	93	79	60	42	29	21	2.76
R11. Pumicite	—	100	99	99	99	99	99	98	0.07
R12. Perlite[f]:									
Coarse	100	98	50	8	5	4	4	3	5.28
Fine	—	100	79	19	4	3	3	3	4.89
R13. Perlite	100	98	65	28	13	8	7	6	4.75
R14. Perlite	—	—	100	95	69	34	8	4	2.90
R15. Perlite	—	—	—	100	92	42	13	4	2.49
R16. Perlite:									
Coarse	—	100	88	16	9	8	8	6	4.65
Medium	—	—	100	84	6	3	3	2	4.02
Fine	—	—	—	—	100	92	70	44	0.94
R17. Perlite	—	—	—	—	100	87	57	29	1.27
R18. Expanded vermiculite	—	100	96	79	46	19	5	1	3.54
R19. Treated expanded vermiculite[h]	—	—	100	88	36	26	14	6	3.30
R20. Diatomaceous earth	100	91	14	3	2	2	2	2	5.84

[a] Determined on saturated-surface dry aggregate.
[b] Color ratings for amount of organic impurities.
[c] Special gradings used in crushing-strength tests.
[d] 39.4 lb for ⅜ to ¾ in. aggregate; 60.0 lb for sand portion; 45.7 lb for No. 4 to ⅜ in. aggregate.
[e] 1.64 for No. 4 to ¾ in. aggregate; 2.08 for sand portion.
[f] Only the aggregate tests were made. Insufficient quantity for making concrete.
[g] Heat-treated pumice having skin covered appearance.

has comparatively high compressive strength; but this varies depending on the type of ore from which the slag was produced. Slag is also expanded to produce another type of lightweight aggregate (see Table 2·4).

UNIT WEIGHT, LB/CU FT	BULK SPECIFIC GRAVITY a	ABSOLUTE SPECIFIC GRAVITY	ABSORPTION, PERCENT BY WEIGHT	COLOR TEST b	CRUSHING-STRENGTH TESTS			
					GRADING c	LB/SQ IN. AT 1-IN. COMPACTION	LB/SQ IN. AT 2-IN. COMPACTION	LB/SQ IN. AT 3-IN. COMPACTION
35.7	1.10	2.59	5.8	—				
44.2	1.40	2.59	7.0	—	1	890	4,100	20,000
56.6	1.80	2.59	11.2	No. 1				
d39.4	e1.64	2.61	15.8	No. 1	1	1,060	6,420	i20,000
25.8	1.18	2.94	8.4	No. 1		85	310	1,840
39.7	1.61	2.93	10.6	No. 1	1			
40.8	2.28	3.09	10.3	No. 1	1	140	610	4,415
33.6	2.22	3.17	18.0	No. 1	1	35	115	820
65.0	2.30	2.83	8.7	Clear	1	170	565	4,245
47.7	1.70	2.62	8.0	—	1	680	4,385	i20,000
40.0	1.29	2.42	18.8	—				
50.2	1.56	2.46	22.2	—	1	380	1,410	3,740
54.4	1.61	2.44	25.9	—				
30.3	1.23	2.41	18.3	—	1	290	1,100	4,555
43.9	1.65	2.33	31.9	Clear	1	350	1,950	13,350
53.7	2.34	2.36	0.7	Clear	—	—	—	—
—	0.96	2.33	20.2	Clear	—	—	—	—
—	0.94	2.33	24.1	Clear	—	—	—	—
16.1	0.88	2.34	11.2	No. 1	1	140	440	1,555
15.3	0.88	2.34	12.1	Clear	2	99	310	1,145
10.0	0.67	2.30	12.4	No. 1	—	—	—	—
9.6	0.95	2.33	31.3	Clear				
11.0	0.95	2.32	30.2	Clear	1	14	60	185
9.1	1.31	2.25	31.0	Clear				
2.9	0.88	2.29	51.0	Clear	—	—	—	—
12.1	0.89	2.66	25.7	No. 1	2	14	43	125
8.1	2.16	2.66	19.8	No. 1	2	14	43	120
22.9	1.29	2.08	50.1	—	1	240	1,275	4,920

hVermiculite with air-entraining agent added in production process.

i Capacity of machine; about 2.5 in. compaction.

Cinder Aggregate

Cinders to be used for concrete aggregate should come from anthracite coal and should be free from such harmful impurities as sulfides, unburned coal, and fine ashes. Concrete made from cinders is not used for structural purposes, but floor and roof slabs, fire walls, fireproofing concrete, and masonry blocks are made from it.

DESIGN AND CONTROL OF CONCRETE

In order to produce concrete that will do its job properly, a great deal of attention must be paid to concrete design—determining the correct amounts of each of the ingredients which should be used in any given case. Mixtures must be designed to give the most practical and economical combination of materials that will produce the necessary plasticity and workability and at the same time produce concrete of the required strength and durability.

The designing of concrete mixtures is based primarily on the *water-cement ratio theory* and the *absolute-volume system* of calculating material amounts. Attention, of course, also must be paid to exposure and placing conditions.

The water-cement ratio theory states that the strength of concrete is inversely proportional to the amount of water used per unit (bag) of cement. This means that if, for example, 60 lb of water per bag of cement will produce concrete capable of developing 2,500 psi in 28 days, then less water per bag will produce stronger concrete and more water will produce concrete of lesser strength. Table 2·5 shows the probable compressive strength, in psi, that can be expected in 28 days using various amounts of water per bag of cement, for both plain and air-entrained concrete.

Table 2·5

Compressive strength of concrete for various water-cement ratios.

WATER-CEMENT RATIO, LB PER BAG OF CEMENT	PROBABLE COMPRESSIVE STRENGTH AT 28 DAYS, PSI	
	PLAIN CONCRETE	AIR-ENTRAINED CONCRETE
66	2,000	1,600
60	2,500	2,000
54	3,000	2,400
50	3,500	2,800
44	4,000	3,200
40	4,500	3,600
36	5,000	4,000
33	5,500	4,400
30	6,000	4,800

The durability of concrete—its ability to withstand frequent freezing and thawing cycles, wide ranges of temperature, alternate wetting and drying, the action of seawater and ground salts, the abrasion of traffic—and its permeability (its watertightness) are also affected by the water-cement ratio. Table 2·6 gives the recommended water-cement ratios to be used for a variety of exposure conditions and thicknesses of section, for both plain and reinforced concrete. When both compressive-strength and exposure conditions are involved, the designer must choose the smaller of the two recommended water-cement ratios for his design.

The maximum size of coarse aggregate, the preferred fine-

Table 2 · 6
Maximum permissible water-cement ratios for different types of structures and degrees of exposure, gal per bag.[a]

TYPE OF STRUCTURE	SEVERE WIDE RANGE IN TEMPERATURE, OR FREQUENT ALTERATIONS OF FREEZING AND THAWING (AIR-ENTRAINED CONCRETE ONLY)			MILD TEMPERATURE, RARELY BELOW FREEZING; RAINY; ARID.		
	AIR	AT WATER LINE OR WITHIN RANGE OF FLUCTUATING WATER LEVEL OR SPRAY		AIR	AT WATER LINE OR WITHIN RANGE OF FLUCTUATING WATER LEVEL OR SPRAY	
		FRESH WATER	SEA WATER OR SULFATES[c]		FRESH WATER	SEA WATER OR SULFATES[c]
Thin sections, such as railings, curbs, sills, ledges, ornamental or architectural concrete, reinforced piles, pipe, and all sections with less than 1 in. concrete cover over reinforcing.	5.1 (4.25)	4.65 (3.88)	4.2[d] (3.5)	5.6 (4.67)	5.1 (4.25)	4.2[d] (3.5)
Moderate sections, such as retaining walls, abutments, piers, girders, beams	5.6 (4.67)	5.1 (4.25)	4.65[d] (3.88)	e	5.6 (4.67)	4.65[d] (3.88)
Exterior portions of heavy (mass) sections	6 (5)	5.1 (4.25)	4.65[d] (3.88)	e	5.6 (4.67)	4.65[d] (3.88)
Concrete deposited by tremie under water	—	4.65 (3.88)	4.65 (3.88)	—	4.65 (3.88)	4.65 (3.88)
Concrete slabs laid on the ground	4⅔	—	—	e	—	—
Concrete protected from the weather, interiors of buildings, concrete below ground	e	—	—	e	—	—
Concrete which will later be protected by enclosure or backfill but which may be exposed to freezing and thawing for several years before such protection is offered	5.6 (4.67)	—	—	e	—	—

[a] Imperial gal quantities given in parentheses; 1 U.S. gal = ⅚ imperial gal.
[b] Air-entrained concrete should be used under all conditions involving severe exposure and may be used under mild exposure conditions to improve workability of the mixture.
[c] Soil or ground water containing sulfate concentrations of more than 0.2 percent.
[d] When sulfate-resisting cement is used, maximum water-cement ratio may be increased by 0.48 gal per bag.
[e] Water-cement ratio should be selected on basis of strength and workability requirements.

ness modulus of fine aggregate, and the proportions of fine to coarse depend on the placing conditions, the thickness of the section, and the requirements of finishing. But the amounts of aggregates to be used with a given cement paste are calculated by the absolute-volume method. The absolute volume of a loose material is the actual total volume of solid matter in all the particles, without taking into account the space occupied by voids between the particles. Absolute volume is computed from the weight of the material and its specific gravity. The formula is as follows:

$$\text{Absolute volume} = \frac{\text{weight of loose dry material}}{\text{specific gravity} \times \text{unit weight of water}}$$

For example, the absolute volume of 1 cu ft of cement, whose specific gravity is 3.13, would be

$$\text{Absolute volume} = \frac{87.5}{3.13 \times 62.4} = 0.45 \text{ cu ft}$$

If the absolute volume of the water and the absolute volume of the cement required for a cubic yard of concrete, plus air content, if any, are added, the result is the absolute volume of the cement paste and air in a cubic yard of concrete. If this figure is subtracted from 27, the remainder will represent the absolute volume of the aggregates required in a cubic yard of concrete.

Publications by the Portland Cement Association and the American Concrete Institute give full details on working out a concrete-mix design by absolute volume.

Designing a concrete mix using expanded shale aggregate requires another method. Because of the difficulties involved in determining a satisfactory value for specific gravity and absorption of the aggregate, a method of proportioning is suggested which does not require the use of these values. The determination of the proportions of cement, water, and aggregates to attain the required strengths and workability is carried out by mixing trial batches based on volume proportions. Table 2·7 gives the recommended proportions to be used in trial batches.

Table 2·7
Trial batches using
Herculite aggregate.

MAX SIZE AGGREGATE, IN.	REQUIRED 28-DAY STRENGTH, PSI	CEMENT, BAGS/ CU YD	LOOSE DRY AGGREGATE, CU FT/CU YD		
			FINE (0 TO ³⁄₁₆ IN.)	MEDIUM (³⁄₁₆ TO ³⁄₈ IN.)	COARSE (³⁄₈ TO ¾ IN.)
¾	2,000	5.25	17.6	4.8	9.6
¾	2,500	5.70	17.45	4.75	9.5
¾	3,000	6.25	17.3	4.7	9.4
¾	3,500	6.7	17.15	4.7	9.4
¾	4,000	7.25	17.0	4.7	9.4
¾	5,000	8.5	16.7	4.6	9.2
⅜	2,000	5.75	19.6	13.0	
⅜	2,500	6.20	19.4	12.9	
⅜	3,000	6.75	19.2	12.8	

It is advisable to use an air-entraining agent of good quality to improve workability and reduce segregation. The recommended air content is from 4 to 6 percent.

Vermiculite concrete can be made with or without sand. The mix design will depend on the use to which the concrete is to be put; manufacturers and the Vermiculite Institute publish design specifications for most uses of vermiculite concrete. For example, for vermiculite-sand concrete for floors on ground, specifications call for 1 cu ft portland cement, 3 cu ft stabilized vermiculite-concrete aggregate, 2 cu ft concrete sand. Enough water must be added to produce a slump of not less than 3 or more than 5 in. For a vermiculite-concrete floor on ground, 1 cu ft portland cement to not more than 6 cu ft of vermiculite is recommended. Enough water should be used to produce a slump of 6 in. This should amount to 17 to 19 U.S. gallons or 14 to 15 imperial gallons.

CONTROL OF CONCRETE MIXES

Freshly mixed concrete must be checked to ensure that the specified slump is being attained consistently. This is done by taking slump tests. A standard slump cone, 12 in. high and 8 in. in diameter at the bottom, is used (Fig. 2·5). The cone is filled in three equal layers, each being rodded 25 times with a standard ⅝-in. bullet-nosed tamping rod. Figures 2·5(a) and (b) illustrate the process of filling and tamping a slump cone.

When the cone has been filled and leveled off, it is lifted carefully (Fig. 2·6a) and the amount of slump measured (Fig. 2·6b).

The compressive-strength test of cylindrical concrete specimens is the most common quality-control test of concrete. The tests may be conducted for any time interval but generally are based on 7- and 28-day curing periods.

Concrete specimens are usually cylindrical with a length equal to twice the diameter. The standard size is 12 in. high

(a)

(b)

Figure 2 · 5
(a) Filling slump cone.
(b) Tamping slump cone.
(Soiltest, Inc.)

(a)

(b)

Figure 2 · 6
(a) Lifting cone.
(b) Measuring slump.
(Soiltest, Inc.)

and 6 in. in diameter, if the coarse aggregate does not exceed 2 in. in size (Fig. 2·7a). The mold is filled in three equal layers, each one being rodded 25 times with a standard tamp-

(a)

(b)

Figure 2 · 7
(a) Filling test cylinder.
(b) Tamping cylinder.
(c) Leveling off.
(Soiltest, Inc.)

(c)

ing rod (Fig. 2·7b). When the mold is full, it is struck off level (Fig. 2·7c) and covered with a glass or metal plate to prevent evaporation. The specimens are removed from the mold after 24 hours and placed in the curing location for the designated period. Some will be placed in a curing cabinet under moist, warm conditions, and some may be placed in field conditions.

At the end of the curing period the specimens are subjected to a compression test. First the ends are capped with a thin layer of sulfur to provide completely even bearing surfaces at both ends. Figures 2·8(a), (b), (c), and (d) illustrate the procedure for capping the test specimens.

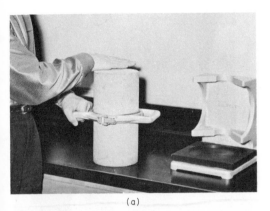

(a)

(b)

(c)

Figure 2·8

(a) Capping test cylinders.
(b) Capping material.
(c) One end being capped.
(d) Ends capped.
(Soiltest, Inc.)

(d)

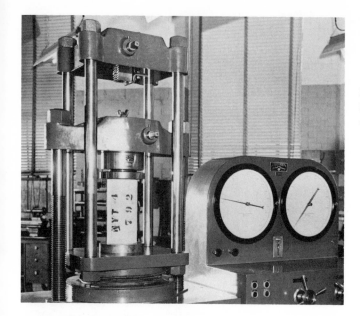

Figure 2 · 9
Compression-testing machine.
(Tinius Olsen Co.)

(a)

(b)

(c)

(d)

Figure 2 · 10
(a) Preparing test beam.   (b) Tamping concrete.   (c) Consolidating concrete.
(d) Leveling off concrete.   (Soiltest, Inc.)

Each specimen is then placed in a compression-testing machine and loaded to rupture. Figure 2·9 shows a typical compression tester in operation.

Tests are also made on concrete to determine its flexural (bending) strength. The test specimen is in the form of a beam with a length of at least 2 in. greater than three times the depth. The minimum cross-sectional dimension must be at least three times the maximum size of the coarse aggregate used and in no case less than 6 × 6 in.

The mold should be filled in two equal layers, with each layer rodded one stroke for each 2 sq in. of area. The edges are spaded as shown in Fig. 2·10(c). The top must be finished off with a wood or metal float. Figures 2·10(a), (b), (c), and (d) illustrate quite clearly the procedure in forming a flexure specimen.

After the specified curing period, during which the specimen should be kept in a moist condition at a temperature between 60 and 80°F, each one is tested. The machine subjects the specimen to third-point loading and the piece is broken under the load. The load required to rupture the specimen is read as ultimate flexural strength in pounds per square inch. Figures 2·11(a), (b), (c), and (d) describe the procedure for making the flexural test.

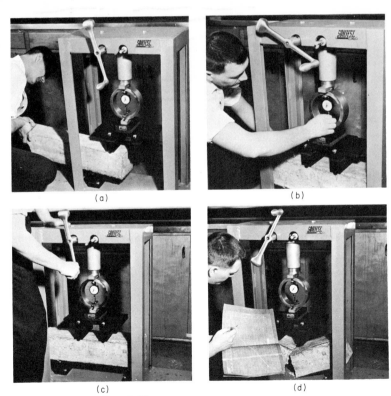

(a) (b)

(c) (d)

Figure 2·11
(a) Testing a specimen for flexural strength. (b) Machine being adjusted.
(c) Applying test load. (d) Beam broken. (Soiltest, Inc.)

(a)

(b)

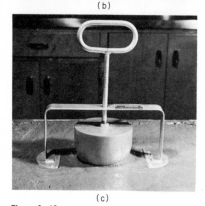

(c)

Figure 2 · 12
(a) Ball penetration test.
(b) Setting instrument in place.
(c) Ball penetrates concrete.
(Soiltest, Inc.)

A ball penetration test—a consistency test—is also carried out on fresh concrete. The apparatus consists of a cylinder with a half-round bottom and an attached handle. The complete unit weighs about 30 lb. A frame guides the handle and serves as a reference for measuring the depth of penetration. The instrument is set on a freshly poured smooth concrete surface, and the ball is set on the level concrete surface with the handle vertical. The ball is allowed to settle under its own weight; after the weight has come to rest, the ball penetration is read to the nearest ¼ in. A minimum of three readings should be taken from each batch or location. Figures 2 · 12(a), (b), and (c) depict the instrument and its use in making the penetration test.

Still another test carried out on freshly mixed concrete is one to determine the air content. This is carried out by an air meter such as the one illustrated in Fig. 2 · 13. The container, holding ¼ cu ft of concrete, is filled in three layers, with each one being tamped 25 times with a standard rod (Fig. 2 · 13a). When the container is full, the top is struck off level and the top is put on and locked in place. Complete instructions, which accompany each unit, describe the steps to take to obtain a reading on the dial.

PRECAST CONCRETE

The concept of building with concrete structural members which have been cast and cured in a factory rather than in place on the site has found general acceptance in recent years. These prefabricated, reinforced units go under the general heading of *precast concrete,* and the rapid growth in the use of precast concrete is one of the important developments in the construction industry.

The idea has gained popularity for a number of reasons. Casting and curing conditions, as well as concrete design, can be rigidly controlled, resulting in consistently high-quality concrete. The cost of forms is reduced since they can be placed on the ground rather than having to be suspended or supported in position. Where mass production of a unit is possible, forms can be made very precisely of steel, ensuring long use and very smooth surfaces. Structural members can be mass-produced in a plant while excavations and foundation work are taking place at the site. Precast-concrete members are then delivered as called for in work schedules and in most cases erected directly from truck bed to the structure, without rehandling at the site. Close supervision and control of materials and a specialized work force in a centralized plant result in a high-quality product. Finishing work on concrete surfaces can be done more easily in the plant than in position on the site. Because of superior reinforcing techniques the dead load of the structural members themselves can be reduced. Plant production is not normally subject to

(a)

(b)

(c)

Figure 2·13
(a) Measuring air content of freshly mixed concrete.
(b) Leveling off concrete.
(c) Obtaining an air-content reading.
(Soiltest, Inc.)

delays due to adverse weather conditions, as so often happens to job site operations.

Structural units which are precast include floor and roof slabs, columns, girders, beams and joists, wall panels, and stairs. Whole wall sections are precast and later raised to position in what is called tilt-up construction. Figure 2·14 illustrates such a technique. Reinforced piles, posts, and

Figure 2·14
Raising a precast wall section.
(Portland Cement Association)

63

pilons are also made. In addition, precast members for high-way and railroad bridges are being made in increasing quantity.

Precast structural members fall into two general classifications: *normally reinforced* or *prestressed*. Prestressed units are again divided into two groups, those that are *pre-tensioned* and those that are *post-tensioned*.

Normally reinforced precast members are designed according to accepted reinforced-concrete practice. The main difference is that the reinforcing can be made up as a unit and placed in position in the completed form. It should be noted, however, that high-strength concrete is produced, with factory control, whether required or not, since it is more economical to design reinforced concrete for higher strengths, in the 5,000-psi range.

A prestressed-concrete unit is one in which engineered stresses have been placed before it has been subjected to a load. When pre-tensioning is employed, the reinforcement, in the form of high-tensile steel strands, is first stretched through the form or casting bed between two end abutments or anchorages. Concrete is then poured into the form, en-casing the strands (Fig. 2·15). As the concrete sets, it bonds to the tensioned steel; when it has reached a specified strength, the ends of the tensioned strands are released. This prestresses the concrete, putting it under compression and creating built-in tensile strength. Having been prestressed,

Figure 2·15
Pouring pre-tensioned members in a long bed.
(Portland Cement Association)

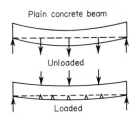

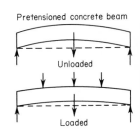

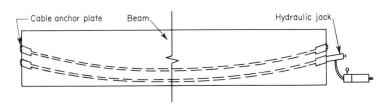

Plain concrete beam

Pretensioned concrete beam

Unloaded

Unloaded

Loaded

Loaded

Figure 2 · 16
Comparison of plain and pre-tensioned concrete beams.

members have a slight arch or camber (Fig. 2 · 16). The action of the highly tensioned steel produces a high compression in the lower portion of the member. An upward force is thus created which in effect relieves the beam of having to carry its own weight and counteracts the load applied to the member.

To hold the tremendous force of tension which is placed on the strands, the end abutments are built into each end of the casting bed. They may be a heavy steel framework or be made of reinforced concrete. Strands are anchored to the dead-end abutment and pass through the casting bed and through the live-end abutment to the tensioning equipment installed behind it.

Post-tensioning involves pouring and curing a precast member which contains normal reinforcing (Fig. 2 · 17) and in addition, a number of channels through which poststressing cables or rods may be passed (Fig. 2 · 18). The channels

Figure 2 · 17
Normal reinforcement for a poststressed folded-plate roof member.

Cable anchor plate   Beam   Hydraulic jack

Figure 2 · 18
Cable channels in beam to be post-tensioned.

Figure 2 · 19
Using portable hydraulic jack to
post-tension large girder.
(Portland Cement Association)

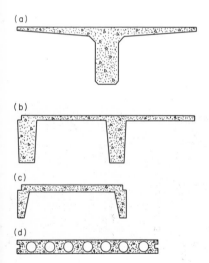

Figure 2 · 20
Some typical roof slab sections:
(a) lin T
(b) monowing
(c) channel slab
(d) hollow-core slab.

are generally formed by suspending inflated tubes through the form and casting around them. When the concrete has set they are deflated and removed. After the concrete has reached a specified strength, the post-tensioning *tendons* are placed in the channels and anchored at one end. They are then stressed from the opposite end by a portable hydraulic jack (Fig. 2·19) and anchored by one of several automatic gripping devices. One such device consists of two ribbed cones, one fitting into the other. Each strand or rod is held between two ribs and is firmly anchored as one cone is pulled tightly into the other.

Post-tensioning may be done at a plant or at the job site. Members may be tensioned individually, or two or more members may be tensioned together after erection. Post-tensioning is usually carried out when the member is very large or when only one or a very few of one particular kind of unit are to be made. In general post-tensioning will be used if the unit is over 45 ft long or over 7 tons in weight. However, some types of pre-tensioned roof slabs will be considerably longer and heavier than this.

Members which are relatively small in section or which can be readily mass-produced are normally pre-tensioned. These include several types of precast roof slabs, such as those shown in Fig. 2·20 and *double-T* slabs (Fig. 2·21), floor slabs, precast joists, and bridge slabs. The versatility of precast roof slabs is illustrated in Fig. 2·22, where double-T slabs have been used to form the roof shown there.

Figure 2 · 21
Double-T roof slabs.
(Portland Cement Association)

Figure 2 · 22
Double-T slabs used to form curved roof.
(Portland Cement Association)

GLOSSARY

absolute volume	The volume of the solid particles of a loose granular material
air-entraining agent	A material which introduces tiny air bubbles into a concrete mixture
calcine	To become powdery by the action of heat
clinker	A stage in the manufacture of cement in which the ingredients are fused into small pieces
fineness modulus	Relative fineness or coarseness
flexural strength	Strength in bending
haydite	A lightweight aggregate made from vitrified shale

hydraulic cement	A cement which will set under water
incipient fusion	Initial stage of the melting process
perlite	A light mineral consisting of volcanic glass
pozzolan cement	A cement made from volcanic rock containing a large proportion of silica
tendon	Steel rods or cables used in prestressing concrete units

REVIEW QUESTIONS

1 Define each of the following terms:
  (a) Calcareous
  (b) Argillaceous
  (c) Pozzolan cement
  (d) Incipient fusion
  (e) Hydration
2 (a) Name the four basic ingredients of portland cement.
  (b) List five types of portland cement produced.
  (c) Basically, how are these five types produced?
  (d) What are the main ingredients of aluminous cement?
  (e) List four advantages to be gained in using concrete made with aluminous cement over concrete made with portland cement.
  (f) How does masonry cement differ from normal portland cement?
3 What do the results of each of the following tests, made on fine aggregate indicate?
  (a) Colorimetric test
  (b) Fineness modulus test
  (c) Silt test
4 Name five types of aggregate, other than stone, which are used in making concrete.
5 Briefly outline the *design* of a concrete mixture.
6 What two major difficulties are encountered in designing concrete containing lightweight aggregates by the absolute-volume method?
7 Draw a properly proportioned diagram to illustrate a standard slump cone.
8 Describe briefly the test specimens made to determine compressive strength and those used to determine flexural strength.
9 (a) What is the purpose of making and testing both *lab-cured* and *field-cured* concrete specimens?
  (b) What is the purpose of a sulfur cap placed on specimens to be tested for compressive strength?
  (c) What is the purpose of a ball penetration test on fresh concrete?

(d) What unit compressive strength is indicated if a 6 × 12-in. cylindrical specimen of concrete ruptures at 126,500-lb load?
10 List the three major advantages of *precasting* concrete structural members.
11 Outline the major difference between *pre-tensioned* and *post-tensioned* concrete units.
12 Under what conditions is post-tensioning normally employed?

SELECTED SOURCES OF INFORMATION

American Concrete Institute, Detroit, Mich.
Ciment Fondu Lafarge Corp., Montreal, Que., and New York, N.Y.
Expanded Shale, Clay and Slate Institute, Washington, D.C.
Portland Cement Association, Chicago, Ill.
Vermiculite Institute, Chicago, Ill.
Perlite Institute, New York, N.Y.

3

CONCRETE MASONRY BUILDING UNITS

Concrete masonry units are designed and made for use in all types of masonry construction. They are made from both heavyweight and lightweight materials in a great variety of shapes and sizes. Some of the uses are exterior and interior load-bearing walls, firewalls, party walls, curtain walls, panel walls, partitions, backing for other masonry facing materials, fireproofing over structural-steel members, piers, pilasters, columns, retaining walls, chimneys and fireplaces, concrete floor units, fillers for ribbed concrete floors, and patio paving units.

CONCRETE BLOCK

The most common concrete masonry unit is the concrete block, made with both stone and lightweight aggregates. They are made in five basic types: (1) hollow load-bearing concrete block, (2) solid load-bearing concrete block, (3) hollow, non-load-bearing concrete block, (4) concrete building tile, and (5) concrete brick.

A hollow load-bearing concrete block of 8 × 8 × 16 in. nominal size will weigh approximately 40 to 50 lb when made with heavyweight aggregate and 25 to 35 lb when made with lightweight aggregate. Heavyweight blocks are made from such aggregates as sand, gravel, crushed stone, and air-cooled slag. Lightweight units are made from cinders, expanded shale, pumice, and scoria.

A solid concrete block is one which is defined by ASTM as having a core area of not more than 25 percent of the gross cross-sectional area. A hollow concrete block is one in which the core area exceeds 25 percent of the cross-sectional area; generally the core area of such units will be from 40 to 50 percent of the gross area.

Concrete blocks are made in a wide variety of shapes and sizes to fit different construction needs. Figure 3·1 illustrates a large number of these. Many blocks are made in half- as well as full-length units; half-height blocks (4 in. instead of the standard 8 in.) are also available in some areas.

Block sizes are usually referred to by their nominal dimensions. Thus No. 4 in Fig. 3·1 is called an 8 × 8 × 16-in. block. When laid with a ⅜-in. mortar joint, these sizes are in accordance with the modular coordination of design based on a 4-in. module.

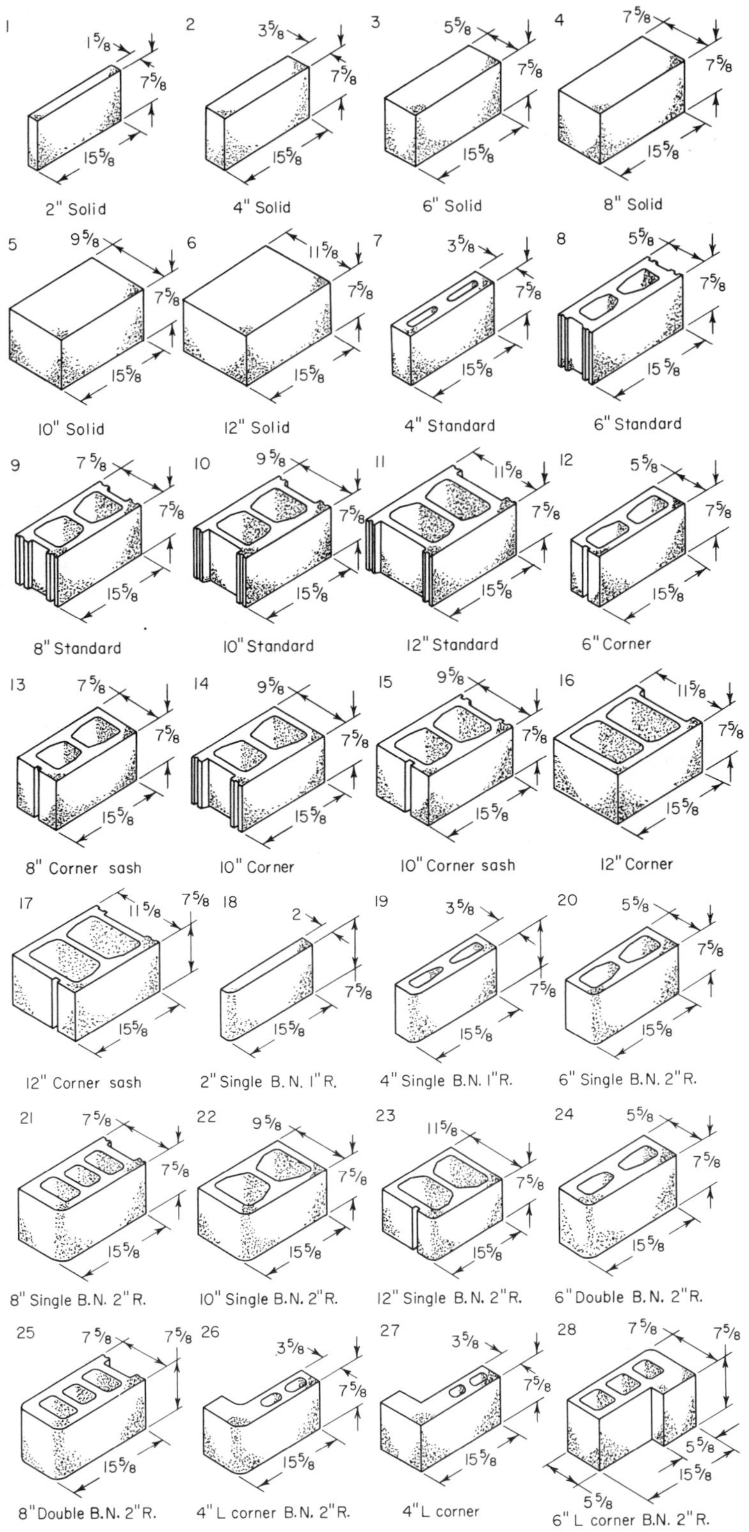

Figure 3·1
Concrete block shapes.
(Edmonton Concrete Block Co.)

2" Solid   4" Solid   6" Solid   8" Solid

10" Solid   12" Solid   4" Standard   6" Standard

8" Standard   10" Standard   12" Standard   6" Corner

8" Corner sash   10" Corner   10" Corner sash   12" Corner

12" Corner sash   2" Single B.N. 1"R.   4" Single B.N. 1"R.   6" Single B.N. 2"R.

8" Single B.N. 2"R.   10" Single B.N. 2"R.   12" Single B.N. 2"R.   6" Double B.N. 2"R.

8" Double B.N. 2"R.   4" L corner B.N. 2"R.   4" L corner   6" L corner B.N. 2"R.

71

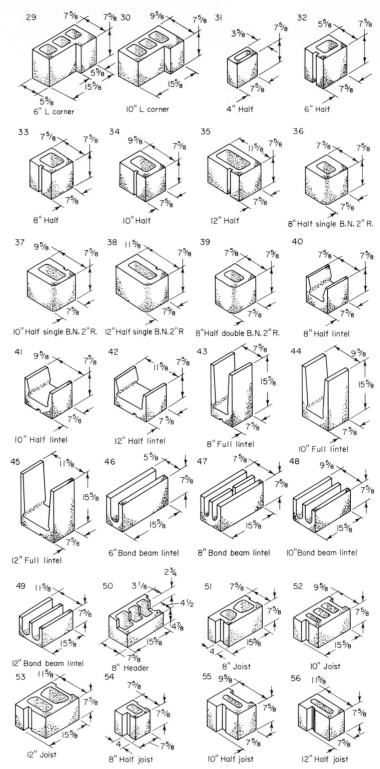

Figure 3·1 (continued)

29 7⅝ 7⅝ 5⅝ 15⅝ 5⅝
6" L corner

30 9⅝ 7⅝ 15⅝
10" L corner

31 3⅝ 7⅝ 7⅝
4" Half

32 5⅝ 7⅝ 7⅝
6" Half

33 7⅝ 7⅝ 7⅝
8" Half

34 9⅝ 7⅝ 7⅝
10" Half

35 11⅝ 7⅝ 7⅝
12" Half

36 7⅝ 7⅝ 7⅝
8" Half single B.N. 2" R.

37 9⅝ 7⅝ 7⅝
10" Half single B.N. 2" R.

38 11⅝ 7⅝ 7⅝
12" Half single B.N. 2" R

39 7⅝ 7⅝ 7⅝
8" Half double B.N. 2" R.

40 7⅝ 7⅝ 7⅝
8" Half lintel

41 9⅝ 7⅝ 7⅝
10" Half lintel

42 11⅝ 7⅝ 7⅝
12" Half lintel

43 7⅝ 15⅝ 7⅝
8" Full lintel

44 9⅝ 15⅝ 7⅝
10" Full lintel

45 11⅝ 15⅝ 7⅝
12" Full lintel

46 5⅝ 7⅝ 15⅝
6" Bond beam lintel

47 7⅝ 7⅝ 15⅝
8" Bond beam lintel

48 9⅝ 7⅝ 15⅝
10" Bond beam lintel

49 11⅝ 7⅝ 15⅝
12" Bond beam lintel

50 3⅛ 2¾ 4½ 4⅞ 15⅝ 7⅝
8" Header

51 7⅝ 7⅝ 15⅝ 4
8" Joist

52 9⅝ 7⅝ 15⅝
10" Joist

53 11⅝ 7⅝ 15⅝
12" Joist

54 7⅝ 7⅝ 4 7⅝
8" Half joist

55 9⅝ 7⅝ 7⅝
10" Half joist

56 11⅝ 7⅝ 7⅝
12" Half joist

72

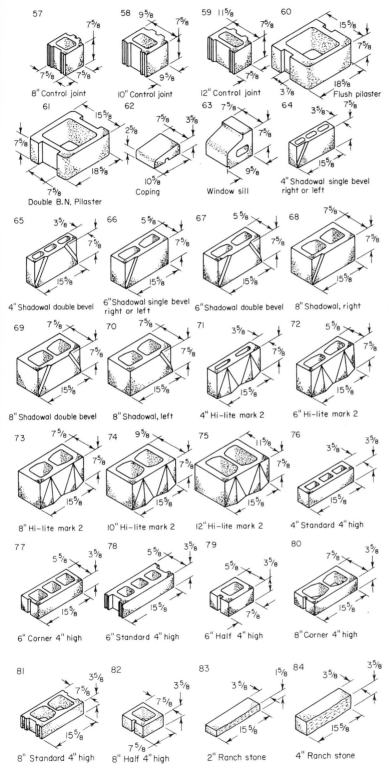

Figure 3·1
(continued)

57   7⅝ 7⅝ 7⅝
8" Control joint

58 9⅝ 7⅝ 9⅝
10" Control joint

59 11⅝ 7⅝ 7⅝
12" Control joint

60 15⅝ 7⅝ 3⅞ 18⅝
Flush pilaster

61 15⅝ 7⅝ 18⅝ 7⅝
Double B.N. Pilaster

62 7⅝ 3⅝ 2⅝ 10⅝
Coping

63 7⅝ 7⅝ 9⅝
Window sill

64 3⅝ 7⅝ 15⅝
4" Shadowal single bevel
right or left

65 3⅝ 7⅝ 15⅝
4" Shadowal double bevel

66 5⅝ 7⅝ 15⅝
6" Shadowal single bevel
right or left

67 5⅝ 7⅝ 15⅝
6" Shadowal double bevel

68 7⅝ 7⅝ 15⅝
8" Shadowal, right

69 7⅝ 7⅝ 15⅝
8" Shadowal double bevel

70 7⅝ 7⅝ 15⅝
8" Shadowal, left

71 3⅝ 7⅝ 15⅝
4" Hi-lite mark 2

72 5⅝ 7⅝ 15⅝
6" Hi-lite mark 2

73 7⅝ 7⅝ 15⅝
8" Hi-lite mark 2

74 9⅝ 7⅝ 15⅝
10" Hi-lite mark 2

75 11⅝ 7⅝ 15⅝
12" Hi-lite mark 2

76 3⅝ 3⅝ 15⅝
4" Standard 4" high

77 5⅝ 3⅝ 15⅝
6" Corner 4" high

78 5⅝ 3⅝ 15⅝
6" Standard 4" high

79 5⅝ 3⅝ 7⅝
6" Half 4" high

80 7⅝ 3⅝ 15⅝
8" Corner 4" high

81 7⅝ 3⅝ 15⅝
8" Standard 4" high

82 3⅝ 7⅝ 7⅝
8" Half 4" high

83 3⅝ 15⅝ 15⅝
2" Ranch stone

84 3⅝ 3⅝ 15⅝
4" Ranch stone

73

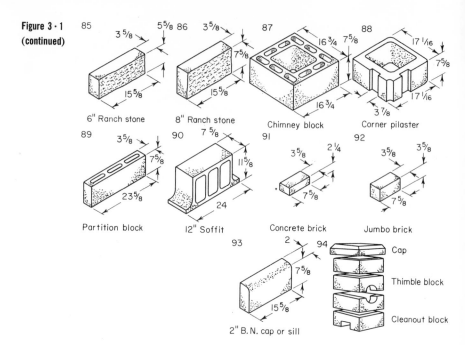

Figure 3·1 (continued)

85 6" Ranch stone — 3⅝, 5⅝, 15⅝

86 8" Ranch stone — 3⅝, 7⅝, 15⅝

87 Chimney block — 16¾, 7⅝, 16¾

88 Corner pilaster — 17¹/₁₆, 7⅝, 17¹/₁₆, 3⅞

89 Partition block — 3⅝, 7⅝, 23⅝

90 12" Soffit — 7⅝, 11⅝, 24

91 Concrete brick — 3⅝, 2¼, 7⅝

92 Jumbo brick — 3⅝, 3⅝, 7⅝

93 2" B. N. cap or sill — 2, 7⅝, 15⅝

94 Cap, Thimble block, Cleanout block

The ingredients for most concrete blocks are mixed in a paddle-type mixer, and the very dry mix is fed into a block-forming machine where the blocks are molded under heavy pressure and vibration. Blocks are then transported to a curing room, where they are cured by steam, and from there to a storage yard.

Concrete blocks are made to comply with certain requirements, notably compressive strength, absorption, and moisture content. These are laid down by local or national building codes and by the applicable specifications of ASTM or other specifying agencies.

Compressive-strength requirements provide a measure of the block's ability to carry loads and withstand structural stresses. Absorption requirements provide a measure of the density of the concrete, while the moisture-content requirements are intended to indicate whether the unit is sufficiently dry for use in wall construction.

Concrete shrinks slightly with loss of moisture down to an air-dry condition. If moist units are placed in a wall and this natural shrinkage is restrained, as is often the case, tensile and shearing stresses are developed which may result in cracking. Units should be dried to at least the moisture-content limitations of the applicable specifications. Table 3·1 gives a summary of physical requirements for a number of the common types of concrete masonry units.

The maximum allowable working stress on all types of concrete-block construction is governed by building codes and specifications. Using mortars specified in Table 3·5, the

74

Table 3·1

Physical requirements for hollow and solid concrete block. (Portland Cement Association)

SPECIFICATION, SERIAL DESIGNATION, AND LATEST REVISED DATE	MINIMUM FACE-SHELL THICKNESS, IN.	COMPRESSIVE STRENGTH, MINIMUM, PSI, AVERAGE GROSS AREA — AVERAGE OF 5 UNITS	COMPRESSIVE STRENGTH, MINIMUM, PSI, AVERAGE GROSS AREA — INDIVIDUAL UNIT	WATER ABSORPTION, MAXIMUM, LB PER CU FT OF CONCRETE, AVERAGE OF 5 UNITS	MOISTURE CONTENT, MAXIMUM, PERCENT OF TOTAL ABSORPTION, AVERAGE OF 5 UNITS
Hollow load-bearing concrete masonry units ASTM C90, 1952	1¼ or over: Grade A[a,c] Grade B[b,c] Under 1¼ and over ¾	1,000 700 1,000	800 600 800	15 — 15	40 40 40
Hollow non-load-bearing concrete masonry units ASTM C129, 1952	Not less than ½	350	300	. . .	40
Solid load-bearing concrete masonry units ASTM C145, 1952[d] Grade A Grade B	. . . . . .	1,800 1,200	1,600 1,000	15 15	40 40
Concrete units; masonry, hollow Federal SS-C-621, 1935				AVERAGE OF 3 UNITS	AVERAGE OF 3 UNITS
Load-bearing units	1¼ or more ¾ to 1¼	700 1,000	600 800	16 16	40 40
Non-load-bearing units	Not less than ¾	350	—	—	40

[a]For use in exterior walls below grade and for unprotected exterior walls above grade that may be exposed to frost action.

[b]For general use above grade in walls not subjected to frost action or where protected from the weather with two coats of portland cement paint or other satisfactory waterproofing treatment approved by the purchaser.

[c]Regardless of the grade of unit used, protective coatings such as portland cement paint may be desirable on exterior walls for waterproofing. In this connection purchasers should be guided by local experience and the manufacturer's recommendations.

[d]Units with 75 percent or more net area. The classification is based on strength.

maximum allowable compressive working stresses in load-bearing walls made of hollow concrete blocks are 80 psi for walls using a cement-lime mortar and 100 psi for walls using a cement mortar. The use of lime mortar is not permitted.

Comprehensive tests have established relationship between the compressive strength of hollow concrete blocks and the wall in which they are laid. These tests showed that the compressive strength of axially loaded walls in pounds per square inch was approximately 42 percent of the compressive strength of the unit when laid with face-shell mortar bedding and 53 percent when laid with full mortar bedding. Figure 3·2 illustrates the difference between full and face-shell mortar bedding.

Thus a wall built of hollow concrete blocks with a minimum compression stress of 800 psi (see Table 3·1) and laid up with cement-lime mortar in face-shell bedding will have an

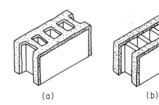

(a)　　　　(b)

Figure 3·2
(a) Full mortar bedding.
(b) Face-shell mortar bedding.

Table 3 · 2

Coefficients of heat transmission, U. (Portland Cement Association)

BASIC WALL CONSTRUCTION*		PLAIN WALL NO PLASTER	INTERIOR FINISH		
			½-IN. PLASTER ON:		
			WALL DIRECT	¾-IN. FURRING WITH:	
				⅜-IN. PLASTER-BOARD	½-IN. RIGID INSULATION
Concrete masonry (cores not filled)	8-in. sand and gravel or limestone	0.53	0.49	0.31	0.22
	8-in. cinder	0.37	0.35	0.25	0.19
	8-in. expanded slag, clay, or shale	0.33	0.32	0.23	0.18
	12-in. sand and gravel or limestone	0.49	0.45	0.30	0.22
	12-in. cinder	0.35	0.33	0.24	0.18
	12-in. expanded slag, clay, or shale	0.32	0.31	0.23	0.18
Concrete masonry (cores filled with insulation)†	8-in. sand and gravel or limestone	0.39	0.37	0.26	0.19
	8-in. cinder	0.20	0.19	0.16	0.13
	8-in. expanded slag, clay, or shale	0.17	0.17	0.14	0.12
	12-in. sand and gravel or limestone	0.34	0.32	0.24	0.18
	12-in. cinder	0.20	0.19	0.15	0.13
	12-in. expanded slag, clay, or shale	0.15	0.14	0.12	0.11
Cavity walls (with 2-in. or larger cavity. Cavity not filled with insulation)	10-in. wall of two 4-in. sand and gravel or limestone units	0.34	0.33	0.24	0.18
	10-in. wall of two 4-in. cinder, expanded-slag, clay, or shale units	0.26	0.24	0.19	0.15
	10-in. wall of 4-in. face brick and 4-in. sand and gravel or limestone units	0.38	0.36	0.25	0.19
	10-in. wall of 4-in. face brick and 4-in. cinder, expanded-slag, clay, or shale unit	0.33	0.31	0.23	0.18
	14-in. wall of 4-in. face brick and 8-in. sand and gravel or limestone units	0.33	0.31	0.23	0.18
	14-in. wall of 4-in. face brick and 8-in. cinder, expanded-slag, clay, or shale unit	0.26	0.25	0.19	0.16
	14-in. wall of 4-in. and 8-in. sand and gravel or limestone units	0.30	0.28	0.21	0.17
	14-in. wall of 4-in. and 8-in. cinder, expanded-slag, clay, or shale units	0.22	0.21	0.17	0.14
4-in. face brick plus:	4-in. sand and gravel or limestone unit	0.53	0.49	0.31	0.23
	4-in. cinder, expanded-slag, clay, or shale unit	0.44	0.42	0.28	0.21
	4-in. common brick	0.50	0.46	0.30	0.22
	8-in. sand and gravel or limestone unit	0.44	0.41	0.28	0.21
	8-in. cinder, expanded-slag, clay, or shale unit	0.31	0.30	0.22	0.17
	8-in. common brick	0.36	0.34	0.24	0.19
	1-in. wood sheathing, paper, 2 x 4 studs, wood lath and plaster	—	0.27	0.27	0.20
4-in. common brick plus:	4-in. sand and gravel or limestone unit	0.45	0.42	0.28	0.21
	4-in. cinder, expanded-slag, clay, or shale unit	0.38	0.36	0.26	0.19
	8-in. sand and gravel or limestone unit	0.37	0.35	0.25	0.19
	8-in. cinder, expanded-slag, clay, or shale unit	0.23	0.27	0.20	0.16
	8-in. common brick	0.31	0.30	0.22	0.17
	1-in. wood sheathing, paper, 2 x 4 studs, wood lath and plaster	—	0.25	0.25	0.19
Wood frame	wood siding, 1-in. wood sheathing, 2 x 4 studs, wood lath and plaster	—	0.25	0.24	0.19

* All concrete masonry shown in this table are hollow units. All concrete masonry wall surfaces exposed to the weather have two coats of portland cement base paint. Surfaces of all walls exposed to the weather subject to a wind velocity of 15 miles per hour.

† Values based on dry insulation. The use of vapor barriers or other precautions must be considered to keep insulation dry.

allowable compressive stress of 80 psi. If the actual bearing capacity is 42 percent of 800 psi (336 psi), then the factor of safety is 4.2. Similarly, a wall constructed with 1,000-psi blocks will have a safety factor of 6. Both exceed the generally accepted factor of safety of 4 for concrete-block construction.

The insulation value of concrete block has been determined by tests conducted at the University of Minnesota. Table 3·2 shows the insulation values for various types of concrete-block walls compared with other types of construction. The overall coefficient of heat transmission U represents the amount of heat transmitted in Btu (British thermal units) per hour, per square foot of wall, for each degree Fahrenheit difference in temperature between the air on the warm and cool sides of the wall. It can be seen from Table 3·2 how the insulating value of concrete-block walls can be affected by the type of construction, kind of wall finish, type of aggregate used, use of insulating fill in block cores, and use of air spaces.

A considerable amount of attention has been paid in recent years to the reduction of noises in buildings, and studies have been conducted to determine the sound-absorbing values of various building materials. Results have shown that concrete blocks with open surface texture will absorb sound readily. Paint applied to concrete-block walls tends to reduce the sound-control values, with spray painting having less effect than brush painting.

The ability of walls to resist the transmission of sound is important. Hollow blocks made from lightweight aggregates have very good sound-reduction factors, in most cases. Table 3·3 gives the reduction factors in sound transmission

Table 3 · 3

Reduction factors in sound transmission through walls of hollow concrete masonry. (Portland Cement Association)

WALLS OF HOLLOW CONCRETE MASONRY	WEIGHT PER SQ FT OF WALL AREA, LB	AVERAGE REDUCTION FACTOR, DECIBELS
3-in. Cinder, ⅝-in. plaster on both sides[a]	32.2	45.1
4-in. Cinder, ⅝-in. plaster on both sides[a]	35.8	45.6
4-in. Cinder, 1-in. plaster[b]	32.3	47.0
8-in. Expanded slag, 1-in. plaster[b]	56.0	52.6
4-in. Celocrete, ½-in. plaster on both sides[c]	30.0	42.6
8-in. Celocrete, unplastered[c]	28.6	43.7
8-in. Celocrete, ½-in. plaster on both sides[c]	40.0	52.9
Cavity wall, two 4-in. Celocrete, ½-in. plaster on one inner face[c]	45.0	57.1
3-in. Haydite, unplastered[c]	—	36.0
3-in. Haydite, 1-in. plaster[c]	—	42.0
4-in. Haydite, unplastered[c]	—	37.0
4-in. Haydite, 1-in. plaster[c]	—	43.0
6-in. Haydite, unplastered[c]	—	44.8
6-in. Haydite, 1-in. plaster[c]	—	48.5
8-in. Haydite, unplastered[c]	—	47.8
8-in. Haydite, 1-in. plaster[c]	—	50.5
12-in. Haydite, unplastered[c]	—	52.0

[a] National Bureau of Standards Report BMS17.

[b] Data reported in *Acoustics and Architecture* by Paul E. Sabine.

[c] Tests conducted by Riverbank Laboratories.

[d] National Bureau of Standards Supplement to Report BMS17.

WALLS OF HOLLOW CONCRETE MASONRY	WEIGHT PER SQ FT OF WALL AREA, LB	AVERAGE REDUCTION FACTOR, DECIBELS
12-in. Haydite, 1-in. plasterᶜ	—	54.0
4-in. Pumice, ½-in. plaster on both sidesᵈ	25.3	37.4
4-in. Pumice, ½-in. plaster on one side only	20.4	34.6
4-in. Waylite, ½-in. plaster on both sidesᶜ	31.0	50.0
8-in. Waylite, ½-in. plaster on both sidesᶜ	47.0	53.0
3-in. Waylite, 2 coats cement paint each sideᶜ	16.75	44.1
4-in. Waylite, unpaintedᶜ	16.5	33.2
4-in. Waylite, 2 coats cement paint each sideᶜ	16.5	46.7
6-in. Waylite, unpaintedᶜ	21.0	39.7
6-in. Waylite, 2 coats cement paint each sideᶜ	21.0	52.2
Cavity wall, two 3-in. Waylite, ⅜-in. plaster on one unexposed faceᶜ	17.0	56.1

ᵃNational Bureau of Standards Report BMS17.
ᵇData reported in *Acoustics and Architecture* by Paul E. Sabine.
ᶜTests conducted by Riverbank Laboratories.
ᵈNational Bureau of Standards Supplement to Report BMS17.

Table 3 · 4
Relation between sound transmission loss through a wall and hearing conditions on quiet side.*
(Portland Cement Association)

TRANSMISSION LOSS IN DECIBELS	HEARING CONDITION	RATING
30 or less	Normal speech can be understood quite easily and distinctly through the wall.	Poor
30 to 35	Loud speech can be understood fairly well. Normal speech can be heard but not easily understood.	Fair
35 to 40	Loud speech can be heard but is not easily intelligible. Normal speech can be heard only faintly, if at all.	Good
40 to 45	Loud speech can be faintly heard but not understood. Normal speech is inaudible.	Very good, recommended for dividing walls between apartments.
45 or more	Very loud sounds such as loud singing, brass musical instruments, or a radio at full volume can be heard only faintly or not at all.	Excellent, recommended for band rooms, music practice rooms, radio and sound studios.

* This table is based on the assumption that a noise corresponding to 30 decibels is continuously present on the listening side and that noises passing through the wall are audible despite this noise level. A decibel is roughly equivalent to the smallest change in sound energy that the average ear can detect, and 30 decibels corresponds approximately to the average background noise in a quiet apartment.

Table 3·5
Recommended mortar mixes.*

TYPE OF SERVICE	CEMENT	HYDRATED LIME OR LIME PUTTY	MORTAR SAND IN DAMP, LOOSE CONDITION
For ordinary service	1—masonry cement† or 1—portland cement	. . . 1 to 1¼	2 to 3 4 to 6
Subject to extremely heavy loads, violent winds, earthquakes or severe frost action. Isolated piers.	1—masonry cement† plus 1—portland cement or 1—portland cement	. . . 0 to ¼	4 to 6 2 to 3

* Proportions by volume.
† Tentative C.S.A. Specification A8.

through various types of lightweight hollow concrete blocks.

Table 3·4 shows the relation between sound transmission loss through a wall and the hearing conditions on the quiet side.

Mortars for concrete-block walls must be either cement or cement-lime mortars of good workability and water retentivity, with the strength and durability for its particular purpose.

Workability is obtained through proper grading of sand, use of cement intended specifically for mortar, and thorough mixing. Water retentivity is the ability of a mortar to resist the loss of water to masonry units which may possess high absorption. Well-graded sand, thorough mixing, and the use of masonry cement all help to increase the water retentivity of the mortar.

Table 3·5 lists mortar mixes which provide adequate strength and durability for most conditions.

The large number of shapes and sizes of concrete blocks, indicated in Fig. 3·1, lend themselves to a great many uses. Figure 3·3 illustrates a few of the wall patterns that can be developed using various pattern bonds and block sizes with blocks having a plane face. Blocks with a patterned face allow still more variations in wall design (Fig. 3·1, shapes 64 to 75).

Still another type of wall, called a *pierced* wall, is made using blocks having apertures through them—*screen* blocks.

Figure 3·3
Block wall patterns.
(National Concrete Masonry Association)

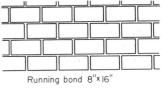

Running bond 8"x16"

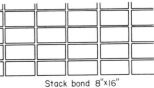

Stack bond 8"x16"

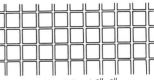

Stack bond 8"x8"

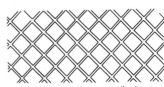

Diagonal stacking 8"x8"

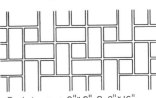

Basket weave 8"x8" & 8"x16"

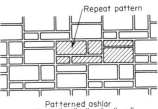

Patterned ashlar
4"x8", 4"x16", 8"x8", 8"x16"

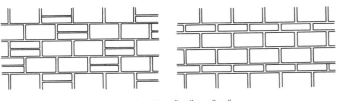

Coursed ashlar 4"x16" & 8"x16"

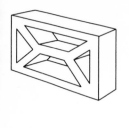
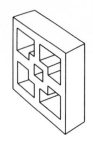

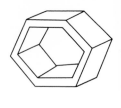

Figure 3 · 4
Screen block designs.
(Edmonton Concrete Block Co.)

A number of styles of screen blocks are available; a few are illustrated in Fig. 3·4.

Other effects are produced by laying some of the courses in relief (Fig. 3·5) or by using concrete block and glass block together. Extruded mortar joints are used to give a roughcast effect, and *slump* blocks are used for a similar purpose. (See Fig. 3·6.)

Bond beam lintel blocks are used for two purposes. One is to form a reinforced concrete lintel over door and window openings (Fig. 3·7). The other is to form a solid reinforced-concrete beam in a block wall, in order to provide extra structural strength. This may be done by using either one or two courses of bond beam blocks (Fig. 3·8). Precast reinforced lintels and sills are also available for use over and under openings in concrete-block construction.

Soffit blocks are made in various thicknesses for use in light-, medium-, and heavy-duty floors. Figure 3·9 shows how they are laid to form a ribbed concrete floor. Standard blocks

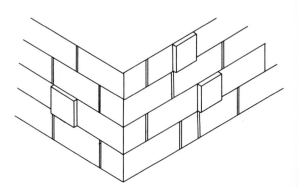

Figure 3 · 5
Blocks laid in relief.

80

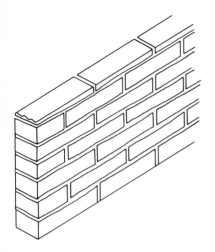

Figure 3 · 6
Extruded mortar; slump blocks.
(National Concrete Masonry Association)

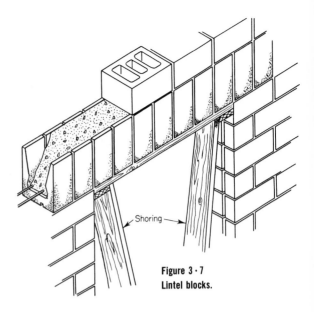

Shoring

Figure 3 · 7
Lintel blocks.

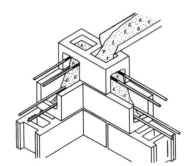

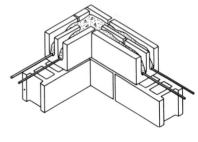

Figure 3 · 8
Forming bond beams.
(Besser Technical Center)

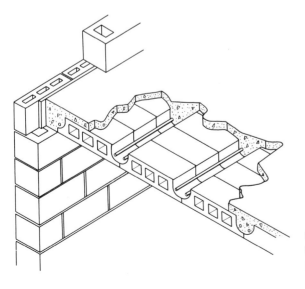

Figure 3 · 9
Forming ribbed concrete floor with soffit blocks.
(Besser Technical Center)

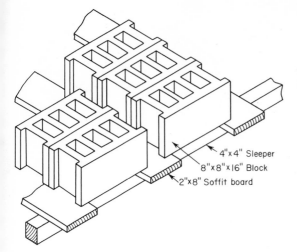

Figure 3 · 10
Standard blocks to form ribbed floor.

4"x 4" Sleeper
8"x 8"x 16" Block
2"x 8" Soffit board

Figure 3 · 11
Reinforced pilaster blocks.

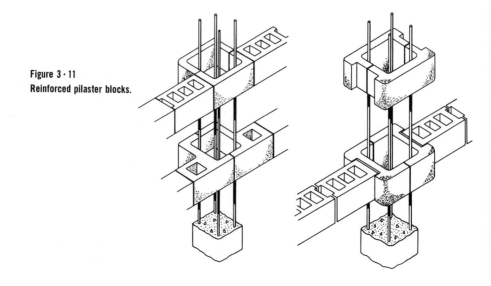

Figure 3 · 12
(a) Sill blocks.
(b) Coping blocks.

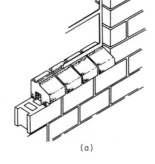

(a)

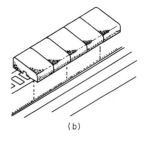

(b)

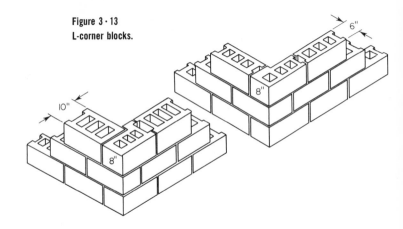

Figure 3·13
L-corner blocks.

may be used for the same purpose; the method used to form the ribbed floor is shown in Fig. 3·10.

Figure 3·11 shows two kinds of pilaster blocks being used, the flush wall pilaster (a) and the full pilaster (b). Pilaster blocks provide greater lateral strength in a wall and provide a greater bearing area for beams and girders carried on the wall. As shown, these blocks may be poured with reinforced concrete, thus producing a reinforced-concrete column.

Sill blocks are used to form a sill or bottom ledge of a window opening in a block wall, while coping blocks cap a block wall and shed water from it to the roof. L-corner blocks are used as illustrated in Fig. 3·13, producing a square corner, while bullnose blocks (Fig. 3 ·14) are used to produce rounded corners.

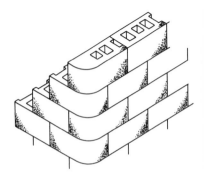

Figure 3·14
Bullnose corner blocks.

CAST STONE

Several methods are used to make simulated stone from concrete. One is by splitting a solid concrete block to expose two rough surfaces (Fig. 3·1). Figure 3·15 illustrates the use

Figure 3·15
Concrete blocks split to simulate stone.

of such units, which may be used for either exterior or interior work.

Another method involves making a mortar of cement and very-high-quality silica sand and casting it in molds which produces a unit with the face shaped to simulate chipped sandstone, shale, or slate. Some manufacturers cover the face of the mold with a coloring material and cast the mortar against it. As a result this unit has only the face colored. Others mix the color into the mortar so that the unit is colored through its entire thickness. The units are attached to a wall by a coat of mortar. In one type of application, the mortar is applied to the wall and allowed to dry. The cast stone units are made on the job and applied to the hard but damp mortar backing while they are still fresh. In another system, the units are cast and cured in a plant and pressed to a freshly applied coat of mortar. Both flat and corner units are made, the normal sizes being 4×4 in., 4×8 in., 8×8 in., and 8×16 in., all approximately 1 in. thick.

Still another method of making cast stone units is to mix granite or marble chips with a mortar made with white cement and cast the mortar in a mold with a hard, smooth face. When the unit is partially cured, it is ground off to expose some stone in the surface, resulting in a terrazzo-like appearance.

PRECAST FACING SLABS

Stone and terra-cotta have long been used as exterior facing, and with the development of precast concrete, facing slabs precast with either stone or lightweight aggregates have become quite common. Units can be custom-made any size to fit a particular structure.

Normally slabs are cast in the required dimensions, 2, 3, or 4 in. thick as specifications require. Sometimes they may be made in two layers, the outer one using white cement. After the slabs have been cured, the exterior face is ground smooth and treated with a sealer to prevent water absorption. Another style of precast slab is made by covering the face of a freshly poured unit made with stone aggregate with a set inhibitor. It prevents the cement paste on the surface from bonding to the aggregates. When the unit has set, the unbonded, hardened paste on the surface is brushed, washed, or sandblasted away, leaving a rough surface of exposed aggregate.

Precast facing slabs are normally fixed to the building in the same way that stone facing would be anchored, by pins or dowels to a steel frame and by metal strap anchors to a concrete or brick backup wall.

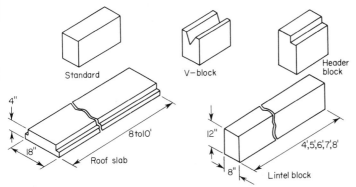

Figure 3 · 16
Cellular concrete blocks.

Standard V–block Header block

4"

8 to 0'

18" Roof slab

12"

4',5',6',7',8'

8" Lintel block

CELLULAR CONCRETE BLOCKS

Another type of building block is available which is very lightweight and possesses outstanding thermal and sound-insulation qualities. The basic ingredients are cement—made from silica-rich sand and lime—water, and aluminum powder. The three are mixed to form a slurry, which is poured into steel vats about 4 ft wide by 8 ft long by 30 in. deep. Vats are filled to about two-thirds of their depth.

A chemical reaction takes place which generates heat and hydrogen gas. The gas causes the slurry to expand, and the heat sets the foamed product in the cellular form. After completion of the set, the slab is removed from the form and wire-cut into blocks of various sizes. These are then cured under steam pressure in autoclaves.

Blocks weigh between 30 and 40 lb per cu ft and have an ultimate compressive stress ranging from 450 to 1,000 lb per cu in. They have outstanding thermal-insulation properties, low sound transmission values, and a high fire-resistance rating.

They can be easily cut or sawed to any desired shape with woodworking tools and are laid up in masonry cement or cement-lime mortar. Stucco and plaster can be applied directly to the face of the block, and other materials may be nailed directly to them, preferably with cut nails.

Blocks made in this manner are used for bearing walls for light construction, residences, etc.; backup walls for larger buildings; interior fire walls; fireproofing for steel; and roof slabs. Figure 3·16 shows some of the common units produced; Fig. 3·17 illustrates some of the common uses of this type of block.

Another type of lightweight block is made by mixing chemically treated wood shavings with cement paste and forming the resulting mixture into blocks. Three types are

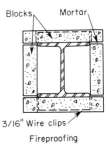

Blocks Mortar

3/16" Wire clips
Fireproofing

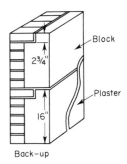

Block

2¾"

Plaster

16"

Back–up

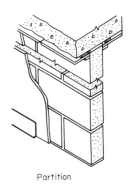

Partition

Figure 3 · 17
Applications of cellular blocks.
(Ytong Ltd.)

85

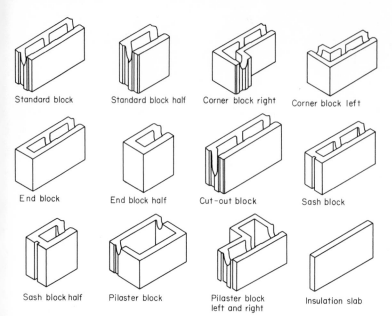

Standard block

Standard block half

Corner block right

Corner block left

End block

End block half

Cut-out block

Sash block

Sash block half

Pilaster block

Pilaster block
left and right

Insulation slab

Figure 3·18
Woodchip form blocks.
(Du-al Block Co.)

made, *form blocks, insulation slabs,* and *ceiling blocks.* Form blocks (Fig. 3·18) are so called because they are intended to be stacked into a wall without mortar and filled with concrete, thus acting as a form. The blocks bond to the concrete and act as insulation on both sides. Standard blocks are 12×24 in., made in various thicknesses. The standard block weighs about 30 lb and has an ultimate compressive strength of 150 lb per sq in. Blocks may be cut with woodworking tools and fastened with nails.

Ceiling blocks are made to form ribbed concrete floor slabs. Two styles and a special block made to accommodate recessed ceiling lights are shown in Fig. 3·19.

Another type of concrete masonry unit combines some

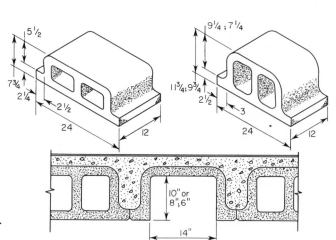

Figure 3·19
Woodchip ceiling blocks.
(Du-al Block Co.)

features of both conventional block and brick. It is made with lightweight aggregate and weighs about 68 lb per cu ft. Cell walls are sloped so that the webs are thicker on one side than the other (Fig. 3·20). Units are made in two sizes, 12 × 8 × 3½ in. and 12 × 4 × 3½ in., the same general proportions as brick. Both sizes are made in halves and corner units and are available in a range of colors.

Standard concrete blocks made with expanded-shale aggregate are also produced with glazed surface for facing purposes. A number of methods are used to do this. One of them is to coat one face with a mortar of silica sand, cement, and color; another is to coat one surface with a mixture of colored liquid plastic and marble chips which sets hard and is ground to a smooth finish.

Quality concrete masonry construction depends not only on high-quality masonry units but also on good design, good mortar, and good workmanship. Suggested specifications for handling and laying concrete block of all kinds are available from manufacturers' associations. Information on suitable mortars, good mortar bedding, and methods of making mortar joints is also available. In addition, literature covering patterns and bonds, control joints, block ties, waterproofing, and block cleaning may be obtained from the same sources.

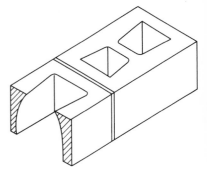

Figure 3·20
Units with tapered webs.

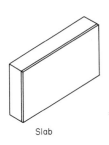

Slab

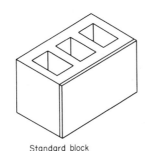

Standard block

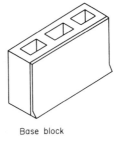

Base block

Figure 3·21
Face-glazed units.

GLOSSARY

bond beam	A beam that ties an upper and lower section of wall together giving them added stiffness
cast stone	Simulated stone made from concrete cast in units with artificially colored surface
cellular concrete	Lightweight concrete made by introducing large numbers of air cells into the mix
cement-lime mortar	Mortar made with a proportion of slaked lime added to the cement
extruded mortar joint	Joint between two masonry units in which some of the mortar has been squeezed out and allowed to set without trimming

lintel	A beam over an opening in a wall
party wall	A wall which is common to two buildings
pilaster	A built-in column in a masonry wall, intended to stiffen the wall
slump block	A block made from a wet mix, so that it will sag after being removed from the mold
slurry	A very sloppy mixture of water and mortar or cement ingredients
soffit	The underface of a floor or eave
water retentivity	Ability of a mortar to retain the mixing water for hydration purposes

REVIEW QUESTIONS

1   (a) What is the reason for using a vibrated mold in the manufacture of concrete blocks?
    (b) Why are blocks usually cured by steam?
2   Outline ASTM specifications with regard to:
    (a) Compressive strength of load-bearing concrete blocks;
    (b) Allowable absorption rate of load-bearing blocks;
    (c) Moisture content of blocks.
3   Describe the difference between face-shell and full mortar bedding of blocks.
4   (a) Explain why blocks with open surface texture have better sound-absorbing qualities than smooth-faced blocks.
    (b) Why does paint applied to blocks tend to reduce their sound-control value?
5   (a) Explain why good water retentivity of mortar used in laying blocks is important.
    (b) Name two ways of improving the water retentivity of mortar.
6   (a) What is the purpose of a bond beam in a block wall?
    (b) Describe the method used to form a lintel over an opening in a block wall by the use of lintel blocks.
    (c) What is the alternative to the use of lintel blocks?
7   (a) What is the difference between a flush wall pilaster block and a full pilaster block?
    (b) Give two reasons for using pilasters in a block wall.
8   What is a "cast stone" masonry unit?
9   Name three advantages of using cellular concrete blocks.
10 List five factors basic to the construction of a good-quality block wall.

SELECTED SOURCES OF INFORMATION

Besser Company, Alpena, Mich.
Brikcrete Association, Inc., Holland, Mich.
Canada Cement Co., Montreal, Que.
Consolidated Concrete, Limited, Calgary, Alberta
Expanded Shale, Clay and Slate Institute, Washington, D.C.
National Concrete Masonry Association, Washington, D.C.
Portland Cement Association, Chicago, Ill.

4

CONCRETE ADDITIVES

In addition to the basic ingredients of concrete—cement, water, and aggregates—other materials are often added to the mix or applied to the surface of freshly placed concrete to produce some special result. These materials, known as *concrete additives,* may be used for any one of the following reasons:

1 To speed up the initial set of concrete
2 To retard the initial set
3 To make the concrete more resistant to deterioration due to repeated freezing and thawing cycles
4 To prevent the bleeding of water to the surface of concrete
5 To improve the workability of the mix
6 To improve the hardness or denseness of the concrete surface
7 To render the concrete more watertight
8 To improve the bond between two concrete surfaces
9 To inhibit the set of cement paste
10 To produce a colored surface
11 To produce a nonskid surface
12 To prevent the evaporation of water from the newly placed concrete
13 To help develop all the potential strength of a given water-cement paste
14 To decrease the weight of concrete per cubic foot

ACCELERATORS

An admixture which is used to speed up the initial set of concrete is called an *accelerator*. Such a material may be added to the mix to increase the rate of early-strength development for several reasons. For example, this will allow earlier removal of forms and in some cases reduce the whole curing period. With proper protection it will partly compensate for the retardation of strength development due to low temperatures. This does not mean, however, that an accelerator makes it possible to pour concrete in cold weather without proper protection.

The most common accelerator is calcium chloride ($CaCl_2$), but other materials are also used for this purpose. Among them are some of the soluble carbonates, silicates, fluosilicates, and triethanolamine.

Calcium chloride is generally used in pellet form at a rate of not more than 2 lb per bag of cement. The rate of heat evolution is increased at early ages, with the result that the initial setting time is reduced and the rate of strength development increased, particularly during the first three days. For this reason the addition of the accelerator may be beneficial where the concrete is likely to be exposed to low temperatures—not below freezing—when it is newly placed. The addition of calcium chloride lowers the freezing point of concrete only very slightly.

Calcium chloride in the concrete does not cause corrosion of embedded steel but does increase the resistance of concrete to erosive and abrasive action. On the other hand, shrinkage of concrete due to drying is likely to be increased when calcium chloride is used, and the resistance of concrete to sulfate attack is lowered.

Accelerators such as the fluosilicates and triethanolamine can produce a very pronounced accelerating effect, and great care must be taken in their use. Some are capable of reducing the period during which concrete remains plastic to less than 10 minutes. Sternson's Quicksets, for example, added to neat portland cement, produce setting in a matter of seconds. This makes this type of accelerator valuable for making cement plugs to stop pressure leaks.

Aluminous cement is accelerated by the use of small amounts of portland cement. The portland cement is actually used as an accelerator in this case. The combination usually recommended for field use is about 70 percent aluminous cement and 30 percent portland cement. Some experimenting has been done, using small amounts of aluminous cement (5 to 20 percent) to accelerate the setting time of portland cement.

RETARDERS

The function of a *retarder* is to delay or extend the setting time of the cement paste in concrete. In hot weather hydration is accelerated by the heat, thus cutting down the time available to place, consolidate, and finish the concrete. This speedup of hydration means that some of the water usually available to provide plasticity is used by the cement. Therefore more water is required for equal slump, which in turn means lower concrete strength. High temperatures, low humidity, and wind cause rapid evaporation of water from the mix during summer. This drying of the concrete leads to cracking and crazing of the surface.

An initial set retarder will hold back the hydration process, leaving more water for workability and allowing concrete to be finished and protected before drying out. A retarder usually has water-reducing characteristics as well, making further reductions possible in the water-cement ratio.

There are also other reasons for using a retarder. For example, in bridge construction, girders or beams are designed with a camber and will be deflected as the load of the bridge deck is applied. Paving bridge decks is a relatively slow operation and deflection takes place progressively as the load is increased. The initial pours may be partially set before paving is complete if a retarder is not used. As further deflection takes place, this concrete, being no longer plastic, will be subjected to stress and may crack.

In casting prestressed members, a retarder is often important. Since prestress beds are usually quite long—300 ft or more—it takes a considerable time to place and consolidate the entire pour. It is desirable to keep the concrete plastic until vibrating is completed to ensure a good bond between concrete and prestressed steel along the entire length of the bed. It is also believed that steam, used to cure prestressed members, is more effective if the concrete has not passed a certain point in the hydration process. An initial set retarder will help to ensure this.

Retarders are also helpful for concrete that has to be hauled long distances in transit mix trucks, to ensure that it reaches its destination in a plastic and placeable condition.

A wide variety of chemicals have a retarding effect on the normal setting time of portland cement. Some act as retarders when used in certain quantities and as accelerators when used in others. The more commonly known retarders are carbohydrate derivatives and calcium lignosulfonate, used in fractions of a percent by weight of the cement. One of these is a highly purified metallic salt of a modified lignin sulfonic acid in the form of a brown liquid. It is used at the rate of 8 fluid ounces per sack of cement at 70°F. This amount will extend the vibration time and retard the set by two to four hours. As a general rule the addition rate should be increased or decreased by 1 ounce per sack for each 10°F increase or decrease in temperature from 70°F. The use of retarding agents is not generally recommended if the temperature is below 60°F.

AIR-ENTRAINING AGENTS

The introduction of controlled amounts of air into a mix has proved to be an important advance in concrete engineering. It is generally recognized that proper amounts of entrained air result in improved workability, easier placing, increased durability, better resistance to frost action, and reduction in bleeding and water gain.

The increased resistance to frost action is particularly marked where freezing conditions are severe or where salts are used for ice removal. The reduced tendency for bleeding and water gain indirectly aids in promoting durability because

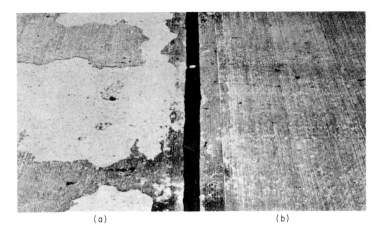

Figure 4 · 1
Comparison of (a) plain versus
(b) air-entrained concrete subjected
to frost action.

(a)   (b)

uniformity is increased and weak sections at the top of vertical lifts can be eliminated.

Air-entrained concrete contains microscopic bubbles of
air formed with the aid of a group of chemicals called surface
active agents, materials that have the property of reducing
the surface tension of water. This enables water to hold air
when agitated, resulting in a foam. There are a large number
of these compounds available, but only a relatively few can
be used satisfactorily in concrete. Among them are a number
of natural wood resins, various sulfonated compounds, and
some fats and oils.

A satisfactory air-entraining agent must not react chemically with cement. It must be able to produce air bubbles of a
definite size, approximately 0.001 in. in diameter, and must
produce bubbles that will not break too rapidly. These entrained air bubbles constitute a definite part of the fine
aggregate and, like water and fine sand, lubricate the con-

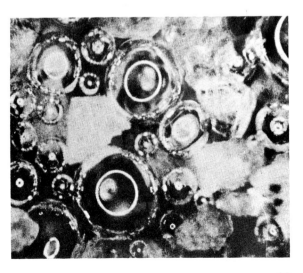

Figure 4 · 2
Air bubbles in concrete mix magnified
250 times.

93

crete. They also act like ball bearings to help concrete to move more easily.

Air entrainment, while improving durability and plasticity, may have an adverse effect on the strength of the concrete. Within the normal range of air contents (see Table 4·1) the decrease in strength usually is about proportional to the amount of entrained air. The maximum reduction in compressive strength rarely exceeds 15 percent, and in the case of flexural strength the maximum reduction is about 10 percent. These figures are for equal cement content and with the sand and water content reduced by the amount permitted by the increased workability of an air-entrained mix.

Table 4·1
Air-entrained concrete.

MIXTURE	COARSE AGGREGATE MAX SIZE, IN.	OPTIMUM AIR CONTENT, % BY VOLUME
Sand mortar (masonry)	No coarse aggregate; max No. 4 sieve	14 ± 2
Sand mortar (concrete)	No coarse aggregate; max No. 4 sieve	9 ± .5
Concrete	½	7.5 ± 1.5
Concrete	1	6 ± 1.5
Concrete	1½	4.5 ± 1.5
Concrete	3	3.5 ± 1

The amount of entrained air which will normally be most beneficial will vary, depending on the maximum size of coarse aggregate used in the mix. Table 4·1 gives the generally recognized optimum volume of entrained air in a number of mixes. The air content of a concrete mixture can be measured by an air meter, available in a number of styles.

Air-entrained concrete can also be made by using an air-entraining portland cement. This type of portland cement contains an air-entraining agent which has been mixed and ground with the raw material during the manufacture of the cement. A specification covering this type of cement has been issued by the American Society for Testing Materials.

DISPERSAL AGENTS

When cement and water are mixed, the cement particles tend to gather in clumps, or to *flocculate*. As a result water does not reach some of the particles and some are only partially hydrated. This means that less than the full potential strength of the cement paste will be developed. In some instances, with 28 days curing only 50 percent of the cement hydrates.

94

Water trapped within these clumps later bleeds to the surface of the concrete, because of the weight of the other materials. The voids left by the forcing out of the water later become passages through which water can penetrate the concrete.

These relatively large clumps of cement particles have rough, abrasive surfaces and resist movement of one past another. It is then necessary to use more water to produce concrete that is workable.

A cement dispersal agent such as calcium lignosulfonate causes cement particles to separate by imparting like electrostatic charges to them. Dispersal of the cement brings a great deal more of the particles into contact with water, resulting in better hydration. With a film of water surrounding them, the particles move easily in relation to one another, thus rendering the mix more workable. Water hitherto trapped is made available for hydration, so bleeding is greatly reduced.

Most cement dispersal agents also contain some air-entraining agents; some also contain a set-control agent.

CONCRETE HARDENERS

Plain concrete surfaces which are subjected to rolling live loads, the impact action of foot traffic, and other types of wear begin to dust and crumble at the surface after a period of time. This condition worsens with time, finally resulting in the destruction of the surface.

To prevent this, two types of concrete hardeners are used. One is a chemical hardener, the other a fine metallic aggregate which is introduced into the surface to increase its hardness and wear-resistance.

Chemical hardeners are liquids containing silicofluorides or fluosilicates and a wetting agent. The latter reduces the surface tension of the liquid and allows it to penetrate the pores of the concrete more easily. The silicofluorides or fluosilicates combine chemically with the free lime and calcium carbonate which are present in the concrete and bind the fine particles into a flintlike topping, which is highly resistant to wear and dusting.

Metallic hardeners are specially processed and graded iron particles which are dry-mixed with portland cement, spread evenly over the surface of freshly floated concrete, and worked into the surface by floating. The result is a hard, tough topping which is highly resistant to wear and less brittle than normal concrete.

CONCRETE WATERPROOFERS

Water under pressure and in contact with one surface of the concrete can be forced through channels between the inner and outer surfaces. A measure of the amount of water passing in this way is a measure of permeability; any admixture used to reduce this flow is really a *permeability reducer*.

Water also can pass through concrete by the action of capillary forces. If one side is exposed to moisture and the other to air, the water reaching the dry side evaporates, resulting in a flow of moisture through the concrete. Materials used to reduce or stop this type of flow are more properly called *dampproofers*.

Before water can pass by either of these means there must be channels through which it can travel. It is possible, through careful design, placing, and curing of concrete, to make it impermeable without using an admixture. But for some types of concrete, lean mixes in particular, it is often advantageous to use an admixture to reduce permeability.

The production of concrete of low permeability depends largely on uniform placing of the material and some means of preventing or limiting bleeding. Air-entraining agents increase the plasticity of concrete and therefore help to make placing easier and more uniform. They also reduce bleeding by holding the water in films about the air bubbles. For these reasons air-entraining agents may also be considered as permeability-reducing agents. It is also believed that the small disconnected voids produced by air entrainment break up the capillaries in the concrete and therefore offer a barrier to the passage of water by capillary action. This means that an air-entraining agent may also be classed as a *dampproofing* agent.

A cement dispersal agent may also be considered as a permeability reducer since it also tends to reduce voids formed when water is trapped in groups of cement particles.

Water repellents are also used as dampproofing agents. Materials commonly used for this purpose are compounds containing calcium or ammonium stearate, calcium or ammonium oleate, or butyl stearate. These substances are generally combined with lime or calcium chloride. Because these materials are water repellents, their effectiveness depends on the uniformity of distribution throughout the concrete.

Another type of concrete waterproofer consists of a film applied to the surface, preferably the one adjacent to the water source. Several materials are used for this purpose, the three most common ones being those containing asphalt or sodium silicate and one which contains a metallic aggregate.

The asphaltic products, thick viscous liquids, form an impervious coating over the surface. The sodium silicate compounds enter the surface pores and form a gel which prevents water from entering the concrete. The metallic-aggregate type of waterproofer consists of fine cast-iron particles, to which is added a chemical that causes them to oxidize rapidly when mixed with portland cement and wetted. It is applied over a concrete surface in the form of a slurry; rapid oxidation results in an expansion of the iron particles, causing them to knit the coating to the surface by means of the many tiny fingers thrust out in the process of oxidation. Successive coats build up a thin but dense watertight film over the surface.

BONDING AGENTS

When fresh concrete is poured against another concrete surface already set and at least partially cured, it is often difficult to obtain a bond between the two surfaces unless special precautions are taken. Fresh concrete shrinks when setting, and unless there is a very good bond this shrinkage makes the new concrete pull away from the old surface. If the old surface is treated so that the aggregates are exposed and clean, the cement paste in a new pour will bond to them in the same way that it bonds to the aggregates in the new mix. A cement-paste slurry is often applied to such an old surface immediately prior to pouring new concrete to increase the amount of paste available at the surface for bonding purposes.

Where such a treatment cannot be applied, bonding agents can be used to join the two surfaces. Two types of bonding agent are in common use, one in which the bonding is accomplished by a metallic aggregate and the other consisting of a synthetic latex emulsion.

The metallic-aggregate bonding agent is similar to a permeability reducer made with the same materials, except that in the bonding agent, the iron particles are larger. Bonding takes place through the oxidation and subsequent expansion of the iron particles. The tiny fingers that thrust out into both the old and the new concrete bind them together.

There are a number of types of synthetic latex bonding agents, but basically they consist of a highly polymerized synthetic liquid resin dispersed in water. Since it is an emulsion, a bonding agent must lose water for its adhesive ingredients to set. When it is sprayed or painted on a concrete surface the pores in the concrete absorb the water and allow the resin particles to coalesce and bond. When a bonding agent is mixed with cement paste or a mortar the water is used in the hydration of the cement and the resin is left to bind to both surfaces involved.

CONCRETE COLORING AGENTS

There is a considerable demand for colored concrete surfaces in modern construction, and a number of methods of producing these have been developed. One, of course, is to use concrete paint, applied after the concrete surface has been neutralized, either through exposure or by using a neutralizing agent such as zinc sulfate.

Other methods involve integrating color into the surface

concrete while it is still fresh. Both natural and synthetic mineral oxides are used for this purpose.

The natural metallic oxides of cobalt, chromium, iron, etc., have distinctive colors. The ochres and umbers are fine dry powders. They are usually mixed into a topping mix, since this is the best way of distributing the color evenly throughout the concrete.

The coloring agents made with synthetic oxides are usually a mixture of the oxide with one or more additional drying ingredients. The color is sometimes mixed with fine pure silica sand and applied by shaking the mixture over the freshly poured and floated surface. The coloring mixture is floated in, troweled and cured like any other concrete surface. The colors are also available mixed with metallic aggregate. In this case the material is mixed dry with cement and applied as a dry shake over the surface. The mix is floated, troweled, and cured as before.

SET-INHIBITING AGENTS

Specifications sometimes require that concrete surfaces be produced in which the aggregates are exposed for architectural effect. Exposed aggregates also provide a good bonding surface for concrete toppings. Normally these aggregates will be covered by a coating of cement-sand mortar which bonds to them as curing progresses and results in a smooth, uniformly colored surface.

Certain inhibiting agents will prevent the cement paste from bonding to the surface aggregates but will not interfere with the set throughout the remainder of the pour. Two materials are used for this purpose, a liquid which is applied to forms for vertical surfaces immediately before pouring concrete and a powder which is applied directly to freshly poured horizontal surfaces. In the latter case, the depth of penetration of the inhibitor depends on the amount used per square foot. Usual rates of application will vary from 1½ to 3 lb per 100 sq ft of surface.

After three or four days of curing, the retarded surface concrete should be hosed or brushed off, exposing clean aggregate and leaving a roughcast effect.

NONSKID SURFACES

Well-troweled concrete surfaces can be made very smooth, and under certain conditions these surfaces tend to be slippery. A nonskid surface can be produced in several ways. One is to leave out the steel troweling operation during the floor-finishing process. Instead the floor can be finished with wood or cork floats which will leave a rough surface. This can be done either with a plain concrete floor or with a floor topped with a metallic-aggregate coating.

Another method is to use an abrasive material in the topping, applied as a dry shake in much the same way as metallic-aggregate topping is applied. The abrasive material is floated into the top and the steel trowel operation is omitted. Materials commonly used for this purpose are fine particles of flint, aluminum oxide, silicon carbide, or emery.

SURFACE-SEALING AGENTS

Surface-sealing agents are used for two purposes. One is to form a watertight coating which will prevent water from evaporating from a concrete surface and allow it to be retained for hydration. The other is to seal the pores of a concrete surface after it has hardened in order to prevent the passage of water and the absorption of spilled materials such as oil, grease, or paint.

Sealing agents used to prevent water evaporation are usually liquid waxes which can be sprayed over the surface but which are easily removed after curing is complete. The type of sealer applied after the concrete is cured is used primarily to reduce maintenance. This kind of sealer may be a heavy-bodied wax which is rubbed into the surface, or a synthetic resin emulsion. Both must be reapplied periodically because of normal wear on the floor.

GAS-FORMING AGENTS

Under normal conditions concrete undergoes settlement and drying shrinkage, which, in some situations, can result in undesirable characteristics in the hardened concrete. For example, voids on the underneath side of forms, blockouts, reinforcing steel, or other embedded parts such as machinery bases may interfere with the bond and allow passage of water and reduce uniformity and strength.

One method of reducing such voids is to add an expanding agent to the concrete. Aluminum powder, when added to mortar or concrete, reacts with the hydroxides in hydrating cement to produce very small bubbles of hydrogen gas. This action, when properly controlled, causes a slight expansion in plastic concrete or mortar and thus reduces or eliminates voids caused by settlement. The effect on the strength of the concrete depends to a large extent on the restraint offered to expansion. With complete restraint imposed, the strength is not affected appreciably. Very small amounts of aluminum powder are used for this purpose, usually about one teaspoonful per sack of cement.

When larger amounts of powder are used, the expansion is greatly increased, resulting in a lightweight, low-strength concrete. Such concrete is useful for floor and roof slabs, fire walls, nonbearing partitions, etc. Aluminum powder for this purpose is used at a rate of approximately one quarter pound per bag of cement.

POZZOLANIC ADMIXTURES

A pozzolan (see Chap. 2), finely ground and in the presence of moisture, will react with calcium hydroxide at ordinary temperatures to form compounds which have cementitious properties. These materials are sometimes used in structures where it is desirable to avoid high temperature or in structures exposed to seawater or water containing sulfates. These pozzolanic materials are generally substituted for 10 to 35 percent of the cement. This substitute produces concrete that is more permeable but much more resistant to the action of salt, sulfate, or acid water. Strength gain is usually slower than for normal concrete.

Pozzolans may be added to concrete mixes—rather than substituting for part of the cement—to improve workability, impermeability, and resistance to chemical attack. The results depend on the aggregates used in the concrete. Where the aggregates are deficient in fine material the results are best.

Some pozzolans have been found to reduce the expansion caused by alkali-aggregate reaction in concrete and mortar. The expansion is caused by the interaction of alkali in portland cement and certain siliceous types of aggregates. The result of this action is excessive expansion and pattern cracking of the concrete.

The amount of suitable pozzolan required to control this type of expansion varies with the type of aggregate used and the alkali content of the cement. Normally protection can be obtained by using quantities ranging from 2 to 35 percent by weight of the cement. In the case of a few specific pozzolans of high opal content, less than 15 percent by weight is sufficient to prevent expansion.

GLOSSARY

aluminous cement	Cement made from aluminum ore
bleeding	The migration of mixing water to the surface of freshly poured concrete
concrete bond	The knitting together of two concrete surfaces
hydration	The chemical action between cement and water which results in the hardening of concrete
initial set	The original stiffening of the cement paste which results in the concrete losing its plasticity

lean mix	A concrete mix with a low proportion of cement to aggregates
permeability	A measure of the rate of the passage of water through concrete
plasticity	Ability of freshly mixed concrete to flow
water gain	Absorption of water by hardened concrete

REVIEW QUESTIONS

1 (a) Give a concise definition of a concrete additive.
(b) List reasons for the use of additives in concrete.
2 (a) What is the basic purpose of an accelerator?
(b) How does an accelerator do its job?
(c) What is the material most commonly used as an accelerator?
3 Give two important reasons for using a retarder in concrete.
4 (a) What is air-entrained concrete?
(b) List three important purposes for which an air-entraining agent is used.
(c) Explain how air entrainment of concrete reduces water bleeding and how air entrainment increases workability of concrete.
5 (a) What is meant by cement dispersal?
(b) Name one commonly used dispersal agent.
6 Explain how chemical concrete hardeners differ in their action from metallic hardeners.
7 (a) Explain what is meant by concrete permeability.
(b) Name two methods by which permeability may be reduced.
8 (a) Explain what is meant by a concrete bonding agent.
(b) Under what conditions is a bonding agent advisable?
(c) Name two types of concrete bonding agent.
9 What is the purpose of using a neutralizing agent such as zinc sulfate on a concrete surface?
10 Explain the reason for using a set inhibitor.
11 Describe how a nonskid surface can be produced by the use of abrasive material.
12 (a) What is pozzolan?
(b) Why are pozzolans used in concrete mixtures?

SELECTED SOURCES OF INFORMATION

A. C. Horn Co. Ltd., Montreal, Que.
Calcium Chloride Association, Detroit, Mich.
G. F. Sterne & Sons, Brantford, Ont.
Master Builders Co., Cleveland, O.
Portland Cement Association, Chicago, Ill.
Sika Chemical Corporation, Passaic, N.J.
W. R. Grace & Co., Lasalle, Que.

5

BRICK AND TILE

BRICK

MANUFACTURE OF BRICK

Brick is one of the oldest building materials known to man, and the manufacture of these clay products still follows the same basic procedures of the past. Modern plants have been made much more efficient, however, as a result of technological advances during the past hundred years. A more complete knowledge of raw materials and their properties, better kilns and control of burning, and more and better machinery have all aided the development of a highly efficient industry.

The basic ingredient of brick is clay—clay which has some specific properties. It must have plasticity when mixed with water, so that it can be molded or shaped; it must have sufficient tensile strength to keep its shape after forming; and clay particles must fuse together when subjected to sufficiently high temperatures.

Clay occurs in three principal forms, all of which have similar chemical compositions but different physical characteristics: (1) surface clays, (2) shales, (3) fireclays.

Surface clays, as the name implies, are found near the surface of the earth. They may be upthrusts of older deposits or of more recent, sedimentary formation. Shales are clays which have been subjected to high pressure until they have become relatively hard. Fireclays are found at deeper levels than the other types and usually have more uniform physical and chemical qualities. Their most important characteristic is their ability to withstand high temperatures.

Clays are complex materials, but basically they are compounds of silica and alumina with varying amounts of metallic oxides and other ingredients. They may be divided into two classes, depending on basic composition: (1) calcareous clays and (2) noncalcareous clays. The calcareous clays contain about 15 percent calcium carbonate and burn to a yellowish color. Noncalcareous clays are composed of silicate of alumina, with feldspar and iron oxide, the oxide content varying from 2 to 10 percent. These clays burn buff, red, or salmon, the color depending largely on the iron oxide content.

The manufacturing process has six phases: (1) mining or *winning* and storage of raw material, (2) preparing raw material, (3) forming units, (4) drying, (5) burning and cooling, (6) drawing and storing the finished product.

Mining and Storage

Most clays are mined from open pits, although some fire-clays are obtained by underground mining. They are transported to storage bins by truck or rail. Figure 5·1 shows a mine train unloading at a dump station in the background and a conveyor carrying the clay to storage. Blending of clays to minimize variations in chemical composition and physical properties usually takes place during the storage phase. If the clay is in large lumps, it undergoes preliminary crushing before storage. Figure 5·2 shows clay on the way to the crusher.

Figure 5·1
Clay going to storage.
(Hewitt—Robins, Inc.)

Figure 5·2
Clay traveling from car dump to crusher.
(Hewitt—Robins, Inc.)

Preparing Raw Materials

From the storage bins, clay passes to crushers which reduce it to relatively small pieces (2 in. and smaller) and stones are removed. Figure 5·3 shows such a crusher. It then passes to grinders where it is ground very fine and thoroughly mixed. Conveyors, controlled from a console, carry crushed clay to the grinders (Fig. 5·4). Two types of grinder are shown in Figs. 5·5 and 5·6. The ground clay passes over a vibrating screen which passes only the material which has been ground finely enough. The coarse particles are returned to the grinder for further processing, while the fine material is elevated to storage.

Figure 5·3
Reversible clay crusher.
(Jeffrey Manufacturing Co.)

Figure 5·4
Conveyors in grinding house.
(Hewitt—Robins, Inc.)

104

Figure 5 · 5
Dry pan grinder. (Chambers Brothers Company)

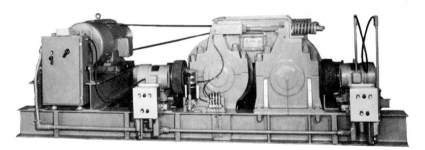

Figure 5 · 6
Roll grinder. (Chambers Brothers Company)

Forming

The first step in the forming process is *tempering,* the mixing of the clay with water in a pug mill. The amount of water used depends on the method being used to form the units. There are three principal methods in use: (1) the stiff-mud process, (2) the soft-mud process, and (3) the dry-press method. In the stiff-mud process, only enough water is used to produce plasticity, usually from 12 to 15 percent by weight. The plastic clay goes through a deairing machine to remove air pockets and bubbles. This also increases workability and increases strength. A stiff-mud pug mill is shown in Fig. 5·7.

The clay is then forced by an auger through a die, pro-

105

Figure 5·7
Pug mill and extruder. (Chambers Brothers Company)

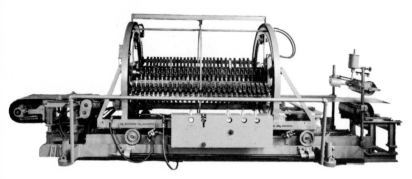

Figure 5·8
Brick cutter. (Chambers Brothers Company)

ducing a continuous column of clay of the desired size and shape. The die head is shown in Fig. 5·7. The column passes through an automatic cutter which cuts off units of the proper length (Fig. 5·8). Textures are applied to the surface as the column emerges from the die. The units are carried by belt to an inspection area where good units are unloaded onto drier cars and the imperfect units are returned to the pug mill. Much brick and all structural clay tile is manufactured by the stiff-mud process.

The soft-mud process is used for making brick only and is employed with clays which contain too much natural water for the stiff-mud process. Twenty to thirty percent water is used in tempering, and the bricks are formed in molds. This is the oldest method of production. Molds are lubricated with sand or water. Brick made with sanded molds is *sand-struck;* brick made with water-lubricated molds is *water-struck.* Figure 5·9 shows a machine for mixing clay for the soft-mud process.

The dry-press process uses the least water in tempering, the maximum being about 10 percent. The relatively dry mix is fed to machines which form the bricks in steel molds under high pressure (Fig. 5·10).

106

Figure 5·9
Soft-mud brick machine. (Posey Iron Works, Inc.)

Figure 5·10
Dry-press brick machine.
(Chisolm, Boyd & White Co.)

Drying

When the units come from the forming machines, they contain from 7 to 30 percent moisture, most of which is removed in drier kilns. Drying causes shrinkage, which must be allowed for when the bricks are being formed so that the finished product will be the proper size.

Drier-kiln temperatures range from 100 to 400°F, and the drying time varies from 24 to 48 hours depending on the type of clay. Heat is usually provided by the exhaust heat from the burning kilns. In all cases the heat and humidity are carefully regulated to avoid too-rapid shrinkage, which causes excessive cracking.

When brick are to be glazed, it is usually done at the end of the drying period, although low-fire glazes can be applied after the brick has been burned. Ceramic glazing consists of spraying a coating of a mixture of mineral ingredients on one or more surfaces of the brick. The glaze melts and fuses to the brick at a given temperature, producing a glasslike coating which is available in almost any color.

Burning and Cooling

Burning is a very important step in the manufacture of brick. The time required varies from 40 to 150 hours, depending on the type of kiln, the type of clay, the type of glaze if any, and other variables. A number of kiln types are in use now, the main ones being tunnel kilns and periodic kilns. In the tunnel kiln, dried brick pass through various temperature zones on special cars. In periodic kilns the temperature is varied periodically—raised and then lowered by steps—until the burning is complete.

Brick must be set on the kiln cars or in the kilns in a prescribed pattern which allows free circulation of hot kiln gases. Fuel may be natural gas, oil, or coal.

Burning may be divided into six general steps: water-smoking, dehydration, oxidation, vitrification, flashing, and cooling. Although temperatures vary, depending on the type of material, each step occurs in a definite temperature zone.

Water-smoking (evaporating free water) takes place at temperatures up to about 400°F; dehydration, at temperatures from about 300 to 1800°F; oxidation, from 1000 to 1800°F; and vitrification, from 1600 to 2400°F.

Near the end of the burning process the brick may be flashed to produce color variations. This is done by injecting natural gas at the appropriate time or place. When this extra fuel burns, patches and variations in color are formed throughout the stack of brick.

Cooling takes from 48 to 72 hours, depending on the type of kiln; it must be carefully controlled because the rate of cooling has a direct effect on color and because too-rapid cooling will cause cracking and checking in the brick.

Drawing and Storing

Drawing is the process of unloading a kiln after the brick are cool. At this time they are normally sorted, graded, packaged, and taken to storage yards or loaded on trucks or railcars for shipment.

BRICK TYPES, SIZES, AND DESIGNS

The unit universally known as a common brick has, in the past, been made in a variety of sizes, depending on the material and the locality. But as the need for standardization became apparent, most structural clay products have been classified by nationally recognized product specifications. Most of these have been done by the American Society for Testing Materials.

A standard size for common brick was adopted—$2\frac{1}{4} \times 3\frac{3}{4} \times 8$ in. (Fig. 5·11). Common brick are used primarily as structural material where strength and durability, rather than appearance, are the important factors. Three grades of common brick are made, as follows:

Grade SW brick is intended for use where high resistance to frost action is desired—for wet locations, below ground, and where the brick may be frozen when permeated with water. The compressive strength rating is 3,000 psi.

Grade MW brick is intended for use in relatively dry locations, exposed to temperatures below freezing. The compressive strength rating is 2,500 psi. In general, brick used in the exterior face of a wall above ground should conform to this grade.

Grade NW brick is intended for use as backup or interior masonry where no freezing occurs. The compressive rating is 1,500 psi.

In addition to this common brick a number of variations are available which have gained recognition and standardization. Table 5·1 lists these and their size.

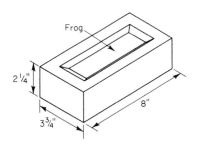

Figure 5·11
Standard brick.

Table 5·1
Nominal modular sizes of brick.
(Structural Clay Products Institute)

UNIT DESIGNATION	THICKNESS, IN.	FACE DIMENSIONS, IN.		MODULAR COURSING
		HEIGHT	LENGTH	
Modular	4	2⅔	8	3C = 8 in.
Engineer	4	3⅕	8	5C = 16 in.
Economy	4	4	8	1C = 4 in.
Double	4	4½	8	3C = 16 in.
Roman	4	2	12	2C = 4 in.
Norman	4	2⅔	12	3C = 8 in.
Norwegian	4	3⅕	12	5C = 16 in.
King Norman	4	4	12	1C = 4 in.
Triple	4	5⅓	12	3C = 16 in.
Structural Clay Research brick	6	2⅔	12	3C = 8 in.

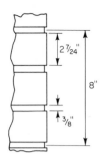

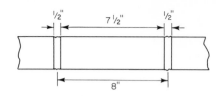

Figure 5·12
Nominal and modular sizes.

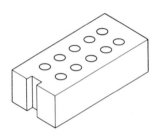

Figure 5·13
Standard extruded brick.

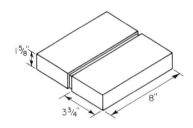

Figure 5·14
Roman brick.

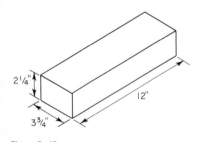

Figure 5·15
Norman brick.

A nominal dimension of a brick or other masonry unit is equal to the specified dimension plus the thickness of the mortar joint with which the unit is designed to be laid, as shown in Fig. 5·12. The standard joint thickness is subtracted from each of the three nominal dimensions of the unit to obtain the specified dimensions. These may vary only by the amount of the permissible tolerance laid down in product specifications.

Thus for modular brick $4 \times 2\frac{2}{3} \times 8$ in. to be laid down with ½-in. mortar joints, the standard dimensions would be $3\frac{1}{2} \times 2\frac{1}{6} \times 7\frac{1}{2}$ in. For Economy brick with ½-in. mortar joints, the standard dimensions would be $3\frac{1}{2} \times 3\frac{1}{2} \times 7\frac{1}{2}$ in. In general the mortar joint thicknesses are ¼ in. for glazed brick, ⅜ or ½ in. for face brick, and ½ in. for common brick. The standard size of a modular glazed brick would be $3\frac{3}{4} \times 2\frac{5}{12} \times 7\frac{3}{4}$ in.

Brick designs have been altered over the years for a number of reasons, including ease of forming, ease of handling, improved mortar bond, architectural appearance, conformation to modular coordination, and changes in building codes.

The oldest brick design produced is that shown in Fig. 5·11, in which the wide faces contain an indentation or *frog*. This design can be produced by a mold (in the dry-press process) but not by the extrusion method (stiff-mud process). In this case the brick are made with a series of holes through them, similar to the one shown in Fig. 5·13.

The S.C.R. (Structural Clay Research) brick was designed when building codes were relaxed to permit 6-in. load-bearing walls for one-story dwellings; it was introduced in 1952. In addition to 10 core holes, it has a ¾ × ¾-in. notch in one end, a window-jamb slot (Fig. 5·13).

Roman brick are made in double form (Fig. 5·14) and broken in two on the job. The breaking leaves a roughcast effect on the exposed edge. Norman brick, with its 12-in. length (Fig. 5·15) is another old design standardized for modern manufacture. Other designs, listed in Table 5·1, have been developed mainly for architectural reasons.

BRICK TEXTURES

Common brick are normally made with smooth surfaces, but bricks to be used for facing are very often given some type of surface treatment—a texture applied as the column of clay leaves the die in the stiff-mud process, a glaze, or a color variation produced by flashing.

Textures are applied by attachments which cut, scratch, brush, roll, or otherwise roughen the surface (Fig. 5·16). Glazes are sprayed on the brick before or after burning. Typical ones are ceramic glaze, described previously, and salt glaze, consisting of a solution of sodium iron silicate. Salt glaze is transparent, so the color of the brick is presented under a lustrous gloss.

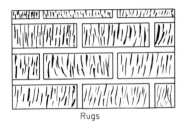

Rugs

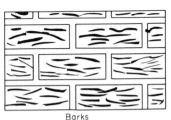

Matt

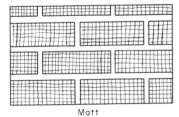

Barks

BRICK BONDS

The term *bond,* used in connection with brick masonry, can be used in three different ways. The method of laying up bricks in a wall in order to form some distinctive pattern or design is referred to as the *pattern bond.* The method by which the individual units in a brick structure are tied together, either by overlapping or by metal ties, is known as the *structural bond.* The adhesion of mortar to bricks or to steel reinforcements used in conjunction with them is called the *mortar bond.*

Structural Bond

Brick are used in walls (1) to form a *solid* brick wall, which, except when S.C.R. brick are used, will be at least 8 in. thick; (2) to build a *cavity* wall, which consists of *wythes* of brick 4 in. thick separated by a 1- or 2-in. cavity; and (3) to face a wall of some other material with a *veneer* of brick, usually 4 in. thick. In all cases there must be some method of tying the units to each other or to the backup material to form a solid structure. This is done by providing a structural bond.

In solid walls the structural bond is provided by header brick which reach through the wall and tie it together (Fig. 5·17). In cavity walls, the two wythes of brick are tied

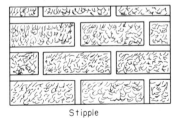

Stipple

Figure 5·16
Brick textures.

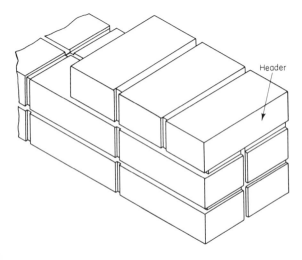

Figure 5·17
Structural header.

111

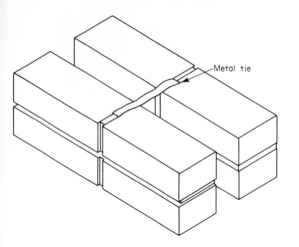

Figure 5 · 18
Cavity wall.

Metal tie

together by metal ties (Fig. 5·18). Structural bond for brick veneer over a wooden backup wall is provided by metal straps. One end of each strap is nailed to the wall; the other end is bonded into a mortar joint (Fig. 5·19). When brick veneer is used over a tile backup wall, header bricks are again employed (Fig. 5·20). Brick veneer over a concrete-block backup wall requires metal ties.

Pattern Bond

There are five basic pattern bonds which are most commonly used in brickwork today: running bond, common bond, Flemish bond, English bond, and Dutch bond (Fig. 5·22). Variations of these basic bonds include double Flemish,

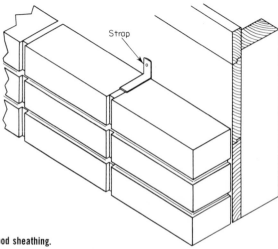

Strap

Figure 5 · 19
Brick veneer over wood sheathing.

Figure 5 · 20
Tile backup, brick veneer.

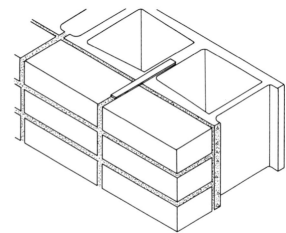

Figure 5 · 21
Concrete block, brick veneer.

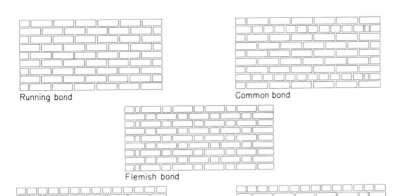

Running bond

Common bond

Flemish bond

English bond

English cross bond

Figure 5 · 22
Basic pattern bonds.

113

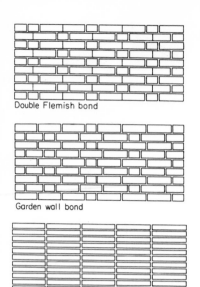

Double Flemish bond

Garden wall bond

Stack bond

Figure 5 · 23
Pattern variations.

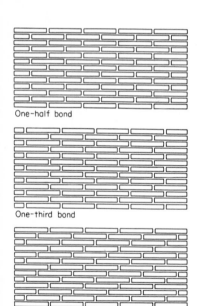

One–half bond

One–third bond

One–third bond diagonal

Figure 5 · 24
Patterns suited to Roman or Norman brick.

garden wall, stack, and many others, some of which are particularly adapted to Roman and Norman brick (Fig. 5·24).

Running bond is the simplest of the basic pattern bonds; it consists of all stretchers (Fig. 5·22). Since there are no headers for structural bond, running bond is used largely in cavity-wall construction and in brick veneering. When used in solid brick walls, metal ties must be used to provide structural bond.

Common bond is a variation of running bond with a complete course of full-length headers at regular intervals, usually at every fifth, sixth, or seventh course. These headers provide structural bond as well as pattern, with the interval depending on the size of the units and the bonding requirements.

In Flemish bond, each course is made up of alternate stretchers and headers, with the headers in alternate courses centered over the stretchers in the intervening courses. When full headers are not required for structural bonding purposes, half-bricks, called *blind headers,* are used.

English bond is composed of alternate courses of headers and stretchers. The headers are centered on the stretchers and the joints between stretchers. Stretchers all line up vertically. Here again, blind headers are used where structural bonding is not required.

English cross or Dutch bond is a variation of English bond and differs only in the position of the stretchers in alternate courses (Fig. 5·22).

Mortar Bond

The building of structures from brick is possible only because a *mortar bond* develops between the mortar and the brick. The strength of brick walls and their ability to resist water penetration depends to a large extent on the strength and completeness of the mortar bond.

The water content of the mortar must be high to obtain a strong bond between mortar and brick. The mortar should be mixed with the maximum amount of water that is possible to use and still maintain plasticity. If mixed mortar loses water by evaporation and stiffens, additional water can be added and the mortar remixed. All mortar should be used within two hours after mixing.

Most building codes recognize four types of mortar, each for a specific purpose. These are:

Type M Mortar. This mortar is suitable for general use and is recommended specifically for masonry below grade and in contact with earth. It consists of 1 part portland cement, ¼ part hydrated lime or lime putty, 3 parts sand by volume *or* 1 part portland cement, 1 part masonry cement, and 6 parts sand by volume.

Type S Mortar. This is also a general purpose mortar bond and is recommended where high resistance to lateral force is required. It consists of 1 part portland cement, ½ part hydrated lime or lime putty, 4½ parts sand by volume *or* ½ part portland cement, 1 part masonry cement, and 4½ parts sand by volume.

Type N Mortar. This mortar is suitable in exposed masonry above grade and is recommended specifically for exterior walls subjected to severe exposure. It consists of 1 part portland cement, 1 part hydrated lime or lime putty, 6 parts sand by volume *or* 1 part masonry cement, and 3 parts sand by volume.

Type O Mortar. This mortar is recommended for load-bearing walls of solid units where the compressive stresses do not exceed 100 lb per sq in. and the masonry will not be subjected to freezing and thawing in the presence of excess moisture. It consists of 1 part portland cement, 2 parts hydrated lime or lime putty, 9 parts sand by volume *or* 1 part masonry cement, and 3 parts sand by volume.

Mortar joints can be treated in several ways to provide some texture in a brick wall. Figure 5·25 shows six types of mortar joints in common use. The tooled, concave, and V joints, which compress the mortar tightly against the brick, offer the best resistance to rain penetration.

TILE

STRUCTURAL CLAY TILE

Bricks are considered to be solid units (having the cross-sectional area of cores, etc., not exceeding 25 percent of the total cross-sectional area of the unit). Clay tile, by contrast, are hollow units. (See Fig. 5·26.)

Tile are made from the same materials as brick, but all clay tile are formed by extrusion in the stiff-mud process. The whole manufacturing process is exactly the same as for brick. A number of types of tile are made, each for a specific purpose: (1) load-bearing wall tile, (2) partition tile, (3) backup tile, (4) furring tile, (5) fireproofing tile, (6) floor tile, (7) structural clay facing tile, (8) structural glazed facing tile.

LOAD-BEARING WALL TILE

This type of tile is used for the bearing walls of light buildings, the height usually being restricted by building codes to four stories, or 40 ft. They are designed for use in either exposed or faced load-bearing walls; their requirements are specified in ASTM Specifications C34. Two grades are in-

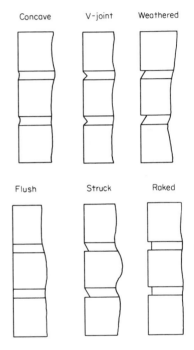

Concave   V-joint   Weathered

Flush   Struck   Raked

Figure 5·25
Mortar joints.

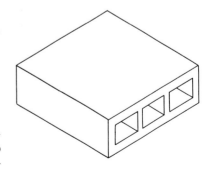

Figure 5·26
Hollow clay tile.

cluded, based on resistance to weathering. Grade LBX is suitable for general use in masonry construction and is especially adapted for use in masonry exposed to weathering. They are also considered suitable for general use in masonry not exposed to frost action or for exposed masonry if it is protected by a facing of at least 3 in. of stone, brick, facing tile, or terra-cotta. The physical requirements for these two grades are given in Table 5·2.

Structural load-bearing wall tile are made in 4-, 6-, 8-, 10-, and 12-in. thicknesses with various face dimensions. Figure 5·27 illustrates various standard shapes in this type of tile.

Modular sizes of structural load-bearing tile are given in Table 5·3. Only the dimensions of full-size units are listed here. Half-lengths, half-heights, corner units, and jamb units are available where required for bonding.

Nominal sizes include the thickness of the standard mortar joint for all dimensions.

Table 5·2
Physical requirements for load-bearing wall tile.
(Structural Clay Products Institute)

| | | | MIN COMPRESSIVE STRENGTH (BASED ON GROSS AREA†), PSI | | | |
| | MAX WATER ABSORPTION* BY 1 HR BOILING, % | | END-CONSTRUCTION TILE | | SIDE-CONSTRUCTION TILE | |
GRADE	AVG OF 5 TESTS	INDIVIDUAL	AVG OF 5 TESTS	INDI-VIDUAL	AVG OF 5 TESTS	INDI-VIDUAL
LBX	16	19	1,400	1,000	700	500
LB	25	28	1,000	700	700	500

*The range in percentage absorption for tile delivered to any one job shall not be more than 12.

†Gross area of a unit shall be determined by multiplying the horizontal face dimension of the unit as placed in the wall by its thickness.

Table 5·3
Nominal modular sizes of structural load-bearing tile.
(Structural Clay Products Institute)

| | FACE DIMENSION IN WALL | |
THICKNESS, IN.	HEIGHT, IN.	LENGTH, IN.
4	5⅓	12
4	8	8, 12
4	12	12
6	5⅓	12
6	12	12
8	5⅓	12
8	6	12
8	8	8, 12, 16
8	12	12
10	8	12
10	12	12
12	12	12

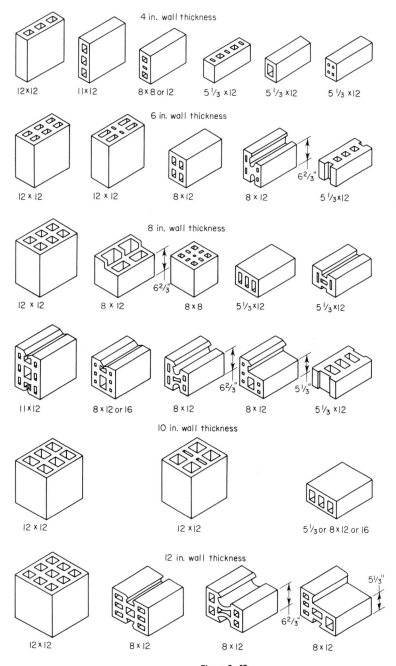

4 in. wall thickness

12×12	11×12	8×8 or 12	5⅓×12	5⅓×12	5⅓×12

6 in. wall thickness

12 × 12	12 × 12	8×12	8 × 12	5⅓×12

8 in. wall thickness

12 × 12	8 × 12	8×8	5⅓×12	5⅓×12

11×12	8×12 or 16	8×12	8×12	5⅓×12

10 in. wall thickness

12 × 12	12 ×12	5⅓ or 8×12 or 16

12 in. wall thickness

12×12	8×12	8×12	8×12

Figure 5·27
Various standard shapes of load-bearing structural clay tile.

PARTITION TILE

Structural clay partition tile are classified as non-load-bearing and only one grade, NB, is included in ASTM Designation C56. The only physical requirement is that dealing with maximum water absorption allowable. Nominal sizes of

117

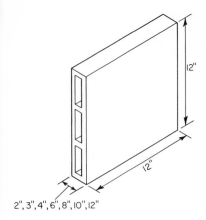

Figure 5·28
Partition tile.

2", 3", 4", 6", 8", 10", 12"

typical partition tile are shown in Fig. 5·28. Partition tile with modular dimensions based on ½-in. mortar joints are available in most areas.

BACKUP TILE

Backup tile are intended for use in both bearing and nonbearing walls which will be faced with brick or facing tile. The facing is bonded to the backup, and the loads are supported by both; consequently backup tile falls into the same grade classifications as load-bearing wall tile. Backup tile include header tile and stretcher units and are available in both vertical and horizontal cell units. Figure 5·29 illustrates some typical backup tile shapes. Modular sizes of load-bearing backup tile are given in Table 5·4. The nominal sizes include the thickness of the standard mortar joint.

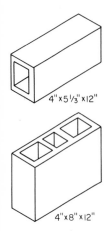

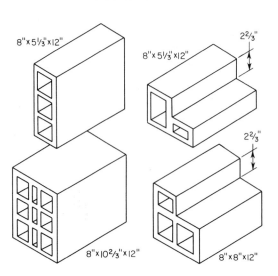

Figure 5·29
Typical backup tile.

Table 5·4
Nominal modular sizes of structural backup tile.
(Structural Clay Products Institute)

THICKNESS, IN.	FACE DIMENSION IN WALL	
	HEIGHT, IN.	LENGTH, IN.
4	2⅔	8, 12
4	5⅓	12*
4	8	8, 12
4	10⅔	12
6	5⅓	12
6	8	12*
6	10⅔	12
8	5⅓	12
8	8	8, 12*
8	10⅔	12

* Includes header and stretcher units.

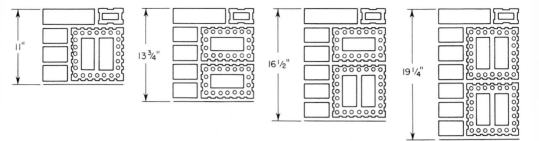

Figure 5·30 shows typical masonry construction using backup tile and face brick. Notice that brick may be bonded every fourth, fifth, sixth, or seventh course. No L-shaped header tile are being used in this case. Mortar joints are ½-in. thick.

Figure 5·30
Backup tile.

FURRING TILE

Furring tile are used on the inside of exterior walls to provide air spaces for insulation, to prevent the passage of moisture, and to provide a suitable plastering surface. They are classified as non-load-bearing and are made in both solid and split types, with modular face dimensions and thicknesses of 1½ and 2 in. for split tile and 2, 3, and 4 in. for solid furring. Typical furring tile are shown in Fig. 5·31. The application of

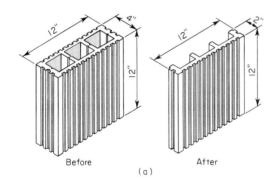

Before   After

(a)

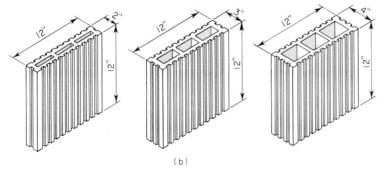

(b)

Figure 5·31
(a) Split furring tile.
(b) Solid furring tile.
(Montreal Terra Cotta, Ltd.)

119

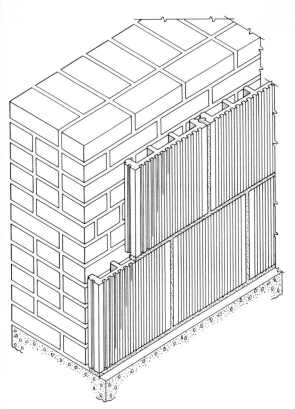

Figure 5 · 32
Application of split furring tile.
(Montreal Terra Cotta, Ltd.)

Figure 5 · 33
Tile furring.
(Montreal Terra Cotta, Ltd.)

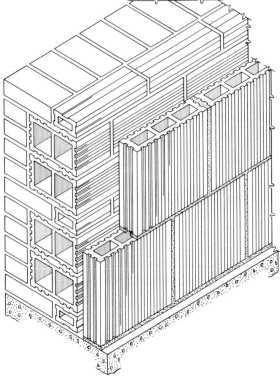

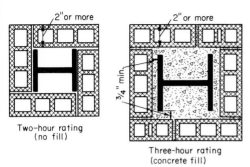

Two-hour rating
(no fill)

Three-hour rating
(concrete fill)

Four-hour rating
(tile fill)

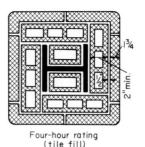

Four-hour rating
(tile fill)

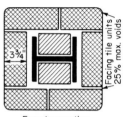

Four-hour rating
(brick fill)

split furring tile is shown in Fig. 5·32; Fig. 5·33 shows a wall built with backup tile faced with brick and furred with 3-in. solid furring tile.

FIREPROOFING TILE

Structural steel must be insulated in fireproof construction. One method of doing this is to cover it with fireproofing tile. Two types of tile are used for this purpose. Units for fireproofing columns may be selected from furring, partition, or wall-tile shapes (Fig. 5·34). Fireproofing tile for beams and girders are made in special shapes to fit around these members. The three basic shapes made are *clip* tile, *angle* tile, and *soffit* tile. Figure 5·35 shows the three shapes and the method of using them.

FLOOR TILE

One-way ribbed concrete floor and roof slabs can be formed by using structural clay floor tile. They are manu-

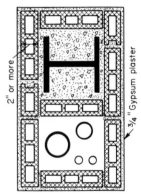

Four-hour rating
(concrete fill)

Figure 5 · 34
Typical structural clay tile column fireproofing details.
(Structural Clay Products Institute)

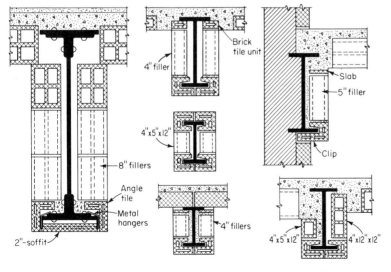

Figure 5 · 35
Typical structural clay tile girder and beam fireproofing details.
(Structural Clay Products Institute)

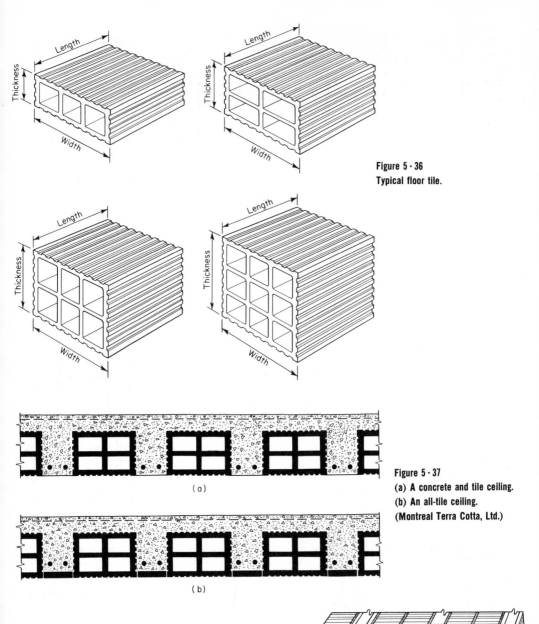

Figure 5 · 36
Typical floor tile.

Figure 5 · 37
(a) A concrete and tile ceiling.
(b) An all-tile ceiling.
(Montreal Terra Cotta, Ltd.)

(a)

(b)

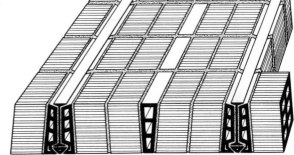

Figure 5 · 38
Flat arch tile floor.

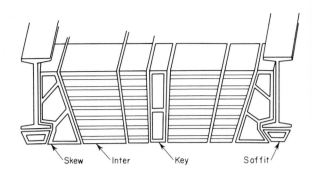

Figure 5 · 39
Floor arch tile.

Skew Inter Key Soffit

factured in both load-bearing and non-load-bearing grades in standard thicknesses ranging from 3 to 12 in. and standard lengths and widths of 12 in. *Starter* lengths of 6 in. are also made; auxiliary 8-in. widths to provide wider joists at the supports can be obtained on order. Standard units contain 3, 4, 6, or 9 cells (Fig. 5·36). Where an all-tile ceiling is required, soffit tile are available for forming the bottom of the joists. They are about 1 in. thick, 4, 5, or 6 in. wide, and are made in 6- and 12-in. lengths. Figure 5·37 shows ribbed floors with and without an all-tile ceiling.

Another type of structural clay floor tile is made for forming segmental and flat clay-tile floor arches. These are patterned after the old brick segmental floor arches.

Figure 5·38 indicates how these tile are used to form a flat-arch floor. The frame is of I beams, normally on 6-ft centers. Four tile shapes are required to form the arch: (1) *skews,* to fit around the beam web and lower flange, (2) *soffits,* to cover the underside of the lower flange, (3) *inters,* to form the main body of the arch, and (4) *key tile* to form the wedge at the center of the arch. Figure 5·39 illustrates how skews and soffit tile fit the I beam.

STRUCTURAL CLAY FACING TILE

Facing tile falling into this category are unglazed and may have either a smooth or a rough textured finish. They are designed to be used as exposed facing material on either exterior or interior walls and partitions. There are two classes of unglazed facing tile, standard and special duty, based on the thickness of the face shell. Standard tile are suitable for general use in either exterior or interior locations. Special-duty tile have heavier shells and webs and are intended for greater resistance to impact and moisture penetration.

Both classes of tile are produced in two types, the differences being based mainly on appearance. The two types are:

Type FTX. This is a smooth-face tile, suitable for general use for either exterior or interior work. It is low in absorption, easily cleaned, and resists staining. The color range is narrow, but the variation in face dimensions very small.

Type FTS. This type may be either smooth or textured, for exterior or interior use. The absorption rate is higher than for type FTX and the variation in dimensions greater. It is produced in a wider color range but may have minor surface defects.

Probably the most popular sizes in facing tile are 5⅓ × 12 in. and 4 × 12 in. face, but this type of tile is produced in a variety of modular sizes. Table 5·5 lists these.

Some of the common stretcher units available in unglazed facing tile are shown in Fig. 5·40.

Table 5·5
Nominal modular sizes of structural facing tile.*
(Brick and Tile Manufacturers' Association of Canada)

| | FACE DIMENSION IN WALL | |
THICKNESS, IN.	HEIGHT, IN.	LENGTH, IN.
2, 4, 6, 8	4	8, 12
2, 4, 6, 8	5⅓	8, 12
2, 4, 6, 8	6	12
2, 4, 6, 8	8	12, 16

* Nominal sizes include the thickness of the standard mortar joint for all dimensions.

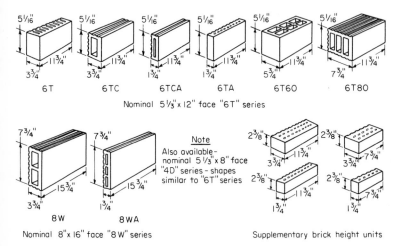

Nominal 5⅓" x 12" face "6T" series

6T   6TC   6TCA   6TA   6T60   6T80

Nominal 8"x 16" face "8W" series

8W   8WA

Note
Also available–
nominal 5⅓"x 8" face
"4D" series – shapes
similar to "6T" series

Supplementary brick height units

Figure 5·40
Unglazed facing tile stretcher units.
(Brick and Tile Manufacturing Assn. of Canada)

STRUCTURAL GLAZED FACING TILE

This type of facing tile is produced from high-grade light-burning clay which is suitable for the application of ceramic or salt glaze. Two grades are produced:

Grade S (select). Intended for use with comparatively narrow (¼-in.) joints.

124

Grade G (ground edge). Used where the variation in face dimension must be very small.

Two types of glazed tile are made, single-faced units (Type I) and units with two opposite faces glazed (Type II). Type I is used where the tile is used to face a backup wall, while Type II is used where the tile is exposed on two opposite faces. ASTM Designation C126, which covers this type of tile, specifies requirements for compressive strength, absorption rate, number of cells, shell and web thickness, tolerances on dimensions, and the properties of the ceramic finish.

Shapes and sizes are similar to those of unglazed facing tile except that ceramic glazed tile units are available in 2- and 4-in. thicknesses in 16-in. lengths only.

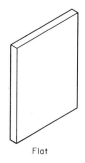

Flat

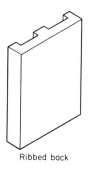

Ribbed back

TERRA-COTTA

Terra-cotta, meaning "fired earth," is a clay product which has been used for architectural decorative purposes since the days of ancient Greece and Rome. Modern terra-cotta is machine-extruded and molded or pressed. The machine-made product, usually referred to as *ceramic veneer,* is a unit with flat face and flat or ribbed back (Fig. 5·41). The molded or pressed units, called *architectural* terra-cotta, are available in sculpture or bas-relief as well as in plain surfaces.

Ceramic veneer is made in two types, *adhesion* type and *anchor* type. Adhesion-type units are held to the wall by the bond of the mortar to the ceramic veneer back and to the backing wall. Anchor type are held by mortar and by wire ties between the terra-cotta and the wall behind.

Adhesion-type ceramic veneer is available in face sizes up to 600 sq in. with maximum widths of 24 in. and lengths up to 36 in. The thickness is limited to 1⅝ in. The actual face dimensions will vary with the manufacturer and, of course, with the overall dimensions of the structure for which the facing is intended. It can be applied over brick or tile, concrete, metal, or wood surfaces by setting it in a mortar coat applied over the surface of the wall (Fig. 5·42).

Anchor-type ceramic veneer is used where the architect desires a larger slab than those available in adhesion-type

Figure 5·41
Adhesion-type ceramic veneer.

Figure 5·42
Ceramic veneer applications.

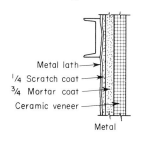

Metal lath
¼ Scratch coat
¾ Mortar coat
Ceramic veneer

Metal

Sheathing
Building paper
¼ Scratch coat
¾ Mortar coat
Ceramic veneer

Wood

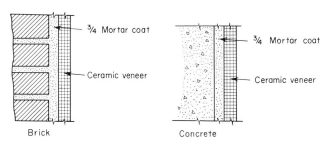

¾ Mortar coat

Ceramic veneer

Brick

¾ Mortar coat

Ceramic veneer

Concrete

125

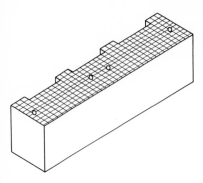

Figure 5·43
Anchor-type ceramic veneer.

veneer. The slab thickness will range from 2 to 2½ in. and the face dimensions, within reason, are a matter of choice. The back of the units are scored or ribbed, and anchor holes are provided in the bed edges. Figure 5·43 illustrates the cross section of a typical anchor-type unit. One method of anchoring this type of terra-cotta involves the use of heavy copper wire loops. The wire is passed around a pencil rod fastened to the backing wall, and the ends of the loop are bent down to fit into the anchor holes in the edge of the unit (Fig. 5·44). The spaces between the back of the terra-cotta units and the backing wall are poured full of grout to provide mortar bond and to hold the anchors in place.

All ceramic-veneer units are designed and sized to be laid with uniform ¼-in. mortar joints, and deviation from a plane surface is restricted to from $\frac{1}{16}$ to $\frac{3}{16}$ in. depending on the face area of the units.

Before architectural terra-cotta units are made, detailed drawings must be prepared, showing size, shape, profile, joint sizes, location, type of anchors and hangers, expansion joints, etc.

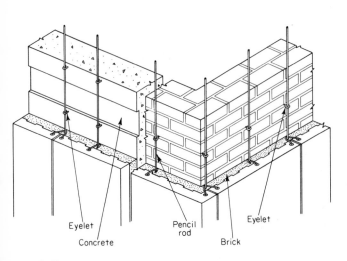

Eyelet Pencil rod Eyelet

Concrete Brick

Figure 5·44
Ceramic veneer anchored in place.

CLAY MASONRY SOLAR SCREENS

Solar screens may be made from brick, tile units originally intended for some other use, or screen tile made especially for this purpose. The latter are made in a wide variety of patterns and sizes and colors, glazed and unglazed. Figure 5·45 illustrates a number of the patterns available.

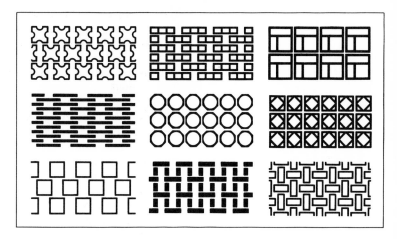

Figure 5 · 45
Solar-screen patterns.

GLOSSARY

backup wall   A wall to support a facing material

bas-relief   A slight projection of ornament from a background

feldspar   A crystalline mineral, aluminum silicate, with potassium, sodium, calcium, or barium

frog   A depression in the wide surface of a brick

furring   The building out or leveling of a surface

modular size   A size which allows a material to conform to a given module or standard measurement

pencil rod   A thin rod used as an anchor for stone or terra-cotta facing

pug mill   A machine for mixing clay with water

salt glaze   Transparent glazing

solar screen   A pierced wall, made from masonry or tile units, intended to act as a sunshade

veneer   A surface coating

vitrification   The process of changing to a glassy substance through heat

winning   Mining or removal of clay

wythe   A 4-in. thickness of brick wall

REVIEW QUESTIONS

1   What are the basic properties which clay must have to be suitable for making brick?

2   What is the reason for blending two or more clays in the process of manufacturing brick?

3   (a) What is meant by tempering clay?
     (b) Where is this done?
4   (a) Which process is most commonly used in molding brick?
     (b) What is the purpose of the die at the end of a pug mill?
5   Explain why heat and humidity must be carefully controlled in brick drying kilns.
6   What is meant by each of the following terms:
     (a) Flashing brick
     (b) Textured brick
     (c) Ceramic glaze
7   Explain the meaning of these terms:
     (a) Pattern bond
     (b) Structural bond
     (c) Mortar bond
8   Illustrate by means of a sketch the difference between English bond and Dutch bond.
9   Why should brick be soaked before being laid up in a wall?
10 What is the basic difference between brick and tile?
11 List the two basic functions of backup tile.
12 Where would you use:
     (a) Type I glazed facing tile
     (b) Type II glazed facing tile
13 Outline two basic differences between ceramic veneer and architectural terra-cotta.
14 Explain why:
     (a) There is a maximum allowable area and thickness for adhesion-type ceramic veneer.
     (b) Architectural terra-cotta is a relatively costly type of facing material.

SELECTED SOURCES OF INFORMATION

Brick and Tile Manufacturers' Association of Canada, Toronto, Ont.
Cooksville-Laprairie Brick Ltd., Montreal, Que.
Division of Building Research, N.R.C., Ottawa, Ont.
Federal Seaboard Terra Cotta Corporation, New York, N.Y.
Ludowici-Celadon Co., Chicago, Ill.
Medicine Hat Brick & Tile Co. Ltd., Medicine Hat, Alberta
Structural Clay Products Institute, Washington, D.C.
United States Ceramic Tile Co., Canton, O.

6

STONE

The term "stone" usually designates blocks or pieces of the basic material rock. It is one of the oldest building materials known to man. Because of its unique characteristics, stone has been regarded as the preferred material in the construction of permanent buildings. It was, in fact, the predominant material used in buildings built prior to the turn of the twentieth century.

CLASSIFICATION

Rock can be divided into three general categories, depending on its geological origin: (1) *igneous*, (2) *sedimentary*, and (3) *metamorphic*. Igneous rock was formed as the result of the cooling of molten matter. Sedimentary rock was formed by the action of water, either depositing minerals at the bottom of a water body or depositing them on the earth's surface. The latter took place when water flowed to the surface from the earth's interior, bringing minerals which were deposited as the water evaporated. Metamorphic rocks have been changed from their original structure by the action of extreme pressure, heat, moisture, or various combinations of these forces.

Stone used for building purposes also can be classified according to the form in which it is available commercially: (1) rubble (fieldstone), (2) dimension (cut stone), (3) flagstone (flat slabs), and (4) crushed rock. Rubble includes rough fieldstone which may merely have been broken into suitable sizes, or it may include irregular pieces of stone that have been roughly cut to size. Dimension stone makes up the largest portion of the stone used in building; it consists of pieces that have been cut or finished according to a set of drawings. Flagstone consists of thin pieces (½ in. and up) which may or may not have had their face dimensions cut to some particular size. Crushed stone consists of pieces varying in size from ⅜ to 6 in. and is used to a large extent in the concrete industry.

Despite the abundance of rock, relatively few stones satisfy the requirements as building stones. The important requirements are (1) strength, (2) hardness, (3) workability, (4) durability, (5) color and grain, (6) porosity and texture, (7) ease of quarrying, (8) accessibility.

Many stones satisfy the requirements of strength. For most purposes in building, a compressive strength of 5,000 psi is satisfactory. In a few instances good shear strength is important. Hardness is vitally important only where the stone is to be used in floors, steps, walks, etc.; but hardness does have a bearing on workability. It varies all the way from soft sandstone, which can be easily scratched, to some stones harder than steel. Workability is important since the ease of producing the required sizes and shapes has a direct bearing on the cost. Durability—the ability of the stone to withstand the effects of rain, spray, wind, dust, frost action, heat, and fire—determines the maintenance-free life of a stone structure. This will vary from about ten to two hundred years. Color is very important from the standpoint of aesthetics and location but is also partially a matter of taste and fashion. The grain or surface appearance of stone affects its desirability for decorative purposes.

Porosity has a direct bearing on the ability of the stone to withstand frost action and the marking and staining caused by the dissolving of some mineral constituents in water. Texture, the fineness of grain, affects workability and therefore cost. Fine-textured rock splits and dresses more readily than coarse rock. For many ornamental purposes, also, the texture is important.

The ease of quarrying is a prime consideration in judging the suitability of stone for building. The bedding and joint planes must be such that the stone can be produced in sizable, sound blocks. The rock exposure should be free from closely spaced joints, cracks, and other lines of weakness. Deep and irregular weathering is also undesirable. The nearness of the deposit to the surface is also important. Building stone is seldom obtained from underground. Accessibility also affects cost. Transportation over long distances is expensive but in some cases becomes a necessity.

COMPOSITION

Rock can be classified according to its composition. Although a great many minerals occur in rock formations throughout the world, stone used in construction comes from rock that usually falls into one of three classifications: (1) rock containing mainly *silica,* (2) rock containing chiefly *silicates,* and (3) rock containing *calcareous* minerals.

The main silica mineral is *quartz,* the most abundant mineral on the earth's surface. It is the chief constituent of sand and is found in most clays and in several of the building stones.

Silicate minerals include *feldspar, hornblende, serpentine,* and *mica.* Feldspar is a silicate of alumina in combination with lime or potash. Depending on the combination, colors may be red, pink, or clear. Hornblende is a silicate of alumina with lime or iron. It is a strong, tough mineral appearing in green, brown, and black crystals. Mica is mainly silicate of alumina but may be in combination with other minerals such as iron or potash. It appears in soft, usually clear crystals that split easily into flat flakes. Serpentine, a silicate of magnesia, appears often in combination with lime. It is a light green or yellow and has no defined planes along which it splits readily.

The calcareous minerals include *calcite,* which is basically carbonate of lime, and *dolomite,* a carbonate of lime in combination with varying amounts of magnesia.

BUILDING STONES

Stones which do, in general, satisfy the foregoing requirements and which are commonly used in building include granite, limestone, travertine, marble, serpentine, sandstone, and slate.

Granite is of igneous origin, composed of quartz, feldspar, hornblende, and mica. It is generally very hard, strong, durable, and capable of taking a high polish. Colors include red, pink, yellow, gray, and brown. Quartzite is a type of stone sometimes confused with granite but quite different in composition. It is made up of grains of quartz sand cemented together with silica and is usually distinguishable by its coarse, crystalline appearance.

Limestone is a sedimentary rock, with three distinct types being found.

Oolitic limestone is a calcite-cemented calcareous stone formed of shells and shell fragments, particularly noncrystalline in nature. It has no cleavage lines and is usually very uniform in composition and structure.

Dolomitic limestone is rich in magnesium carbonate and frequently somewhat crystalline in character. It usually has greater compressive and tensile strength than oolitic limestones, with greater variety of texture.

Crystalline limestone is predominantly composed of calcium carbonate crystals. It has high compressive and tensile strength, is very low in absorption, and has a smooth texture. The color is a fairly uniform light gray.

Some of the better-known limestones are Carthage limestone, which is a crystalline limestone; Kasota stone, Mankatostone, and Winonastone, which are dolomitic limestones; and Indiana limestone, Tyndallstone, Cordova limestone, and golden shell limestone, which are oolitic limestones.

Travertine is also a sedimentary rock, composed mainly of calcium carbonate. It has been formed at the earth's surface through the evaporation of water from hot springs. It is used as an interior decorative stone because of its pleasing texture and its tendency to show small, natural pockets on a cut surface.

131

Marble is an example of a metamorphic rock, one that has been changed from its original structure. In this case limestone and dolomite have been recrystallized to form marble. A number of types of marble have come to be recognized, among them carrara, parian, numidian, onyx, Vermont, and brecciated marbles.

The colors of marble range from pure white through all shades of gray to black, as well as violet, red, yellow, pink, and green. The great range of colors is due to the presence of various oxides of iron, silica, graphite, mica, and carbonaceous matter, which are scattered through the rock in streaks, blotches, or grains. Brecciated marbles are made up of small fragments embedded in a colored paste or cementing material. Certain varieties of marble deteriorate quite readily when exposed to the weather and are suitable only for interior work.

Serpentine is an igneous rock which takes its name from the mineral serpentine, its chief constituent. The mineral, a magnesium silicate, is olive green to blackish green, but impurities may give the rock other colors. The stone is massive appearing and takes a high polish but is often subject to deterioration due to weathering. For this reason it is used mainly for interior or in sheltered locations.

Sandstone is a class of rocks composed of cemented silica grains. The cement may be silica, iron oxide, or clay; the hardness and durability of the particular sandstone depend on the type of cement. Other materials such as mica, lime, or feldspar, in addition to the silica, appear in some sandstones, resulting in considerable variation in color and texture. Colors include gray, buff, light brown, brown, and red. Textures range from very fine to very coarse and some are quite porous, with as much as 30 percent of their volume composed of pores. Some common sandstones are berea stone, linroc stone, ledgestone, Kaibab stone, and Pearl sandstone.

Slate rock is formed by the metamorphosis of clays and shales deposited in layers. A unique characteristic of the rock is the relative ease with which it may be separated into thin tough sheets, called slates, ¼-in. or more thick. Slates are black, green, red, gray, or purple; in some cases, the color changes after long exposure.

PRODUCTION OF STONE

The process of removing stone from its natural bed is known as quarrying. The method of quarrying depends on the nature of the stone. Drilling and splitting are the basic methods and, in the case of stratified rocks, this is facilitated by the natural cleavage lines in the stone. The spacing of the cleavage lines, however, limits the thickness of the stone produced.

Bush–hammered

Patent–hammered

Peen–hammered

Crandalled

Pick–pointed

Figure 6·1
Hand finishes on stone.

Holes are drilled close together along the faces of the rock. For stratified rock, the holes are drilled only on the face at right angles to the cleavage lines. When this method is used for unstratified rock, both horizontal and vertical holes are drilled. Wedges are driven into the holes in order to split the rock along a drilled line. The stones thus produced are large, with irregular faces, and these are first cut or split to the desired rough size. Power saws (chat saws, shot saws, and diamond saws) are used to cut the blocks to the required dimensions. Each type of saw produces a surface texture which is different from the others.

In addition to the sawed finishes, a number of other surface treatments can be applied to a stone face. Machine finishes include a planer finish, carbo-finish, rubbed finish, and various machine-tool finishes. A carbo-finish is a very smooth finish produced by the use of a carborundum machine instead of a planer. A rubbed finish requires the rubbing of the stone with an abrasive after it has been planed.

A variety of hand finishes are also applicable to cut stone. They include the bush-hammer, peen-hammer, patent-hammer, pick-point, crandalled, and hand-rubbed finishes (Fig. 6·1).

Stone varies widely in its characteristics, both between types of stone and within a group of stones of the same kind. Table 6·1 outlines the strength characteristics of the more common commercial building stones.

STONE CONSTRUCTION

The building industry today uses stone largely as a facing material for large buildings with steel or concrete frames. In some instances it is used in bearing walls for buildings two or three stories in height.

In either case, the stonework may be divided into three general categories: rubblework, ashlar, and trim. Rubblework involves using stones which have not been cut but which may have had one face—the face that is to be exposed—split or chipped. Two styles of rubblework are used, random and coursed. In the first case no attempt is made to produce either horizontal or vertical course lines. Spaces too small for a regular stone are filled with *spalls;* small stones (Fig. 6·2) and bond stones must be provided for structural bonding, unless ties are being used for this purpose. In

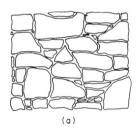
(a)

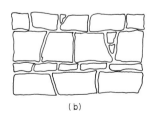
(b)

Figure 6·2
(a) Random rubble.
(b) Coursed rubble.

133

Table 6 · 1

Strength characteristics of commercial building stones.

STONE	COMPRESSIVE STRENGTH, PSI, RANGE	MODULUS OF RUPTURE, PSI, RANGE	SHEAR STRENGTH, PSI, RANGE	TENSILE STRENGTH, PSI, RANGE	ELASTIC MODULUS, PSI, RANGE	TOUGHNESS		WEAR RESISTANCE	
						RANGE	AVG	RANGE	AVG
Granite	7,700-60,000	1,430-5,190	2,000-4,800	600-1,000	5,700,000-8,200,000	8-27	13	43.9-87.9	60.8
Marble	8,000-50,000	...	1,300-6,500	150-2,300	7,200,000-14,500,000	2-23	6	6.7-41.7	18.9
Limestone	2,600-28,000	500-2,000	800-4,580	280-890	1,500,000-12,400,000	5-20	7	1.3-24.1	8.4
Sandstone	5,000-20,000	700-2,300	300-3,000	280-500	1,900,000-7,700,000	2-35	10	1.6-29.0	13.3
Quartzite	16,000-45,000				...	5-30	15		
Serpentine	11,000-28,000	1,300-11,000	...	800-1,600	4,800,000-9,600,000	...	...	13.3-111.4	46.9
Basalt	28,000-67,000	...	...	...	...	5-40	20		
Diorite	16,000-35,000	...	...	...	...	6-38	23		
Syenite	14,000-28,000	...	...	...	...	...			
Slate	...	6,000-15,000	2,000-3,600	3,000-4,300	9,800,000-18,000,000	10-56	...	5.6-11.7	7.7
Diabase	...	...	...	...	...	6-50	19		
Building limestone	...	...	...	...	...	3-8	4.4		

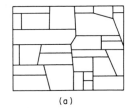
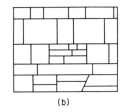
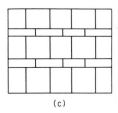

(a) (b) (c)

Figure 6·3
(a) Broken ashlar.
(b) Irregular coursed ashlar.
(c) Regular coursed ashlar.

Figure 6·4
Stone quoins.

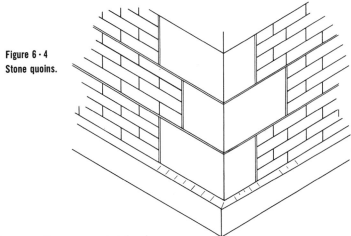

coursed rubblework, horizontal course lines are maintained, but no vertical course lines used.

Ashlar work requires the use of cut stone and includes broken ashlar, irregular coursed ashlar, and regular coursed ashlar (Fig. 6·3).

Stone trimming involves the use of stones cut for a specific purpose and includes quoins, jambs, sills, belts, copings, cornices, lintels, steps, and arch stones.

Quoins (Fig. 6·4) are stones laid at the intersection of two walls. They can be emphasized by letting them project beyond the vertical plane of the wall or by using a contrasting color or type. Usually they are laid so that they appear alternately as long and short stones on each side of the corner.

Jambs are stones which form the sides of window and door openings. Some of the jamb stones should be bond stones, running through the wall; the joints of the short ones should come at the rabbet of the jamb.

Sills are the stones which form the bottom of window and door openings. There are two types, slip sills and lug sills. The ends of the lug sills extend under the jambs and consequently carry a part of the wall load (Fig. 6·5), while slip sills fit between the jambs (Fig. 6·6). All sills should have a wash —a slope—on the upper surface to provide for water runoff.

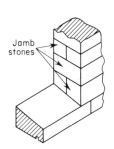

Jamb stones

Figure 6·5
Lug sill.

Figure 6·6
Slip sill.

135

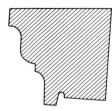

Figure 6·7
Wash and drip.

Sills should also be provided with a drip to prevent water from running back to the wall along the underside of the sill (Fig. 6·7).

Belts are special stone courses which are built into a wall for a particular purpose. One reason for a belt course is to provide architectural relief to a large wall of one material or to provide a break in the vertical plane of the wall. A belt course also provides a convenient means of hiding a change in wall thickness. Figure 6·8 illustrates the use of a belt course for these two purposes.

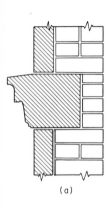

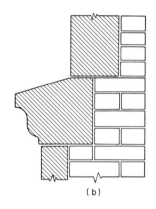

Figure 6 · 8
(a) Belt course for architectural relief.
(b) Belt course for change in wall thickness.

(a) (b)

A coping stone is one which is cut to fit on the top of a masonry wall. It prevents the passage of water into the wall, sheds water to either the inside or the outside, and gives a finished appearance to the wall (Fig. 6·9).

Cornice stones are also specially cut stones which are built into and project from a masonry wall near the top to provide the appearance of an eave. Sometimes two or more stones of varying widths are used to provide the projection with adequate support (Fig. 6·10).

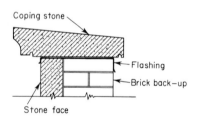

Coping stone
Flashing
Brick back–up
Stone face

Figure 6 · 9
Stone coping.

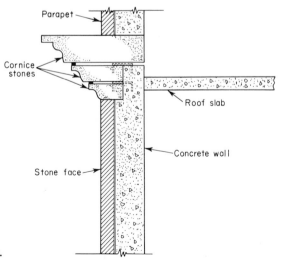

Parapet
Cornice stones
Roof slab
Concrete wall
Stone face

Figure 6 · 10
Three-piece cornice.

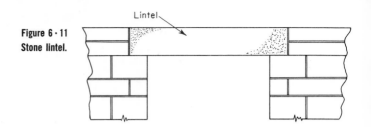

Figure 6 · 11
Stone lintel.

Lintels are stones which bridge the top of door and window openings (Fig. 6·11).

Stone steps are made to fit over an inclined concrete slab (Fig. 6·12) or to cap steps cast in concrete. It is important to use stone that can withstand weathering and that has uniform hardness to allow for even wear on the treads.

Arch stones are cut to form some particular type of arch over a door or window opening. An arch is thus used in place of a lintel. A number of arch types are used, including semicircular, elliptical, segmental, Gothic, and flat. In each case the stones are cut to form the type of arch required. Figure 6·13 illustrates the use of stones in forming a Gothic arch.

Stone floors, walks, and patios are made by covering a base of stone, concrete, brick, or tile with flagstones. They may be random flagstone, trimmed flagstone, trimmed rectangular, or square and rectangular. Random flagstone consists of natural irregularly shaped pieces laid without any

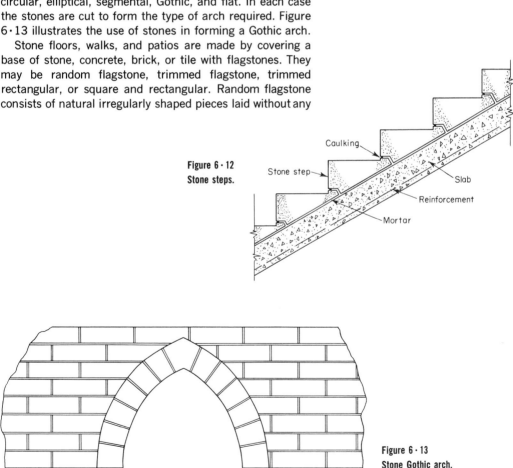

Figure 6 · 12
Stone steps.

Figure 6 · 13
Stone Gothic arch.

Figure 6·14
Random flagstone.

attempt at pattern, as illustrated in Fig. 6·14. Trimmed flag-stones consist of natural random pieces, a percentage of which have one or two edges saw-trimmed. Trimmed rectangular flagstones have four straight sawed edges with right-angle corners but are of no specific dimensions. Square and rectangular flagstones have straight edges, right-angle corners, and are cut to specific sizes often 4 × 4 in. or 6 × 6 in. but may be cut to any specified size.

GLOSSARY

bedding plane	The position and direction of the joints between strata or layers of rock
chat saw	A stone saw using small pieces of hard steel as the cutting agent
cleavage lines	Natural lines of weakness along which stone can be broken most easily
joint plane	The position and direction of the breaks or joints in an individual rock layer, roughly perpendicular to the bedding plane
shot saw	A stone saw using chilled steel shot as the cutters

REVIEW QUESTIONS

1 Explain what a metamorphic rock is. Show why marble is an example of a metamorphic rock.
2 Why are relatively few stones used as building stones?
3 What is meant by:
   (a) The porosity of a stone
   (b) The texture of a stone

4 Explain why stone is today largely limited to a facing material.

5 How does oolitic limestone basically differ from other types of limestone?

6 What is the chief use of travertine as a building stone?

7 What kinds of stone are most commonly used for exterior work?

8 Why is it considered necessary to prevent water from running back to a stone wall along the underside of a sill, coping, or cornice?

9 Explain how flagstones are usually set over a masonry base.

10 Illustrate by diagram one method of anchoring a stone facing to a concrete backup wall.

SELECTED SOURCES OF INFORMATION

Adirondak Stone Quarries Inc., Malone, N.Y.
Building Stone Institute, Indianapolis, Ind.
Chicago Cut Stone Contractors' Association, Chicago, Ill.
Cold Springs Granite Co., St. Cloud, Minn.
Indiana Limestone Co., Bedford, Ind.
Sinclair Cut Stone Co., Hamilton, Ont.
Tennessee Marble Co., Knoxville, Tenn.

7

STEEL AND NONFERROUS METALS

STEEL

PRODUCTION

Three basic raw materials are needed in large quantities for the production of steel—iron ore, coal, and limestone. The operations of the mines and quarries supplying these raw materials are in themselves major industries. Figure 7·1 shows a ship unloading coal at a steel plant, and Fig. 7·2 shows an iron ore storage dock.

The iron ore goes through primary processes of crushing and concentrating at the mine and the concentrated ore is shipped to a steel plant, often in the form of pellets. Lime-

Figure 7·1
Unloading coal at steel plant.
(The Steel Co. of Canada, Limited)

Figure 7 · 2
Iron ore storage dock. (The Steel Co. of Canada, Limited)

Figure 7 · 3
Discharging flaming coke into a quenching car.
(The Steel Co. of Canada, Limited)

stone is quarried, crushed, screened, and shipped to the steel plant in various sizes for use in the sinter plant, and in blast and steel furnaces. Coal is converted into coke in coke ovens, and the coke is then used in the manufacture of steel.

Fine particles of all three basic ingredients of steel, which otherwise would be waste, are blended and burned on a moving grate to cause the formation of clinkers. These are called *sinter,* a high-grade blast-furnace charge material.

141

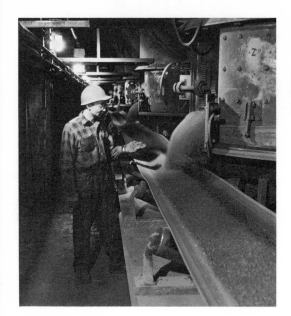

Figure 7 · 4
Material on its way to sinter machine.
(The Steel Co. of Canada, Limited)

Figure 7·4 shows fine raw materials on the way to the sinter-ing machine. Sinter increases the productivity of blast fur-naces. Figure 7·5 shows the sinter machine itself.

The first step in steelmaking begins in the blast furnace. To separate iron from iron ore, alternate layers of ore, coke, limestone, and dolomite are charged into the blast furnace. Blasts of air, heated to 1600°F, cause the coke to burn and

Figure 7 · 5
Sinter machine. (The Steel Co. of Canada, Limited)

142

Figure 7 · 6
Top of blast furnace.
(The Steel Co. of Canada, Limited)

melt the iron, which is drained off through an opening at the base of the furnace. Natural gas is often injected into the furnace to reduce the amount of coke consumed. The dolomite and limestone combine with the nonferrous elements of the ore to form a slag which floats on top of the molten iron and is removed separately.

Figure 7 · 7
Blast furnace.
(The Steel Co. of Canada, Limited)

143

Figure 7 · 8
Charging scrap into open-hearth furnace. (The Steel Co. of Canada, Limited)

The product of the blast furnace is known as pig iron, the basic ingredient of steel. It takes about 2 tons of iron ore, ⅔ ton of coke, ½ ton of limestone, and 4 tons of air to make 1 ton of pig iron. Some of this pig iron goes to foundries to make iron castings, but the vast majority is remelted and used in the production of steel in a steel furnace.

Several types of furnace are used in the production of steel, including the open-hearth furnace, the bessemer converter, the electric furnace, the new oxygen furnace. Because of its efficiency, the open hearth is at present the industry's largest producer.

The open-hearth furnace is called "open" because the charge is exposed to the sweep of flames over the surface.

Figure 7 · 9
Charging open-hearth furnace with molten pig iron.
(The Steel Co. of Canada, Limited)

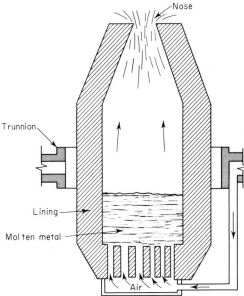

Figure 7 · 10
Bessemer converter.

Nose

Trunnion

Lining

Molten metal

Air

Molten pig iron, scrap iron and steel, limestone, and high-grade iron ore are charged into an open-hearth furnace. Limestone is put in first to act as a flux; then the scrap and the iron ore are introduced. When they have begun to melt, molten pig iron is added (Fig. 7·9).

The ingredients are melted, using fuel oil or gas as fuel, injected along with hot air. Refining takes from 3½ to 7 hours at temperatures up to 3000°F. During this period samples are taken and checked in a laboratory to ensure that the steel adheres to specifications, for each heat of steel is made to a definite formula. It may be necessary to remove some elements and add others. Impurities are removed by oxidizing agents such as limestone. Burnt lime may be added to hasten the absorption of sulfur and phosphorus. In some open-hearth furnaces, oxygen is injected through the furnace roof. As a result of doing this, greater heat is produced and the furnace heat time is reduced.

The bessemer converter is a huge pot, set on massive trunnions so that it can be tilted (Fig. 7·10). The scrap and molten pig iron are charged into the converter first, through the top, and then the limestone or other fluxes are added. Air and fuel are injected from the bottom. When the steel is ready, it is tapped off through a port in the side of the converter.

The new oxygen furnace resembles a bessemer converter, but instead of using air, injected at the bottom, pure oxygen is blown in from the top. The oxygen combines with carbon and other unwanted material and starts a high-temperature churning reaction which burns out the impurities from the pig iron and converts it into steel. The converter is tapped and the chemical content of the steel is adjusted, if necessary, by adding the required chemicals at the ladle.

145

Figure 7 · 11
Drawing off steel from furnace.
(The Steel Co. of Canada, Limited)

An electric furnace is used for making special steels because it is possible to produce intense, rigidly controlled heat and there is no need for oxygen for combustion. Heat is produced by the arcs between the huge electrodes and the scrap charge in the furnace. The charge is mostly scrap of all kinds, along with some iron ore. To this is added the chemicals necessary to make the special alloy steels, which are the chief product of the electric furnace.

Figure 7 · 12
Transporting ingots in molds to stripper building. (The Steel Co. of Canada, Limited)

Figure 7 · 13
Removing molds from ingots.
(The Steel Co. of Canada, Limited)

When it is ready, the molten steel is drawn from the furnace in giant ladles (Fig. 7 · 11) from which it is poured into ingot molds. This pouring into molds is known as *teeming*.

The molds containing the ingots are transported to a stripper building (Fig. 7 · 12) where they are allowed to cool. The molds are then removed, (Fig. 7 · 13) and the ingots placed in soaking pits where they are reheated to a uniform temperature high enough for rolling. Ingots vary in size from about 9 to 23 tons.

Figure 7 · 14
Ingot being placed in soaking pit.
(The Steel Co. of Canada, Limited)

Figure 7 · 15
Blooming mill and operator.
(The Steel Co. of Canada, Limited)

Figure 7 · 16
Slab leaving the blooming mill. (The Steel Co. of Canada, Limited)

A great variety of products used in the construction industry are made from these ingots. They include rolled structural shapes, rods, bars, plates, pipe, wire, bolts, rivets, nails, sheet steel, and many others. Subsequent treatment of the ingots depends to a considerable extent on which of these products is to be made from them.

Hot ingots go into a blooming mill where they receive their first shaping between huge rolls. If the steel is to be made into sheets or other flat products, the ingot is formed into a rectangular slab (Fig. 7·16). If it is to become bars, rods, rolled structural shapes, etc., the ingot is formed into a bloom, roughly square in section.

A bloom which is to be made into a rolled shape is heated to 2200°F in a continuous reheating furnace. It then passes through a series of rolls; as it does so, the grooves and raised areas on the rolls give it shape. A bloom may make as many as 26 passes through the rolls before it is turned into an I-shaped beam.

When rods and bars are being made, the bloom is further reduced to a billet (Fig. 7·17) by passing through a series of billet rolls, becoming smaller in cross section and greater in length with each stand of rolls. Finally the billets are cut into the required lengths and passed on to the rod or bar mills. Prior to being rolled into rods or bars, billets are heated in a

Figure 7 · 17
Billet mill roll stands. (The Steel Co. of Canada, Limited)

Figure 7 · 18
Billets heated in a three-zone furnace.
(The Steel Co. of Canada, Limited)

three-zone furnace as shown in Fig. 7 · 18. Figure 7 · 19 shows bundles of billets being sorted prior to heating, and Fig. 7 · 20, bars being fed into the roll stands of a bar mill. In Fig. 7 · 21, bars are being checked for surface defects.

In the rod mill, up to 12 coils of rod can be bound into one bundle to facilitate subsequent handling and storage (Fig. 7 · 22).

Slabs formed in the blooming mill are rolled into plates of various widths, usually from 24 to 120 in. and in thicknesses from ³⁄₁₆ to 6 in. Steel to be rolled thinner than plate goes to the hot-strip mill where it is further reduced in thickness.

Figure 7 · 19
Sorting bundles of billets. (The Steel Co. of Canada, Limited)

150

Figure 7 · 20
Bars being fed into roll stands. (The Steel Co. of Canada, Limited)

Figure 7 · 21
Checking bars for surface defects. (The Steel Co. of Canada, Limited)

Figure 7 · 22
Bundling coils of rod. (The Steel Co. of Canada, Limited)

Figure 7 · 23
Cold-rolled steel is fed into a continuous annealing line. (The Steel Co. of Canada, Limited)

Steel strips from here may be further reduced in thickness by passing them through a cold-reduction mill. They may be reduced to as thin as 0.007 in. Sheets cut from these coils go into many diversified products such as tin plate, galvanized sheets, steel decking, and automobile stampings.

Cold-reduced steel for tin products must be ductile; it is made so by controlled heating and cooling in a continuous annealing furnace. Figure 7 · 23 shows cold-rolled strip steel being fed into an annealing line, while Fig. 7 · 24 illustrates the type of control panel used on an annealing furnace.

Cold-rolled sheets are galvanized (given a zinc coating) by equipment like that shown in Fig. 7 · 25.

As was mentioned previously, some pig iron is used to make cast iron. Pig iron and scrap iron are melted together in a furnace, using coke as fuel. The resulting molten iron contains essentially the same impurities, such as phosphorus, sulfur, silica, and manganese, but it also picks up carbon from the coke. The molten material is cast into molds of sand.

Cast iron is high in compressive strength but low in tensile strength and, as a result, has little direct use in construction. However, because it is cheap and easy to cast and machine, it has some uses for parts of pumps, motors, engines, etc.; and because of its corrosion resistance it is used for pipes to some extent.

When pig iron is melted in such a way as to remove nearly all of the carbon and other impurities, the result is wrought iron. It is easily worked and welded and is tough and ductile. Its main uses are for roofing sheets, wire, and metal ornaments.

In the manufacture of steel, the amount of carbon, sulfur phosphorus, silica, and manganese in the pig iron must be very carefully controlled.

152

Figure 7 · 24
Control panel for annealing furnace for steel strip. (The Steel Co. of Canada, Limited)

Figure 7 · 25
Galvanizing pot and cooling tower.
(The Steel Co. of Canada, Limited)

Carbon is very important. Its presence controls the hardness and stiffness of the finished steel but at the same time influences the brittleness of steel; hence its proportion is carefully controlled and steel is classified according to its carbon content. In general there are three classes of steel—mild, or low-carbon, with carbon content not exceeding 0.25 percent; medium-carbon steel, with carbon content of 0.25

153

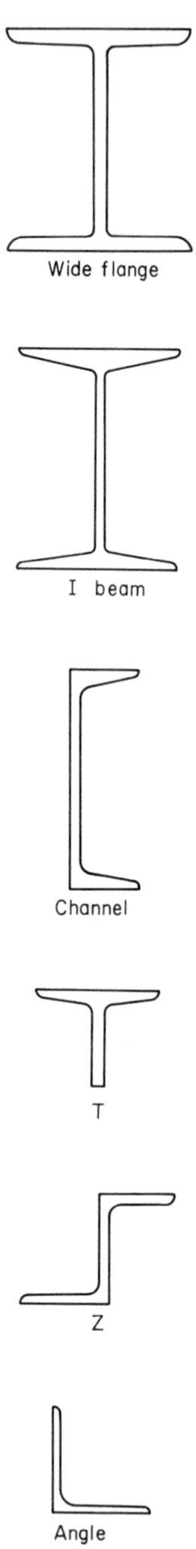

Wide flange

I beam

Channel

T

Z

Angle

Figure 7 · 26
Rolled-steel structural shapes.

to 0.50 percent; and high-carbon steel, with carbon content over 0.5 percent.

Phosphorus causes steel to be brittle at normal temperatures, and the maximum allowable percentage is normally 0.60 percent. Sulfur tends to make steel brittle when heated, and the percentage of this element is limited to 0.05 percent. Silicon has a tendency to cause brittleness, and its presence is limited to a maximum of 0.30 percent. The allowable amount of manganese varies, with the type of steel, from 1.1 to 1.65 percent.

In addition to these three basic types of steel, alloy steels are made by combining other elements with the molten steel. Nickel, chromium, copper, and manganese are all used for this purpose. Nickel steel is stronger than carbon steel and is used to some extent to make structural members for buildings. Chromium steel is very hard and corrosion-resistant. The stainless steels are made with chromium or a combination of nickel and chromium. They are used for buildings, quite extensively in the form of exterior wall panels, frames for doors, and for expansion joints, flashings, copings, fascia, and gravel stops.

Copper-bearing steel has high resistance to corrosion and is used for making sheet steel and metal lath. Manganese steel offers great resistance to abrasion and finds important use in the cutting edges of heavy digging tools.

STEEL PRODUCTS

Rolled structural shapes are among the most important steel products used in building construction. They include standard or I beams, wide-flange beams, channels, angles, Ts, and Zs (Fig. 7·26).

Standard or I beams are designated according to their depth and are made in a variety of sizes from 3 to 24 in. Most sizes are made in two different weights per linear foot, the difference being achieved by changing the width of the flange and the thickness of the web, as illustrated in Fig. 7·27. Thus a 12-in. I beam weighing 35 lb per linear ft, designated 12″ I 35#, is 12 in. deep, with a flange width of 5.078 in. and web thickness of 0.428 in. A 12″ I 31.8# is 12 in. deep, has a flange width of 5 in. and a web thickness of 0.35 in. Tables produced by steel companies and institutes of steel construction provide complete data for designing and detailing for these and other rolled shapes.

Wide-flange units are made in a wider range of sizes and weights than I beams. The regular series are made in depths from 3 to 36 in., in a variety of weights. For example, 14-in. wide-flange units alone are rolled in 39 different weights per linear foot. Weights are changed by altering the width and the thickness of the flange and the thickness of the web (Fig. 7·28). Thus only one weight of this wide-flange group is

154

actually 14 in. deep, the 14″ WF 87 #. A 14″ WF 61 # has a depth of 13.91 in. and a flange width of 10 in.

WF sections which are nearly square in cross section make ideal columns. For example, a 12″ WF 65 # has a depth of 12.12 in. and a flange width of 12 in.

Notice that the flanges of WF members are nearly rectangular in cross section—in fact they have a 5-percent slope, while those of standard members increase in thickness toward the web by a 16⅔-percent slope.

American Standard channels are rolled in depths of from 3 to 18 in., each depth being made in two or more weights per linear foot. The weight is altered in each case by changing the width of the flange and the thickness of the web.

Both equal- and unequal-legged angles are rolled in various sizes. Equal-leg angles range from 1 × 1 in. to 8 × 8 in., each size made in three or more weights per lineal foot. Weights are changed by altering the thickness of the legs. Unequal-leg angles range from 1¼ × 1¾ in. to 9 × 4 in., each size in two or more weights.

Structural Ts are produced by shearing or flame-cutting either standard beams or wide-flange sections. They are available in depths of from 3 to 18 in., in a number of weights.

Zs are rolled in several sizes, from 3 × 2¾ in. to 4 × 3 in., the latter being made in four different weights. Weights are changed by altering the thickness of flanges and web.

A number of special sections are also made, including wide-flange miscellaneous columns and beams, light beams, standard mill beams, junior beams, junior channels, car and ship channels, and special bulb angles. Consult a book of steel tables for details on these special sections.

Sheet piling is another type of rolled section in common use. Sections are made to interlock and are available in several shapes, some of which are shown in Fig. 7·29.

Bearing piles have the same cross section as a wide-flange member, but weights per linear foot are different from those of regular wide-flange sections of the same nominal depth.

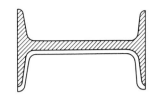

Figure 7 · 27
Increasing the weight of I beam per linear foot.

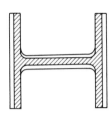

Figure 7 · 28
Increasing the weight of WF beam per linear foot.

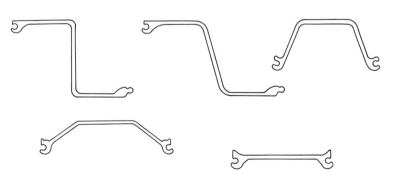

Figure 7 · 29
Sheet piling shapes.

Steel pipe is made by two different methods. Small-diameter pipe can be either seamless or welded, while large-diameter pipe is electrically welded.

Seamless pipe is made by forcing a solid hot rod over a pointed mandrel to form a hollow tube. The tube is then rolled and stretched to produce pipe of the correct diameter and wall thickness.

Either hot-rolled or cold-rolled steel strip, called *skelp,* can be used to make resistance-welded pipe or tubing. Coils of skelp are welded together end to end, and rolls form the strip into a continuous cylinder. The meeting edges are resistance-welded. After cooling, the pipe is passed through cold straightening equipment and hydraulically tested to a pressure of at least 1,000 psi. Pipe to be used for carrying water is galvanized to resist corrosion.

To make large-diameter pipe, plates of the proper width have their edges beveled and are then placed in a press which forms them into cylinders. The two edges are welded together and the pipe is brought to its final diameter by hydraulically expanding the welded shell against a retaining jacket.

Reinforcing steel is a very important part of the production of many steel mills (Fig. 7·30). Most reinforcing bars are rolled from new steel, but sometimes they are made from discarded rails or railway-car axles that are cut and rerolled to the required sizes. The strength grades range from the softest and most ductile, structural grade, up to a grade of very high strength having a specified minimum yield point of 75,000 psi and a minimum tensile strength of 100,000 psi.

Sizes start with No. 2, which is a plain round bar ¼ in. in diameter, and continue all the way up through No. 18S, which

Figure 7 · 30
Reinforcing steel. (The Steel Co. of Canada, Limited)

is a special size approximately 2¼ in. in diameter. Most bars larger than No. 2 are deformed bars, that is, bars which have lugs or deformations rolled on the surface to provide anchorage in the concrete (Fig. 7·31). Table 7·1 lists the essential features of each of the current reinforcing-bar specifications of the American Society for Testing Materials.

A special column-reinforcing material, in the form of a spiral, is made from intermediate or hard-grade hot-rolled coils, corresponding to C.S.A. (Canadian Standards Association) Specification G30.1—1954 or ASTM Specification A432 and from cold-drawn wire meeting ASTM Specification A82. Spirals are available in rod diameters of ¼, ⅜, ½, ⅝, and ¾ in. The diameters of spirals range from 10 to 40 in. A spiral is held at its proper spacing or pitch in a column form by spacer bars (Fig. 7·32).

Another type of reinforcing material is known as welded wire fabric. It consists of parallel, longitudinal wires welded to transverse wires at regular intervals. The wire used is made by the cold-drawing process, to conform to ASTM Designation A82 or C.S.A. Specification G30.3. A loom is used to produce wire fabric, and wire sizes vary from No. 10 (fine) to 0000000 (heavy). Table 7·2 gives wire gauge numbers and wire diameter. Fabric is commonly identified by the term *style,* which refers to the spacing of both longitudinal and transverse wires, as well as the gauge of each. The spacing varies from 2 to 16 in. in both directions, and the spaces may be square or rectangular. For example a fabric identification might read 6 in. × 12 in. × 1 0/4. The first figure indicates that the longitudinal wires are 6 in. apart, the second that transverse wires are 12 in. apart. The third figure refers to the gauge of the longitudinal and the fourth to the gauge of the transverse wires.

Wire fabric is put up in rolls and flat sheets, depending on the gauge of the material. Rolls are normally 5 or 6 ft wide and 200 ft long; sheets can be made up to 32 ft long but are not usually over 8 ft wide.

The fabric made with the heavier gauges of wire, commonly known as structural fabric, is used as primary reinforcement in structural slabs and similar members. Structural fabric can be made to order of material heavier than the 0000000 wire used in welded wire fabric. Both can be made with either plain or deformed wire.

Steel wire is one of the steel industry's most versatile products. Altogether there are over 150,000 uses for wire, including pins, needles, nails, bolts, cables, piano wire,

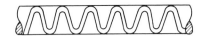

Figure 7·31
Deformed steel rod.

Figure 7·32
Spiral reinforcement spacer bar.

Table 7·1

Kinds and grades of reinforcing bars as specified in ASTM standards.

TYPE OF STEEL AND ASTM SPECIFICATION NO.	SIZE NOS. INCLUSIVE	GRADE DESIGNATION	TENSILE STRENGTH, PSI
Billet steel A-15	2 to 11	Structural	55,000 to 75,000
		Intermediate	70,000 to 90,000
		Hard	80,000 min
Billet steel A-408	14S, 18S	Structural	Same as in A-15, above
		Intermediate	Same as in A-15, above
		Hard	Same as in A-15, above
Billet steel 60,000 psi Yield point A-432	3 to 11	a	90,000 min
	14S, 18S	a	90,000 min
High-strength billet steel A-431	3 to 11 14S, 18S	a	100,000 min
		. . .	. . .
Rail steel A-16	2 to 11	Regular	80,000 min
	3 to 11	Special	90,000 min
Axle steel A-160	2 to 11	Structural	55,000 to 75,000
		Intermediate	70,000 to 90,000
		Hard	80,000 min

Values shown are for deformed bars. See specifications for values for plain bars.
aDesignated by specification title and number.

158

YIELD POINT MIN., PSI	ELONGATION IN 8 IN., MIN PERCENT[b]	COLD BEND TEST[c]	
33,000	1,200,000 tens str min 16%	Under Size No. 6 Nos. 6, 7, 8 Nos. 9, 10, 11	$180°, d = 2t$ $180°, d = 3t$ $180°, d = 4t$
40,000	1,100,000 tens str min 12%	Under Size No. 6 Nos. 6, 7, 8 Nos. 9, 10, 11	$90°, d = 3t$ $90°, d = 4t$ $90°, d = 5t$
50,000	1,000,000 tens str	Under Size No. 6 Nos. 6, 7, 8 Nos. 9, 10, 11	$90°, d = 4t$ $90°, d = 5t$ $90°, d = 6t$
. . .	13	None	
. . .	10	None	
. . .	7	None	
60,000	1,000,000 tens str	Under Size No. 6 Nos. 6, 7, 8 Nos. 9, 10, 11	$90°, d = 4t$ $90°, d = 5t$ $90°, d = 6t$
60,000	7	Nos. 14S, 18S	None
75,000 . . .	Varies with bar size, 5 to 7½%	Size Nos. 3, 4, 5 Nos. 6, 7 Nos. 8, 9 Nos. 10, 11 Nos. 14S, 18S	$90°, d = 4t$ $90°, d = 5t$ $90°, d = 6t$ $90°, d = 8t$ None
50,000	1,100,000 tens str min 5%	None	$180°, d = 2t$ $180°, d = 4t$
60,000	1,000,000 tens str min 5%	None	$180°, d = 6t$ $90°, d = 6t$
33,000	1,200,000 tens str min 16%	Under Size No. 6 No. 6 and over	$90°, d = 6t$ $90°, d = 6t$
40,000	1,100,000 tens str min 12%	Under Size No. 6 No. 6 and over	
50,000	1,000,000 tens str	Under Size No. 6 No. 6 and over	

[b]For base sizes of deformed bars. See specifications for adjustment for small and large sizes and for values for plain bars.

[c]d = diameter of pin around which specimen is to be bent; t = nominal diameter of specimen.

159

Table 7 · 2
Wire details.

STEEL WIRE GAUGE NUMBERS	WIRE		
	DIAMETER, IN.	AREA, SQ IN.	WEIGHT, LB/FT
0000000	0.4900	0.18857	0.6404
000000	0.4615	0.16728	0.5681
00000	0.4305	0.14556	0.4943
0000	0.3938	0.12180	0.4136
000	0.3625	0.10321	0.3505
00	0.3310	0.086049	0.2922
0	0.3065	0.073782	0.2506
1	0.2830	0.062902	0.2136
2	0.2625	0.054119	0.1838
¼"	0.2500	0.049087	0.1667
3	0.2437	0.046645	0.1584
4	0.2253	0.039867	0.1354
5	0.2070	0.033654	0.1143
6	0.1920	0.028953	0.09832
7	0.1770	0.024606	0.08356
8	0.1620	0.020612	0.07000
9	0.1483	0.017273	0.05866
10	0.1350	0.014314	0.04861

fences, etc. Accordingly it must be made in every conceivable degree of strength, hardness, and ductility.

Wire is normally made from hot rolled rods which are first pickled in an acid bath to remove the scale. The rods are then drawn through special tungsten carbide dies into wire of widely varying shapes, diameters, and qualities. Wire diameters range from about 0.006 to 1 in.

Where corrosion resistance is important, as, for example in fence wire, the strands are zinc coated for protection. Wire for mechanical springs is hardened and oil-tempered. Wire with very high tensile strength is twisted into cables to be used for reinforcing prestressed-concrete products.

Wire in coils is fed into nail-making machines, where it is cut to length, headed, and pointed to form nails of all sizes and styles. High-speed cold-heading machines automatically cut wire of the required diameter to length and form a head on each cut length. Another machine slots the heads, and then the blanks are rolled between opposing dies to form the thread and produce a finished screw.

Bolts and nuts may be either hot-forged or cold-formed from wire of the appropriate diameter. For bolts, wire is fed into an automatic bolt-making machine which cuts to length, heads, trims, points, and, in many cases, rolls the thread. Sometimes, however, the thread may be die-cut.

Most of the bolts used in steel erection, as well as the nuts and washers, are made from high-tensile steel which conforms to ASTM Designation A325-58T. Table 7·3 outlines the chemical requirements for steel used for this purpose.

Table 7·4 gives the basic dimensions of high strength bolts and nuts. In determining bolt length, the grip-total thickness of connected material is calculated and to it is added an amount shown in Table 7·5. This compensates for the thickness of the nut, two flat washers, and the bolt point.

			WASHERS	
ELEMENT	BOLTS	NUTS	CARBURIZED	QUENCHED & TEMPERED
Carbon	0.30 min	. . .	0.25 max	
Manganese	0.30 min	. . .	1.00 max	
Phosphorus	0.048 max	0.13 max	0.048 max	0.048 max
Sulfur	0.058 max	0.23 max	0.058 max	0.058 max

Table 7 · 3
Chemical requirements for steel used to make bolts, nuts, and washers, figures in percent.

	BOLT DIMENSIONS		NUT DIMENSIONS*	
NOMINAL BOLT & NUT SIZE, IN.	WIDTH ACROSS FLATS, IN.	HEIGHT, IN.	WIDTH ACROSS FLATS, IN.	THICKNESS, IN.
½	¾	⁵⁄₁₆	⅞	³¹⁄₆₄
⅝	¹⁵⁄₁₆	²⁵⁄₆₄	1¹⁄₁₆	³⁹⁄₆₄
¾	1⅛	¹⁵⁄₃₂	1¼	⁴⁷⁄₆₄
⅞	1⁵⁄₁₆	³⁵⁄₆₄	1⁷⁄₁₆	⁵⁵⁄₆₄
1	1½	³⁹⁄₆₄	1⅝	⁶³⁄₆₄
1⅛	1¹¹⁄₁₆	¹¹⁄₁₆	1¹³⁄₁₆	1⁷⁄₆₄
1¼	1⅞	²⁵⁄₃₂	2	1⁷⁄₃₂

Table 7 · 4
Basic dimensions of high-strength bolts and nuts.

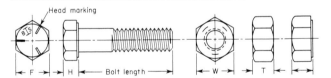

*Nuts may be furnished double-chamfered or washer-faced at manufacturer's option.

Note: Minimum length of thread furnished on bolts is equal to twice the diameter plus ¼ in. on bolts 6 in. and shorter, and twice the diameter plus ½ in. on bolts longer than 6 in.

BOLT SIZE, IN.	ADD TO GRIP, IN.
½	1
⅝	1⅛
¾	1¼
⅞	1½
1	1⅝
1⅛	1¾
1¼	1⅞

Table 7 · 5
Bolt lengths.

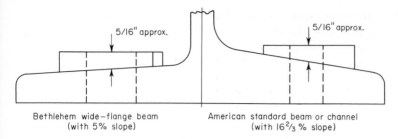

Bethlehem wide–flange beam
(with 5% slope)

American standard beam or channel
(with 16⅔% slope)

Figure 7 · 33
Tapered washers.

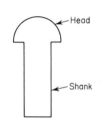

←Head

←Shank

Figure 7 · 34
Steel rivet.

The total length should be adjusted to the next ¼-in. incre-ment up to 5-in. lengths and to the next longer ½-in. incre-ment for lengths over 5 in. If beveled washers are used (Fig. 7·33), an additional ⅛ in. should be added for each.

Rivets used for steel fabrication are made from three grades of steel, soft carbon rivet steel, high-strength rivet steel, and high-strength structural-alloy rivet steel. These have a minimum yield of 28,000, 38,000, and 50,000 psi, respectively, and ultimate shear of 31,000, 40,000, and 60,000 psi, respectively. The first type is used for normal structural rivet applications, the second for structural rivet applications requiring higher strength, and the third is for use with members made from alloy steel.

The manufacturing process consists of cutting short lengths of the rod being used, upsetting one end into a half-round button head (Fig. 7·34) and leaving shanks of various lengths. The rivets are inserted hot into the holes and a second head is formed on the other end by an air hammer. This requires holding a dolly or buck against the original head while the second is being formed. As it cools, the rivet shrinks and draws the two pieces closely together.

Steel strapping is made from high-tensile flat wire in a number of sizes. Table 7·6 gives some details on the com-monly manufactured sizes.

Table 7 · 6
Steel-strapping data.

STRAP SIZE, IN.	FT/LB	LB/1,000 FT	BREAKING STRENGTH, LB
¾ × 0.028	14.04	71.28	2,300
¾ × 0.035	11.25	88.88	3,100
1¼ × 0.035	6.73	148.58	5,000
1¼ × 0.050	4.72	211.86	7,000
2 × 0.050	2.94	340.13	11,000

This type of strapping is used for banding column forms to keep them from bulging under the pressure of freshly poured concrete (Fig. 7·35). Strapping is tightened in place by means of a tightener. It is then held in position by a metal seal which is placed over the two lapped ends and clamped tightly by a sealing tool.

Open-web steel joists are playing an increasingly important part in building construction. They are really lightweight

Warren-type trusses made in several different styles, one of which is illustrated in Fig. 7·36.

Two basic types are made, shortspan and longspan. Shortspan joists are made in lengths of from 4 to 48 ft, with depth ranges from 8 to 24 in. The joist weight per linear foot varies from 4 lb for an 8-in. depth to 13 lb for a 24-in. depth. Tables are available which give the safe load for all the various lengths and depths.

Longspan joists are made of heavier material, in lengths of from 22 to 96 ft. Depths range from 18 to 48 in. and weights per linear foot of joist from about 13 to 68 lb. Safe-load tables are also available for these.

A number of accessories are made which are a part of a complete joist installation. Bottom-chord extensions carry the bottom chords to the wall for ceiling application. Joist bridging holds joists in alignment. Steel rod is often used for this purpose. Bridging anchors secure the ends of bridging lines to masonry walls. Header angles are available to form floor or roof openings and outriggers are used to extend the top chord beyond a wall for an overhanging roof.

Figure 7·37 illustrates a typical installation of longspan joists to support a roof structure.

One of the important uses of sheet steel, both black and galvanized, is in the manufacture of corrugated roofing and siding and formed steel decking.

Corrugated sheets are made both from steel of regular analysis and from rust-resisting alloys, usually copper-bearing steel. Two basic types are produced, Domestic Standard and Export Style. Domestic Standard siding sheets are made 26 in. wide and roofing sheets 27½ in. wide. Export siding sheets are 32 in. wide and roofing sheets 33½ in. wide. General practice is to furnish in even-foot lengths from 5 to 12 ft.

Figure 7 · 35
Steel banding.
(Acme Steel Co.)

Figure 7 · 36
Steel joist.

Figure 7 · 37
Long span joists.
(Bethlehem Steel Co.)

163

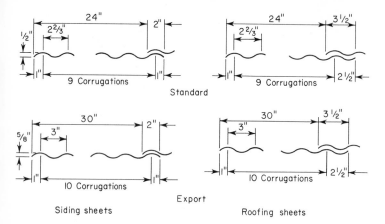

Figure 7·38
Corrugated steel sheets.

Siding sheets are made with both edges turned in the same direction, while roofing sheets have one edge turned up and one turned down. Siding sheets should have a minimum lap of 4 in. Roofing sheets should have an end lap of 6 in. for roof pitches of 4 in 12 or over and 8 in. for roofs of less pitch. Both siding and roofing sheets cover approximately 24 in. net width. (See Fig. 7·38 for details of dimensions.)

Corrugated roofing sheets are also utilized as decking for flat roofs with light loads. In such cases the corrugated deck is used as a base on which to pour a concrete slab or as a base for a built-up roof. In addition to the standard sheets described above, perforated sheets and sheets transversely reinforced with rods are available in decking.

Formed-steel decking is a widely used sheet-steel product. It is produced in a great variety of shapes and styles, using various thicknesses of metal, ranging from 12 to 22 gauge. Depending on the depth, sections are made in spans of from

Figure 7·39
Open-faced steel decking.
(Robertson-Irwin Ltd.)

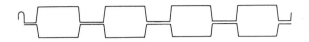

Figure 7 · 40
Cellular steel decking.

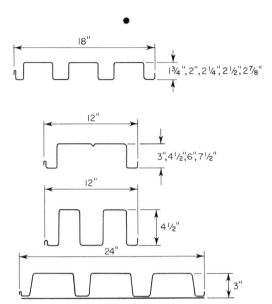

Figure 7 · 41
Some steel decking shapes and depths.

4 to 36 ft. Two basic styles are made, open-faced decking (Fig. 7·39) and cellular decking (Fig. 7·40). Cellular decking not only provides greater strength but also allows easy distribution of electric systems and outlets. Figure 7·41 shows a number of the shapes and depths in which steel decking is available.

Steel deck provides a base for several types of floor or roof. In Fig. 7·42, concrete floor is being placed over a steel deck,

Figure 7 · 42
Concrete over steel deck.
(Bethlehem Steel Co.)

165

but a built-up roof can be applied directly over steel decking. Wood flooring can be applied also, using wood sleepers anchored to the decking.

NONFERROUS METALS

ALUMINUM

Aluminum is a relatively new material, compared with iron, but it is finding increasing use in the building industry. The process now used for extracting aluminum from its ore, bauxite, requires tremendous amounts of electricity—about 10 kilowatt hours for each pound of metal. As a consequence, any large aluminum-extraction industry must be located near the source of abundant low-cost electric power, at present hydroelectric power.

The ore is strip-mined in various parts of the world, and shipped to smelters located near large hydroelectric power developments. In North America, two of the large smelters are at Kitimat, B.C., and Arvida and Isle Maligne, Que. Other essential ingredients in the manufacture of aluminum are petroleum coke, cryolite, and fluorspar.

The reddish-brown ore is washed and treated in a soda solution to yield a chalky-white powder called alumina, containing a high concentration of aluminum. This material is fed into a reduction furnace (pot), where it is dissolved in a bath of molten cryolite, to which aluminum fluoride has been added.

The reduction furnace is lined with a paste of coke which is baked until hard. Carbon blocks are suspended in the molten cryolite, and as electricity flows from the carbon blocks through the molten cryolite to the carbon lining of the furnace, it provides the necessary action to separate the alumina into aluminum and oxygen.

The molten aluminum is siphoned from the pot into rectangular molds producing ingots of various sizes. The ingots are shipped to various production plants which produce one or more aluminum products. Because of its basic characteristics, aluminum can be rolled, spun, drawn, extruded, forged, cast, or powdered. In addition, it is possible to produce a great many alloys of aluminum, some of them many times stronger than the original material.

Ingots for rolling are first trimmed on a scalping lathe, and then preheated in a soaking pit. Each ingot passes through a series of rolls which eventually produce long sheets of metal of various widths and thicknesses. Normally maximum sheet thickness is about ¼ in. The rolling may be continued to produce aluminum foil, which can have a thickness of about one-tenth the diameter of a human hair.

Ingots may also be reduced to long strips which are then extruded (forced through dies) to produce desired shapes

Figure 7 · 43
Some aluminum structural shapes.

166

such as seamless tubing, angles, bars, channels, and many other designs. Figure 7·43 illustrates some structural aluminum shapes; Fig. 7·44 shows a number of architectural shapes.

Another important use of aluminum is in the production of electrical cable. Extruded aluminum wire is wound around a steel core to produce ACSR (aluminum conductor steel reinforced) power cable.

Sand casting and die casting are used to produce aluminum castings of all kinds.

Aluminum structural shapes are used in many framing operations where lightness and corrosion resistance are of prime importance. Spandrel wall frames and frames for curtain-wall paneling are typical cases where aluminum structural shapes may be used in buildings. Bridge and highway railings are frequently made from aluminum, and work is being done in designing aluminum highway bridges.

Architectural shapes are widely used for door and window jambs, curtain-wall panel frames, thresholds, treads, handrails, door and window stiles, rails, muntins and bars, mullions and railings. All of these are available in a variety of shapes.

Sheet aluminum has many uses. Plain sheets are used for flashing, roofing, roof drains, weatherstripping, backing for

Tubing

Framing member

Window stile

Window sill

Door rail

Figure 7 · 44
Some aluminum architectural shapes.

Figure 7 · 45
Aluminum curtain walls.
(Aluminum Co. of Canada, Limited)

167

Figure 7 · 46
Power-plant surge tank covered with aluminum roofing sheets.
(Aluminum Co. of Canada, Limited)

built-up spandrel panels, chimney caps, air ducts, louver blades, etc.

Sheet aluminum is also treated in several ways to improve its appearance and to increase its resistance to weather and corrosion. One of these treatments is called anodizing. This is a combined electrical and chemical process which hardens and increases the thickness of the natural oxide coating on aluminum. It also permits dyeing of the metal in bright colors. Aluminum sheets may be covered with a baked enamel or lacquer finish. Such treated sheets are used for shingles, siding, curtain wall panels, canopies, and acoustic ceiling panels. Aluminum foil is used as a vapor barrier on walls and ceilings and as reflective insulation.

COPPER

The copper content of many copper ores is low, so the first step in the production of this metal is usually concentration. The ore is crushed, screened, and passed through a ball mill to reduce it to small particles. These are mixed with coating oil which wets the copper and iron sulfide particles but not the remainder of the ground mixture. The oil-coated ore is then placed in a water tank and stirred until the oil-coated sulfide particles pick up air bubbles and float to the surface. This froth overflows and is filtered to produce concentrated copper ore.

The concentrate is roasted and then smelted in a reverberatory or blast furnace to produce *copper matte*. This is then converted into *blister copper* in a furnace similar to a bessemer converter. Blister copper is further refined to reduce its oxygen content. When this has been reduced to about 0.04 percent, the material is then called *tough-pitch* copper.

Tough-pitch copper may be electrolytically refined to improve its electrical conductivity or to recover valuable quantities of precious metals such as silver and gold.

Copper and its alloys are widely used in construction, particularly where corrosion resistance, ductility, impact resistance, or high electrical conductivity are required. The treatment of copper during manufacture greatly affects its characteristics. Hot-rolled or soft-rolled copper is soft and malleable; hard-rolled or cold-rolled copper is harder, stronger, and less ductile.

Copper sheets of various thicknesses are the most common copper products used in buildings. They are used for cornice work, spandrel wall panels, roofing, flashing, eaves troughing, and interior and exterior ornamental work. Roofing and flashing sheets are usually made of soft copper, while the remainder are generally made from hard copper.

A great variety of alloys are made with copper, many of which are used for architectural and ornamental purposes. These may be formed into sheets, rods, tubes, or architectural and structural shapes, depending on how they are to be used. Table 7·7 lists the names of a number of the more common copper alloys and their composition.

Copper is an excellent outdoor metal from the standpoint of color as well as corrosion resistance. It first weathers to a brown coloring and then takes on a permanent light-green patina. The green color can also be produced artificially or the original copper color can be preserved by coating the metal with clear lacquer.

NAME	NOMINAL COMPOSITION, %
Copper — 100	99.9+ copper
Everdur	95.8 copper, 3.1 silicon
Everdur casting alloy	94.9 copper, 4.0 silicon, 1.1 manganese
Commercial bronze	90.0 copper, 10 zinc
Red brass	85 copper, 15 zinc
Yellow brass	70 copper, 30 zinc
Muntz metal	60 copper, 40 zinc
Architectural bronze	56 copper, 41.5 zinc, 2.5 lead
Statuary bronze	82.5 copper, 12.5 zinc, 2.5 tin, 2.0 lead, 0.5 nickel
Leaded nickel silver	45 copper, 42 zinc, 10 nickel, 2 manganese, 1 lead
Nickel silver, 10%	65 copper, 24.75 zinc, 10 nickel, 0.25 manganese
Nickel silver, 13%	43.25 copper, 43.6 zinc, 13 nickel, 0.15 manganese
Nickel silver, 15%	56.5 copper, 28.25 zinc, 15 nickel, 0.25 manganese
Nickel-silver casting alloy	55 copper, 20 zinc, 12.5 nickel, 10.5 lead, 2 tin

Table 7·7
Copper alloys.

LEAD

A principal source of lead is ore containing galena, lead sulfide. It is first roasted to form lumps of lead oxide. The lead oxide is charged into a blast furnace with coke, iron oxide, and lime. The lead collects at the bottom of the furnace and is tapped off at intervals. Further refining, which is often necessary, is carried out by heating the lead in a reverbera-tory furnace in the presence of air. Most of the impurities are oxidized and pass off as gases.

Lead is a soft, plastic, malleable metal used in a number of ways in building. In sheets it is used for roofing, flashing, and spandrel wall panels. It can also be readily cast for ornamen-tal work. One of the main advantages of lead sheeting is its

169

extreme pliability, enabling it to be fitted over uneven surfaces. On the other hand, it is heavier than the other metals used in construction.

Hard lead, produced by mixing antimony with lead, is used for gutters and for casting.

TIN

The ore from which tin is commonly produced contains cassiterite, a tin oxide. A reverberatory furnace is used to reduce the ore, and the tin is further refined by electrolytic refining.

Because of its resistance to corrosion, tin is used largely to coat iron and steel roofing sheets. When coated with a mixture of 25 percent tin and 75 percent lead, the sheets are known as terneplate. Plates coated with pure tin are called bright tinplate.

GLOSSARY

alloy steel	A special steel, containing one or more added elements, which impart some special property to the steel
anodize	Coat with a protective film by subjecting to electrolytic action
bloom	The first stage in the formation of an ingot into a rolled steel shape
bottom chord	Lower horizontal member of a steel joist or truss
cast iron	Basic iron, high in carbon content
concentrated ore	Ore from which the major part of the impurities have been removed
corrugated	Shaped into parallel, equally curved ridges and hollows
cryolite	A mineral, sodium-aluminum fluoride
dolomite	A limestone rich in magnesium carbonate
extruded	Shaped by forcing through a die by pressure
fluorspar	A mineral, calcium fluoride
flux	A substance used to promote fusion
ingot	A large mass of metal cast into some convenient shape
matte	A crude mixture of sulfides formed in smelting
patina	A film formed on copper by exposure or by treatment with acids

170

petroleum coke	Residue left when petroleum is distilled to dryness
pig iron	Basic iron from a blast furnace
reverberatory furnace	A furnace in which the flame is reflected from the roof to the material being smelted
slag	Waste material resulting from the refining of an ore
trunnion	A projecting pivot
wrought iron	Basic iron, low in carbon content

REVIEW QUESTIONS

1. Explain what is meant by:
   (a) Sinter
   (b) Slag
   (c) Pig iron
2. Name the ingredients used to make steel in an open-hearth furnace, and indicate the part each plays in the process.
3. Give the average carbon content of low-, medium-, and high-carbon steel, and outline the basic properties of each.
4. Draw neat sketches to illustrate the difference in cross section between an American Standard I beam and a wide-flange beam.
5. Explain how a number of different weights per linear foot for a given nominal depth of wide flange beam are produced.
6. What is the function of:
   (a) A hot-strip mill
   (b) A cold-reduction mill
7. What is meant by annealing, and what is the purpose of this process?
8. Why do wide-flange members, as nearly square as possible in cross section, usually make the best columns?
9. Describe briefly how seamless pipe is made.
10. (a) What is skelp?
    (b) What is resistance welding?
11. (a) What is deformed steel rod?
    (b) What is the purpose of deforming rod?
12. Where and why is spiral reinforcing used?
13. Name two commonly used building products made from sheet steel.
14. List three common uses for aluminum structural shapes.
15. For what purposes are aluminum architectural shapes used?
16. Name one main advantage of using lead sheeting.
17. Outline the difference between terneplate and bright tinplate.

SELECTED SOURCES OF INFORMATION

Aluminum Company of Canada, Ltd., Montreal, Que.
American Institute of Steel Construction, New York, N.Y.
American Iron & Steel Institute, New York, N.Y.
Anaconda American Brass Company, Waterbury, Conn.
Bethlehem Steel Co., Bethlehem, Pa.
Canadian Institute of Steel Construction, Toronto, Ont.
Coseley Buildings Inc., Washington, D.C.
Robertson-Irwin, Ltd., Hamilton, Ont.
Rosco Metal Products, Ltd., Toronto, Ont.
The Steel Company of Canada, Hamilton, Ont.
United States Steel Corporation, Pittsburgh, Pa.

8

GYPSUM AND LIME

GYPSUM

Gypsum has been recognized as a valuable building material for several thousand years. The Greeks and the Egyptians both used it to advantage in structures which still stand.

Gypsum usually is found in rock formation in various parts of the world, notably in Canada, the United States, France, England, Italy, China, Russia, and areas of South America. The rock is crushed, ground, and calcined (heated), which drives off about 75 percent of the combined water, forming the hemihydrate known as plaster of paris. If this product is mixed with water, a chemical recombination takes place and the original rock structure is reformed.

CHEMICAL COMPOSITION

Gypsum is a hydrous calcium sulfate with the chemical formula $CaSO_4(2H_2O)$, which means that it is a compound of lime, sulfur, and water thus:

$$CaSO_4(2H_2O) \rightarrow \begin{array}{l} \text{Calcium Sulfate} \\ CaSO_4 \quad 79.1\% \\ + \\ 2H_2O \quad 20.9\% \\ \text{Water} \end{array} \left\{ \begin{array}{l} \text{Lime} \\ CaO \quad 32.5\% \\ + \\ SO_3 \quad 46.6\% \\ \text{Sulfur Trioxide} \\ \quad\quad 20.9\% \end{array} \right.$$

Gypsum is soluble in hydrochloric acid and also in about 500 parts of water; its specific gravity is 2.3. Anhydrite, calcium sulfate without combined water $(CaSO_4)$, is often found closely associated with gypsum. It has little commercial value but will, in course of time, if exposed to air, absorb sufficient water (2 parts) to convert it into gypsum.

Gypsum is very seldom found in the pure state but usually contains varying amounts of clay, limestone, silica, iron compounds, etc. In the pure state it is white, but combined with impurities, it may be gray, brown, or reddish-brown. Some deposits of gypsum are found close to the surface of the earth; others are buried well below the surface.

Depending on the location of the deposit, gypsum is either mined or quarried. If the rock is near the surface, a stripping operation will allow the material to be removed by the open-pit quarrying method. If it is deeply buried, regular mining operations are necessary.

The raw material is shipped to a mill where it is crushed, dried, pulverized, separated, and ground to the stage where about 93 percent of it will pass a 100-mesh sieve. This product is called "land plaster." It is now ready for calcining, which is the important part of the operation.

Calcining is done in large steel kettles with cast iron bottoms, holding several tons of ground gypsum. It consists of heating the material to a temperature of about 330°F, which drives off about 75 percent of the combined water in the gypsum, leaving the half-hydrate plaster of paris. This is the basic material from which many of the gypsum building materials are made.

GYPSUM PRODUCTS

Plasters

Plaster of paris. Plaster of paris is made from carefully selected white rock. When mixed with water to form a paste, it sets in about 15 to 20 minutes. It is used for small patching jobs on plaster walls and for making molds; when it is mixed with lime putty according to directions, it makes a plaster finish coat which hardens fast and is free from shrinkage cracks.

Keene's cement. If gypsum is subjected to a temperature of 750°F, which must be done in kilns, not kettles, it is completely dehydrated. When this material is ground and has had a positive catalyst such as alum added to it, it is known as Keene's cement. If this product is mixed with water to form a plaster, it sets slowly and becomes very hard. It is highly resistant to moisture penetration and is used where sanitary conditions or excessive moisture makes it necessary to specify a hard, impervious, smooth surface. One ton of Keene's cement, mixed with water and applied as a putty coat, will cover 400 to 500 sq yd of wall surface.

Casting plaster. This plaster is made from specially selected rock and ground much finer than regular plaster of paris. It is slower setting and cooler working, which makes it adaptable for ornamental molded plaster work. This technique requires considerable time to produce sharp, clear lines and extra smooth surfaces associated with molded plaster. Fifty percent lime putty may be added for extra plasticity.

Hard wall plaster. This is a neat gypsum plaster, containing hair or fiber, widely used to form the first (scratch) coat and the second (brown) coat on plastered walls and ceilings. It requires the addition of aggregate and water on the job. The aggregate may be natural sand or a lightweight aggregate such as vermiculite or perlite. A lightweight base-coat plaster is also produced which has the gypsum and aggregate already mixed together and requires only water.

When sand is to be used as the aggregate, 2 parts by weight of dry sand are mixed with 1 part of hard wall for the scratch coat on gypsum, wood, or metal lath. For the brown coat, 3 parts of sand are used to 1 part plaster.

SURFACE	SQ YD/TON
Wood lath	180 to 210 sanded 2 to 1
Metal lath	105 to 135 sanded 2 to 1
Gypsum lath	225 to 240 sanded 2 to 1
Brick and clay tile	165 to 200 sanded 3 to 1
Gypsum tile	235 to 255 sanded 3 to 1

Table 8·1

Average covering capacity of base-coat plaster using sand as aggregate. (Western Gypsum Products, Limited)

By increasing the amount of sand used per bag of hard wall, the plasterer can make his plaster cover more area but only at the expense of reducing the strength of the material. The graph shown in Fig. 8·1, worked out by Western Gypsum Products, Limited, shows the tensile strength of hard wall plaster containing varying proportions of sand.

Cement bond plaster. As the name implies, cement bond plaster is intended for application to concrete surfaces. Almost any finish plaster can then be applied over this base coat.

It requires only water; the mixed material should be allowed to soak for at least 10 minutes before it is used. The plaster is applied in two coats, totaling ⅜ in. thick on ceilings and ⅝ in. on walls. The surface should be roughened to receive the finish coat before the plaster begins to set. One ton of plaster will cover from 90 to 120 sq yd of surface.

Finish plaster. This material is made specially to produce the finish (putty) coat for plastered surfaces. It has to be mixed with hydrated lime putty and water. The lime putty is produced either by mixing hydrated lime and water or by slaking quicklime and using the resulting slaked lime putty. Finish plaster and putty are mixed in the proportion of 1 part plaster to 3 parts lime putty by volume or 1 part plaster to 2 parts dry hydrated lime by weight. Under average conditions 1 ton of finish plaster with 2 tons of dry hydrated lime will cover 1,000 to 1,400 sq yd.

Prepared finish plaster. This type of plaster requires only water. It contains no lime, so the plaster surface can be decorated as soon as it is dry. It does not dry to the degree of whiteness of regular finish plaster and therefore is not recommended when the plaster surface is to be left unpainted. One ton of this plaster will cover from 350 to 400 sq yd.

Texture plaster. Similar in manufacture to prepared finish plaster, texture plaster is used when a rough (texture) surface is required. It is mixed in the proportion of 2 parts plaster

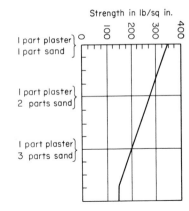

Figure 8·1

Varying strengths in hardwall plaster.

175

to 1 part water by volume and applied in two coats over base coat plaster or gypsum wallboard. The second or texture coat can be applied by trowel, brush, or sponge, depending on the texture desired. One pound of plaster will cover from 2 to 4 sq ft, depending on the kind of texture.

Acoustical plaster. Calcined gypsum is mixed with a lightweight mineral aggregate to make a type of finish plaster that has a high rate of sound absorption (see Table 8·2).

Table 8·2

Absorption coefficients of acoustical plaster for various pitches of sound. (Acoustical Materials Association)

THICKNESS	2,048 CYCLES	1,024 CYCLES	512 CYCLES	256 CYCLES	128 CYCLES	REDUCTION COEFFICIENT
½ in.	0.34	0.30	0.31	0.61	0.69	0.50
¾ in.	0.36	0.37	0.55	0.67	0.67	0.55

It requires only water and is applied over regular gypsum base-coat plasters in two coats each about ¼ in. thick. One ton of acoustical plaster will cover about 100 yd ½ in. thick.

Joint filler. Similar in manufacture and appearance to texture plaster, gypsum joint filler is used to make the paste for filling nail holes and covering joints in gypsum wallboard and also to make the adhesive used in laminating two sheets of board together.

When used as a filler, the material is mixed with lukewarm water in the proportion of approximately 15 pints of water to 25 lb of filler. The mix should be allowed to stand for 30 minutes and can be applied by hand with a broad spatula or by machine.

If it is to be used as an adhesive, 20 pints of lukewarm water are mixed with 25 lb of dry filler. Let the mix stand for 30 minutes and apply to the back of the board to be laminated in a thin layer. 50 to 55 lb of dry filler is required to make enough adhesive for 1,000 ft of wallboard.

Gypsum Boards

Gypsum wallboard. Gypsum wallboard is a fireproof sheathing for interior walls and ceilings. It is made of a core of gypsum covered on each side by a heavy specially manufactured kraft paper. The paper on the exposed surface is ivory colored, while the back is gray.

The board is made by a continuous process in a sheet 4 ft wide and is cut as required into lengths of from 4 to 12 ft, in ⅜-, ½-, ⅝-, and 1-in. thicknesses. The long edges are recessed and reinforced with three layers of paper (Fig. 8·2).

Gypsum board can be applied directly to the wall frame or used over sheathing. It is also used to make partitions in which there is no framework. On walls it can be applied in a single or double layer; ½-in. board is used for single thickness and usually ⅜-in. for double (laminated) application. The board should be applied horizontally wherever possible and nailed with 13-gauge 1½-in. cadmium-coated nails with a

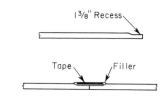

Figure 8·2

Recessed edges of wallboard.

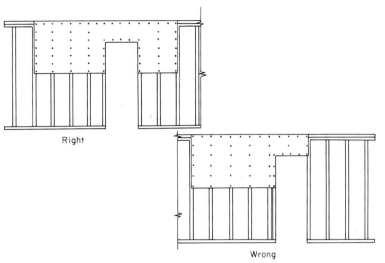

Figure 8·3
Board application at openings.

countersunk head. Nails should be spaced at 7 in. on ceilings and at 8 in. on sidewalls on all framing members. Figure 8·3 illustrates the correct application of wallboard at an opening.

When the laminated system is used, the first layer is applied vertically and the second horizontally. A layer of gypsum cement (joint filler) is applied to the back of the outer layer and is held in place with double-headed nails until the cement is dry. Later the nails are pulled and the holes are filled with the same material used to fill the joints.

Partitions of gypsum board are formed in two ways. One is to use a single layer of board at least ½ in. thick held in place at floor and ceiling by metal channels. Horizontal metal bracing is wired to the board, and it is then plastered on both sides.

The other method requires three layers of board. Wooden strips 1 in. (net) × 1½ in. are fastened to the floor and ceiling and a layer of ½-in. board is nailed to them (Fig. 8·4).

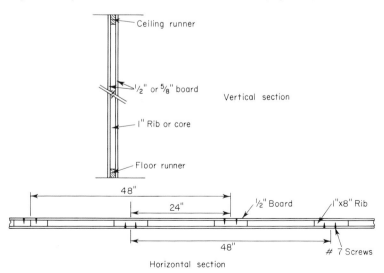

Figure 8·4
Three-ply studless partition.

177

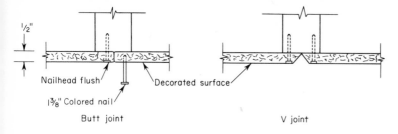

Butt joint   V joint

Figure 8 · 5
Colored nails for decorated wallboard.

Next a solid layer or series of ribs of 1-in. board are set between the strips and cemented to the first layer. Finally a third layer of ½-in. board is nailed and cemented in place on the opposite side.

Gypsum wallboard is also manufactured with a decorated surface, usually a wood-grain pattern. This is normally done by lithographing on both ⅜-in. and ½-in. board. These are produced with either a square edge or a V-joint edge and are fastened with colored nails (Fig. 8·5) or with gypsum cement to a gypsum-board backing. In the latter case, the board is braced in place for from 16 to 24 hours until the cement has set. Nails may be used along the extreme top and bottom edges if they can be covered with trim later.

Gypsum lath. The same basic method of manufacture is used for gypsum lath as for wallboard. A gypsum core is covered on both sides with a heavy paper, but in the case of lath, the same paper is used for both back and front. Laths are 16 × 48 × ⅜ in. and are usually packed six to a bundle.

They are applied in horizontal courses, with 1¼-in. 13-gauge flatheaded blued nails, using four nails per stud. Joints in succeeding courses should be staggered, corners above openings and wide spaces between lath should be reinforced with metal lath, and internal angles should be reinforced with a corner bead.

This lath acts as a base for plaster, providing adhesion for gypsum plaster of about 6 psi if properly applied.

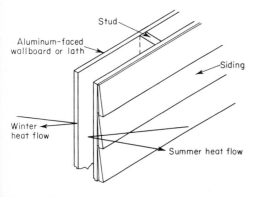

Figure 8 · 6
Reflecting radiant heat.

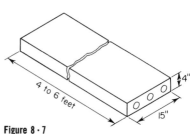

Figure 8 · 7
Square-edged roof plank.

Greater fire protection is provided by using perforated lath, which allows a heavier protective layer of plaster because of an added mechanical bond. Sound insulation can be increased and cracking can be reduced by clipping the lath to the frame.

In order to provide better insulation, gypsum lath and gypsum wallboard are sometimes made with a sheet of aluminum foil attached to the back. This sheet reduces radiant-heat losses in winter and keeps radiant heat from penetrating from the outside in summer (Fig. 8·6).

Gypsum exterior sheathing. This is another gypsum-board product made with asphalt-impregnated paper on both sides for use as exterior sheathing. Boards are made 2 × 8 ft × ½ in. thick, with the long edges tongue-and-grooved for tighter fit. Boards are applied in horizontal courses, using 1¾-in. galvanized roofing nails spaced 8 in. apart. Joints in succeeding courses should be staggered, and let-in wind bracing is used for greater rigidity. Almost any type of exterior finish can be applied over gypsum sheathing, including siding, shingles, stucco, and brick veneer.

Gypsum Precast Roof Decking

Decking panels precast from gypsum containing various types of fiber are made in several styles, two of which are illustrated in Figs. 8·7 and 8·8. The square-edged plank shown in Fig. 8·7 is made in various lengths from 4 to 6 ft to fit any purlin spacing within those limits. They are reinforced with light channel iron.

The metal-edged plank shown in Fig. 8·8 is made 10 ft long, and no attempt is made to make this type fit the purlin spacing. In addition to the metal edge, this plank is reinforced with longitudinal rods and wire mesh. Table 8·3 (right) gives necessary technical data on metal-edged gypsum plank.

Gypsum Tile

Partition and furring tile. Gypsum tile for furring and partitions are made for specially calcined gypsum, to which is usually added about 5 percent wood fiber in the form of chips and sometimes some perlite. The wood fiber allows the tile to bind together better, while the perlite reduces the weight. Both solid and hollow tile are made (Fig. 8·9), the standard dimensions being 12 × 30 in., with thicknesses of from 2 to 6 in.

The thickness of tile used for partitions is determined largely by the ceiling height; 3- and 4-in. tile are generally used where the height does not exceed 15 ft. Two-inch solid tile are used for partitions less than 10 ft high and for covering columns, constructing ducts, cupboards, shafts, etc.

Table 8·3
Technical data table for metal-edge gypsum plank. (Western Gypsum Products, Limited)

DIMENSIONS			WEIGHT, LB/SQ FT	ALLOWABLE LOAD, LB/SQ FT	ALLOWABLE SPAN, FT	THERMAL CONDUCTIVITY, BTU PER SQ FT PER HOUR PER °F DIFFERENCE IN TEMPERATURE		
THICKNESS, IN.	WIDTH, IN.	LENGTH, FT				NO INSULATION	½-IN. INSULATION	1-IN. INSULATION
2	15	10	12	75	7	0.53	0.29	0.20

179

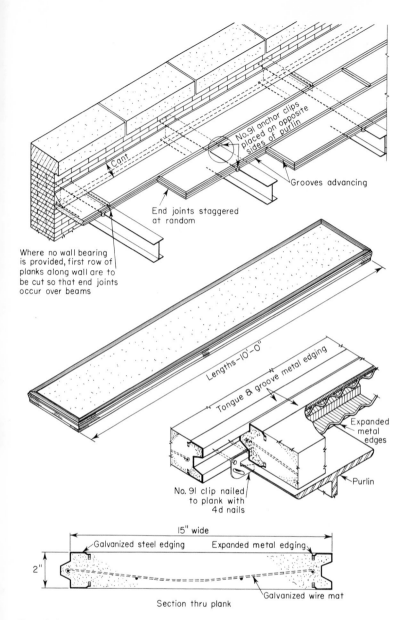

No. 91 anchor clips placed on opposite sides of purlin

Cant

Grooves advancing

End joints staggered at random

Where no wall bearing is provided, first row of planks along wall are to be cut so that end joints occur over beams

Lengths—10'-0"

Tongue & groove metal edging

Expanded metal edges

Purlin

No. 91 clip nailed to plank with 4d nails

15" wide

Galvanized steel edging

Expanded metal edging

2"

Galvanized wire mat

Section thru plank

Figure 8 · 8
Metal-edged gypsum plank.
(Western Gypsum Products, Limited)

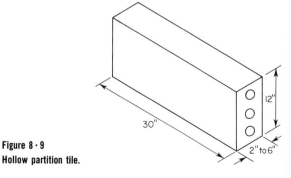

12"

30"

2" to 6"

Figure 8 · 9
Hollow partition tile.

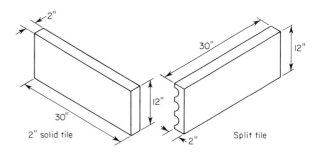

Figure 8·10
Furring tile.

Solid or split furring tile are used against exterior walls (Fig. 8·10).

Gypsum tile are easily cut with a handsaw and are laid up using a mortar made from gypsum cement, sand, and water. Plaster grounds are nailed to the tile, while blocks can be spiked to tile ends to support wood trim, light fixtures, etc. Heavy fixtures can be supported by bolting through the wall. Table 8·4 gives technical data on a number of partition and furring tile.

Fireproofing tile. Since gypsum presents an effective barrier to the passage of heat, specially formed tile are made to cover steel members in a building to protect them against fire. Shoe tile, angle tile, and soffit tile (Fig. 8·11) fit around

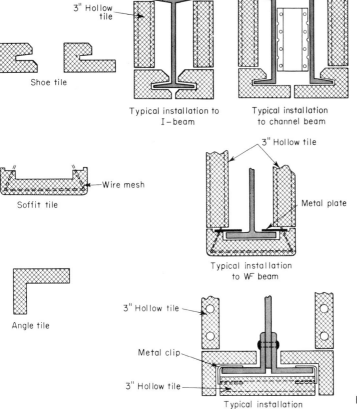

Figure 8·11
Gypsum fireproofing tile.

Table 8 - 4
Sizes and weights of partition and furring tile. (Western Gypsum Products, Limited)

SIZE OF GYPSUM TILE, IN.		RECOMMENDED HEIGHTS, FT	WEIGHT OF TILE, LB/SQ FT	WEIGHT OF MORTAR, LB/SQ FT	WEIGHT OF PLASTER, ONE SIDE, LB/SQ FT ½-IN. GROUNDS	TOTAL WEIGHT PLASTERED, ONE SIDE, LB/SQ FT	WEIGHT PLASTER, TWO SIDES, LB/SQ FT	TOTAL WEIGHT PLASTERED, TWO SIDES, LB/SQ FT	APPROXIMATE MORTAR REQUIREMENTS PER 1,000 SQ FT	
									TILE CEMENT, LB	SAND, CU YD
2-in. split	2 × 12 × 30	Furring	6.4	1.4	3	9.4	...	...	600	0.75
2-in. solid	2 × 12 × 30	10	9.4	1.5	3	12.4	6	15.4	600	0.75
3-in. hollow	3 × 12 × 30	13	9.9	2.0	3	12.9	6	15.9	800	1.00
4-in. hollow	4 × 12 × 30	17	13.0	2.5	3	16.0	6	19.0	900	1.125
6-in. hollow	6 × 12 × 30	30	16.6	3.0	3	19.6	6	22.6	1,100	1.40

the flanges of beams and girders, while regular 3-in. hollow tile are used to fireproof the webs.

Gypsum Precast Wall Panels

Precast wall panels of gypsum are made by casting in a mold. A panel consists of two outer shells ⅝ in. thick, reinforced with viscose fiber and separated by a core of hexagonal cells. It is made 2 ft wide, 2 to 6 in. thick, and up to 10 ft long. Each panel is tongue-and-grooved along its long edges to form an interlocking wall. Both faces of the panel are also recessed along the long edges to allow for taping and filling similar to that done on gypsum wallboard.

Panels to be used for exterior walls may have one face keyed to receive stucco or treated with asphalt for weather protection. Plates may be attached to the top of walls and window and door frames fixed into the panels. Cutting is done with a handsaw. The material has a two-hour fire rating and low sound transmission.

LIME

Lime was commonly used in the past as a constituent of masonry mortar; today cement has largely replaced it for this purpose. It is still used, however, in the making of the finish or putty coat for interior plaster.

The lime used is hydrated or slaked lime, produced by slaking quicklime, which, in turn, is made by burning limestone. The limestone, calcium carbonate ($CaCO_3$), when subjected to heat in a shaft or kiln breaks down into quicklime (CaO) and carbon dioxide (CO_2).

$$CaCO_3 + heat = CaO + CO_2$$

Calcium Carbonate   Quicklime   Carbon
                                       Dioxide

The quicklime is slaked by the addition of water to form hydrated lime, calcium hydroxide [$Ca(OH)_2$].

$$CaO + H_2O = Ca(OH)_2$$

Quicklime   Water   Calcium Hydroxide

The hydrated lime is mixed with water to form a plastic, puttylike material to which is added gauging plaster, a gypsum product. This mixture is applied in a thin coat over the base plaster and troweled to a smooth finish. The setting of the gypsum gives the plaster its initial hardness and permits troweling to a smooth, hard finish. The lime in the putty begins to recarbonate, and this hardening process continues slowly for a long period of time.

The limestone used may be nearly pure calcium carbonate or it may consist of nearly equal parts of calcium carbonate and magnesium carbonate. If the stone contains at least 90 percent calcium carbonate it is classified as a high-calcium limestone. If it contains more than 10 percent magnesium carbonate it is classified as a magnesium limestone, and if it has more than 25 percent magnesium carbonate, it is called dolomitic limestone.

Lime made from magnesium limestone slakes slower and with less heat than high-calcium limestones, and the resulting hydrated lime is more plastic and develops a better ultimate strength.

Slaked lime sets by gradually losing its water through evaporation and absorbing carbon dioxide, changing from $Ca(OH)_2$ to $CaCO_3$, calcium carbonate or limestone.

GLOSSARY

cadmium	A noncorrosive metal used to coat nails
catalyst	A substance which accelerates a chemical reaction without undergoing any significant change in itself
double-headed nails	Nails with two heads, spaced about ½ in. apart on the shank
gauging plaster	Gypsum plaster, added to lime putty to produce a finish plaster with the proper setting time
hemihydrate	A hydrate containing half a molecule of water to one molecule of the other compound involved
hydrated lime	An inert compound formed by the chemical combination of water and calcium oxide—quicklime
neat gypsum	Gypsum free from other compounds
purlin	Roof-framing members which span the space between trusses
slaked-lime putty	A paste made of hydrated lime and water
viscose	A fiber made from cellulose

REVIEW QUESTIONS

1 What is the chemical difference between land plaster, plaster of paris, and Keene's cement?
2 For what particular purpose is Keene's cement commonly used?
3 Explain why casting plaster has to be a slow-setting plaster.

4 What are the results of increasing the amount of sand used par bag of hardwall when mixing plaster?
5 Give one advantage of prepared finish plaster over regular putty coat plaster.
6 Describe briefly the process of filling and finishing a long-edge joint between two sheets of gypsum wallboard using gypsum joint filler.
7 (a) What is meant by the laminated drywall system?
   (b) What is the reason for horizontal application of wallboard?
8 What is the reason for:
   (a) Gray paper on both sides of gypsum lath
   (b) Perforations in gypsum lath
   (c) Aluminum foil on the back of gypsum lath
9 How would a roof decked with gypsum roof plank be waterproofed?
10 Explain the difference between quicklime and slaked lime.

SELECTED SOURCES OF INFORMATION

Kaiser Gypsum Co., Oakland, Calif.
Mechanical Drywall of Canada, Ltd., Hamilton, Ont.
National Gypsum Co., Buffalo, N.Y.
United States Gypsum Co., Chicago, Ill.
Western Gypsum Products, Ltd., Winnipeg, Manitoba

9

GLASS

Of all the mass-produced materials that we use in everyday life, probably none has a more exciting background or adds more to modern living than glass. There is hardly a moment in our daily lives that glass in some form is not performing a service for us.

The art of glassmaking is very old, and today the industry uses basically the same raw materials as did the ancient glassmakers. However, the methods of manufacture have changed and improved, resulting in higher production rates, superior glass, and sheet sizes far greater than anything possible under older methods.

RAW MATERIALS

Glass is described as a soda-lime silicate; that is, it is made from silica (sand), soda, and lime. If sand and soda are melted together, they produce, on cooling, a hard, transparent, glassy substance known as sodium silicate (water glass) which is soluble in water. When lime is added to the mixture, the solubility of the sodium silicate is reduced, and when enough lime is added, a durable glass is obtained which will stand up to the weather and all strong acids except hydrofluoric.

Glass has two peculiar properties which influence the manufacturing process. First, glass does not have a definite melting point. When it is heated, it first softens so that it can be bent. Further heating brings it to the point when it becomes thick, syrupy liquid, a state in which it can be worked. Finally, at still higher temperatures, it becomes a thin, watery liquid.

Second, above a certain temperature, known as the devitrification temperature, glass can be kept in a liquid condition without any change occurring. But if it is kept just below that temperature for any length of time crystallization or devitrification occurs. It is therefore necessary, in any manufacturing process, to complete the operation before devitrification occurs.

MANUFACTURING

Sheet Glass

The raw materials, sand, soda, and limestone, are first ground to a fine state and mixed in the proper proportions. This mixture, known as *frit,* is fed into the filling end of a

186

Figure 9 · 1
Charging raw materials into a glass furnace.
(Pilkington Bros. Ltd.)

furnace and melted. Sometimes the mixing is done by a batcher, which feeds the various ingredients into the furnace. In addition to the three basic materials, *cullet* (broken glass) is also fed into the furnace.

During the initial melting stage a chemical reaction takes place among the three basic ingredients, resulting in a sticky mass full of bubbles. In the next stage, the temperature is raised so that the glass loses its viscous nature and becomes a watery liquid, allowing the gases forming the bubbles to rise to the surface. The third stage consists of cooling the glass down to a temperature at which the material is at the proper consistency to be drawn.

To form the glass into a sheet, it first passes from the fur-

Figure 9 · 2
Batch feeder in operation.
(Pilkington Bros. Ltd.)

nace tank into a drawing kiln, of which there are usually four or five to a furnace. From here it is drawn up in the form of a sheet into a series of rollers. To start the drawing process a *bait* (an iron grille) is lowered into the glass in the kiln. When it has remained there for a short period, the molten glass sticks to the iron and the bait is slowly lifted, drawing behind it a sheet of glass. When the leading edge of the sheet has passed between the first few pairs of rollers, the bait can be cracked off from the glass and the rollers will then draw up a continuous strip or sheet.

The success of this process lies in the provision of devices for maintaining the width of the ribbon of glass being drawn. Since it is in a plastic condition, the ribbon tends to taper off; if this were allowed to occur, the sheet would eventually stop drawing. Basically, these devices consist of knurled rollers which grip the edges of the glass and cool it sufficiently to prevent the tapering from taking place.

These sheets of flat drawn glass are cooled slowly in a cooling chamber known as an *annealing lehr*.

In some manufacturing processes the hot sheet of glass, after being drawn vertically from the surface of the tank, is bent over a roller and sent through the lehr horizontally. Figure 9·3 illustrates the process diagrammatically from furnace to cutting table. In another modern process, the sheet of glass is carried vertically up a tower which acts as an annealing lehr. At a height of about 30 ft the sheet is cool enough to cut. This is done automatically, and the cut sheet is removed and sent to be trimmed.

From the trimming table, the glass is sent to the warehouse where it is examined, sorted, and finally cut into standard sizes.

Flat-drawn sheet glass can be drawn in thicknesses that range in weight from 18 to 32 oz per sq ft, the thickness of the sheet being determined by the speed of the drawing, the skill of the operator, and the accuracy of the machine. This type of glass is used where vision is required but where cost is an important factor. The surface is good but never free from distortion, as the two surfaces of the sheet are not perfectly parallel.

Figure 9·3
Horizontally drawn glass.

Figure 9 · 4
Horizontal annealing lehr.
(Libby-Owens-Ford Glass Co.)

Figure 9 · 5
Sheet of glass cut off at the
top of annealing tower.
(Pilkington Bros. Ltd.)

Figure 9 · 6
Cutting sheet glass.
(Pilkington Bros. Ltd.)

Figure 9 · 7
Plate-glass blank passing from lehr to
twin grinder. (Libby-Owens-Ford Glass Co.)

Figure 9 · 8
Massive twin grinder with 22 grinding heads.
(Libby-Owens-Ford Glass Co.)

Figure 9 · 9
Plate glass passing under polishing head.
(Libby-Owens-Ford Glass Co.)

Plate Glass

In the manufacture of plate glass, molten glass flows from the furnace between rollers of the glassmaking machine. Because of this continuous-flow process, a greater range of thicknesses can be made than is possible with drawn glass. From the rollers, the sheet passes into a lehr for annealing. After it emerges from the lehr, the blank passes to a twin grinder unit, which simultaneously grinds both surfaces of the continuous 100-in.-wide ribbon of glass to make them smooth and parallel. At the end of the grinder line, the ribbon is cut into large sections and polished to give clear, undistorted vision and reflection. Jeweler's rouge is used for polishing the moving glass under the felt-padded revolving

Figure 9 · 10
A line of continuous polishers.
(Pilkington Bros. Ltd.)

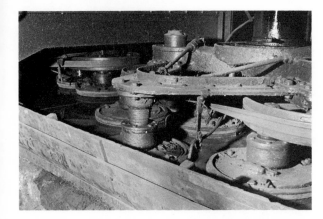

Figure 9 · 11
Closeup of a polishing head.
(Pilkington Bros. Ltd.)

Figure 9 · 12
Inspecting polished plate glass.
(Pilkington Bros. Ltd.)

heads. At the end of the polishing line, the finished glass is washed and inspected before being cut to the desired sizes for shipment.

Plate glass can be produced in thicknesses of from ⅛ to 1¼ in., although the special, thick glasses are usually cast rather than made by the continuous-flow process. However, the grinding and polishing are carried out by the continuous process outlined above.

Float Glass

Float glass is a flat glass produced by a new process. It combines the fire-finish of sheet with the perfect flatness of plate. Figure 9·13 shows the basic layout of a float line, which eliminates the time-consuming grinding and polishing operations.

192

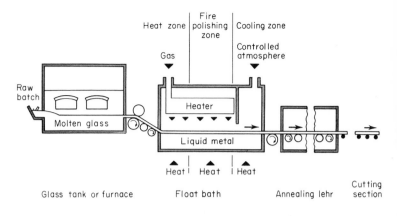

Figure 9 · 13
Diagram of basic float line.
(Pilkington Bros. Ltd.)

In the manufacture of float glass, frit, the usual combination of raw materials, is fed into the charging end of the glass tank, where it is melted in an oil- or gas-fired furnace. The melted glass leaves the furnace and passes to a float bath where it is supported on molten tin. Gravity keeps the liquid tin very flat, and heat, applied from above, melts out any irregularities in the glass, which is free to conform to the perfectly flat tin.

As the ribbon of glass passes through the float bath, the

Figure 9 · 14
General view of float plant glass furnace. (Pilkington Bros. Ltd.)

Figure 9 · 15
Annealing lehr in float plant.
(Pilkington Bros. Ltd.)

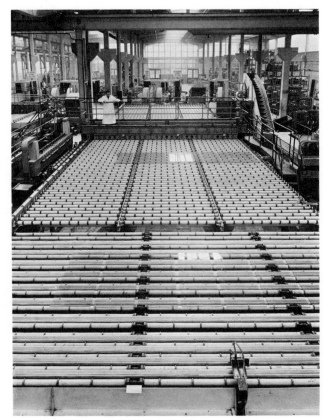

Figure 9 · 16
Glass conveyor on automatic cutting line.
(Pilkington Bros. Ltd.)

heat is reduced until the glass is sufficiently hard to be fed on to the rollers of the lehr without marking the undersurface. After leaving the lehr, the glass is cut into long lengths and transferred to a warehouse where it is cut automatically, inspected, and packed.

The float process does not lend itself to the efficient production of as broad a range of thicknesses as either the sheet-glass or plate-glass processes. But for those thicknesses for which the process is most suitable—⅛, 3/16, and ¼ in.—it produces fire-finished glass with flatter and more parallel surfaces than sheet glass.

Rolled and Roughcast Glass

These types of glass get their name from the fact that originally they were made by casting molten glass on a cast iron table and rolling it out into a sheet. The modern process is the same as the first steps in making plate glass. A ribbon of glass is drawn horizontally from the furnace, passed through rollers, and fed into the annealing lehr. At the end of the lehr it is examined and cut into the required sizes. Glass of this type is used where clear vision is not required, such as for factory roofs and walls, windows for halls and staircases, skylights, and partitions in offices. Cast glass diffuses light, and because of its low reflecting and absorption index, transmits 90 to 93 percent of light rays striking it.

Cathedral and Figured Rolled Glasses

The modern method of manufacture is similar to that described above for rolled and roughcast glasses. However, they contain a pattern or texture impressed usually on one surface by a patterned roller. These glasses are also made a series of standard tints for special uses. Rolled and cast glass is produced in a great many patterns and designs, a few of which are illustrated in Fig. 9 · 17. Thicknesses vary from ⅛ to ⅜ in., depending on pattern and use. Most are produced in stock widths of from 40 to 50 in., with lengths up to 100 in.

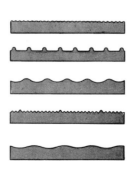
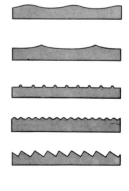

Figure 9 · 17
Rolled glass profiles.

Wired Glass

Wired glass is simply a rolled glass into which wire mesh is inserted during the process of manufacture. The wire greatly increases the resistance to shattering through impact. Wired glass is made in thicknesses of $\frac{7}{32}$, $\frac{1}{4}$, and $\frac{3}{8}$ in. Stock widths 47 to 49 in. and lengths up to 178 in. are produced.

Heat-absorbing Plate Glass

This glass is made by adding ingredients to the mix used in making regular plate glass so that the finished product is pale bluish-green. Because of its chemical composition, this glass absorbs a significant percentage of the sun's radiant energy, thus reducing the buildup of heat within the building. Its color and the fact that it possesses lower light transmission than regular plate means that glare and brightness in the room are reduced. This type of glass is quite widely used for glazing in office buildings, schools, and hospitals.

Tempered Plate Glass

Tempered plate glass is three to five times as strong as regular plate of the same thickness and area in resisting compressive forces and fracture due to strain or thermal shock. It is made by reheating and suddenly cooling plate glass. As a result the outer surfaces are under high compressive stress, while the center portion remains in tension. This produces a condition that is highly resistant to breakage. Tempered plate glass is used for swinging doors, sliding patio doors, windows in gymnasiums and sports arenas, hockey-rink enclosures, etc. Tempered plate is available in thicknesses of $\frac{1}{4}$, $\frac{3}{8}$, $\frac{1}{2}$, $\frac{5}{8}$, $\frac{3}{4}$, and 1 in. Sizes of sheets vary with the thickness, but the normal maximum size is 96×120 in.

Vitreous Colored Plate

Polished plate glass can be heat-strengthened and coated on one side with vitreous color which is fire-fused to the surface. The result is an opaque glass which is widely used in curtain-wall construction, store fronts, showrooms, laboratories, and industrial buildings. It should not be used as a glazing material but instead should be applied against a backup of masonry or have some type of insulative backing. Normal thickness is $\frac{1}{4}$ in.; maximum standard size, 72×120 in.

196

Laminated Safety Glass

Laminated safety glass is made of two thicknesses of plate or sheet glass bonded by a thin, tough layer of polyvinyl butyral resin, a transparent plastic. This type of glass has been widely used in the automotive industry and the transportation industry for many years and is now finding some uses in the building industry.

Safety glass made from sheet glass is produced in thicknesses of $\frac{9}{64}$, $\frac{7}{32}$, $\frac{15}{64}$, and $\frac{1}{4}$ in. The $\frac{9}{64}$-in. thickness is made in a maximum size of 7 sq ft, and the remaining thicknesses have a maximum area of 15 sq ft.

Safety glass made from plate glass is produced in thicknesses of $\frac{1}{4}$, $\frac{3}{8}$, $\frac{1}{2}$, $\frac{5}{8}$, $\frac{3}{4}$, $\frac{7}{8}$, and 1 in. Units of all thicknesses are made in a maximum size of 72 × 138 in.

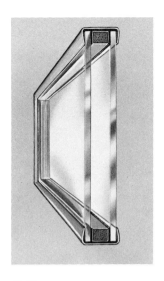

Figure 9 · 18
Cutaway view of insulating-glass unit.
(Canadian Pittsburgh Industries Ltd.)

Insulating Glass

Insulating glass consists of two sheets of plate or sheet glass, separated by an air space, and joined around the edges to produce a hermetically sealed unit. Three methods of sealing are used. One (Fig. 9·18) consists of a rectangular metal spacer sealed to the glass and covered by a stainless steel frame. A $\frac{1}{2}$-in. air space of dehydrated air is left between the sheets, which are $\frac{1}{8}$- or $\frac{1}{4}$-in. polished plate glass, in most cases. However, other types of glass may be used if required. This type of unit is made in 120 standard sizes.

Another method of sealing involves the use of a strip of lead sealed to the edges of the glass (Fig. 9·19). Both $\frac{1}{8}$- and $\frac{1}{4}$-in. plate are used for this type of unit, and a similar range of sizes is available.

The third method of sealing is an electrically fused all-glass edge. Sheet glass $\frac{3}{32}$ or $\frac{1}{8}$ in. thick is used with an air space of $\frac{3}{16}$ in. Units of this type are available in 70 standard sizes with $\frac{1}{8}$-in. glass and 42 sizes with $\frac{3}{32}$-in. glass.

All of these sealed units provide thermal insulation and greatly restrict condensation. In addition, they reduce external noise but still permit the entry of natural light.

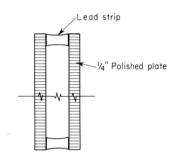

Figure 9 · 19
Lead-sealed unit.

Classification of Sheet Glass

Sheet glass, made by the flat-drawn process previously described, is classified in three types, window glass, heavy sheet glass, and picture glass. Each type is graded according to quality into "AA," "A," "B," and Greenhouse grades. "AA" is specially selected glass for the highest quality work. "A" grade is also selected for its superior glazing quality. "B" grade is suitable for general glazing purposes, while Green-

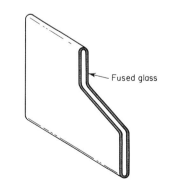

Figure 9 · 20
All-glass seal.

Figure 9·21
Jalousie window.

Figure 9·22
Light-directing block.
(Pittsburgh Corning Corporation)

Figure 9·23
Light-diffusing block.
(Pittsburgh Corning Corporation)

house grade is suitable for horticultural uses. Each type of glass is made in specific thicknesses.

Window glass is used for glazing windows, doors, and storm sash in residential buildings, schools, and other types of buildings where good light and vision are required at moderate cost. It is also widely used for greenhouse glazing, in that one specific grade. Window glass is made in two thicknesses—single strength (18 oz per sq ft), 0.085 to 0.1 in. thick, and double strength (26 oz per sq ft), 0.115 to 0.133 in. thick. Single-strength glass is made in "AA," "A," and "B" qualities, while double-strength is made in all four qualities.

Single-strength grade in all qualities is produced in maximum sizes of 40 × 50 in., or 90 united inches (length plus width). Double-strength in "AA," "A," and "B" qualities is made in maximum sizes of 60 × 60 in., or 120 united inches. Double-strength glass in Greenhouse quality is cut 16 × 18 in., 18 × 20 in., 16 × 24 in., and 20 × 20 in.

Heavy sheet glass is used for glazing windows and doors where greater strength is required but where slight distortion is not objectionable. It is commonly used for display cases, shelving, window ventilators, furniture tops, and jalousies (Fig. 9·21). It is made in two thicknesses, ³⁄₁₆ and ⁷⁄₃₂ in., in "AA," "A," and "B" qualities. The ³⁄₁₆-in. glass weighs about 40 oz per sq ft and is cut in a maximum size of 76 × 120 in.; ⁷⁄₃₂-in. glass weighs 45 oz per sq ft and is also cut 76 × 120 in. maximum.

Picture glass is used for covering pictures, photographs, maps, charts, projector slides, and instrument dials. It is made in three thicknesses, 10 oz (0.043 to 0.053 in.), 13 oz (0.058 to 0.068 in.), and 16 oz (0.07 to 0.08 in.), in three qualities. In each case, the maximum size cut is 60 united inches.

GLASS BLOCKS

Glass blocks, products of the glass industry, are comparable in many ways to unit masonry but have the added feature of transmitting light. They are made in two separate halves which are heat-sealed together to form a hollow unit with reasonably high thermal efficiency and sound insulation. The rib around the middle of the block, where the seal is made, can be seen in Fig. 9·22. The edge surfaces of the block are coated with a gritty mortar bond.

Two general types of block are produced, functional and decorative. Functional blocks direct or diffuse the daylight which passes through them to improve the illumination of the building interior. Decorative blocks are chosen for their ability to contribute to an overall design plan and are not intended to be used as a major control of daylight.

Functional blocks are made in three styles or patterns, each with a specific purpose. A light-directing block (Fig.

9·22) directs incoming light upward toward the ceiling. It should always be used above eye level so that it cannot direct light into the eyes. Eye level is assumed to be approximately 6 ft above the floor. A light-diffusing block diffuses incoming light evenly throughout the interior of the room. It may be used either above or below eye level. A third style is a general-purpose block. All of these patterns are available with a white- or green-tinted fibrous glass insert in the block. The purpose of these inserts is to reduce brightness and instantaneous heat gain; such blocks should be used if direct sunlight strikes the panel during the day. Functional blocks are made in sizes of 8 × 8 in. and 12 × 12 in., both 4 in. thick.

Decorative blocks are made in a variety of patterns, including a number of fluted designs, etched surfaces (Fig. 9·24), and ripple surfaces, in both clear and colored glass. They are available in sizes of 6 × 6 in., 8 × 8 in., 12 × 12 in., and 4 × 12 in.

Glass blocks may be used by themselves to build up curtain wall panels or in conjunction with other unit masonry (Fig. 9·25).

The primary purpose in using glass in a building is to provide for the transmission of light into the interior. The amount of light transmitted varies with the thickness of the glass and the type of surface finish. Plate glass ⅛ in. thick transmits about 91 percent of average daylight, while plate glass 1 in. thick transmits about 78 percent. Sheet glass transmits light at about the same rate as thin plate. Tables supplied by glass manufacturers give light-transmission ratings for all thicknesses of sheet and plate glass.

The use of clear glass often results in undesirable brightness and glare. This may be overcome by the use of patterned glass and neutral-gray plate glass. Light transmission through the latter is reduced to about 44 percent.

Figure 9·24
4 x 12 in. glass blocks.
(Pittsburgh Corning Corporation)

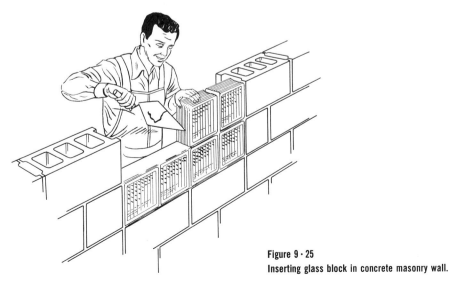

Figure 9·25
Inserting glass block in concrete masonry wall.

When solar radiation falls on glass and other partially transparent material, some of the incident energy is reflected, some is absorbed by the material, and the rest is transmitted to the inside of the building, resulting in a heat gain in the building. For ordinary windows, absorption is quite a small fraction and transmission much the largest part of the total energy involved. The reflection varies considerably with the angle of incidence—the angle between the light rays and a line perpendicular to the reflecting surface. The greater the angle of incidence, the greater the amount of energy reflected. Figure 9·26 shows the variation of the reflection, absorption, and transmission of solar radiation by a single sheet of ordinary glass in a south wall at 45° latitude.

The amount of heat gained by transmission of solar radiation is quite significant. In simple terms, it has been calculated that during the summer months when the sun is low—the angle of incidence less than 40°—100 sq ft of ordinary glass in the west wall of a building would transmit 6.5 kilowatts of energy to the interior of the building. This must be removed by the ventilating and air-conditioning equipment.

It is therefore important to reduce the solar-heat gain as much as possible. This may be done in several ways. The reflectivity of glass can be increased by coating the surface with either a very thin metallic film or a film of dielectric material that has a high index of refraction. Sealed double units are available with a reflective coating on the inner surface of the outer pane. Their reflectivity depends on the angle of incidence just as for uncoated glass, but the value at all angles of incidence is higher than for ordinary glass.

Blinds provide another method of solar control. A light-colored blind reflects some radiation and absorbs the rest. If a light-colored blind can be placed between the panes of a double window, it will help to reduce the room's cooling load.

Heat-absorbing glass is also widely used to reduce solar-heat gain. Glasses are available through which transmission

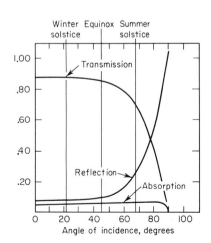

Figure 9 · 26
Absorption, reflection, and transmission of a single sheet of ordinary glass in a south wall at 45° latitude.

to the inside is about 20 percent when the angle of incidence is small and less when it is large. However, this absorbed energy must be dissipated and, to keep the inside heat down, as much as possible must be dissipated to the outside. This can be done if the heat-absorbing glass is used as the outside pane of a double-glazed window. An even greater fraction of the absorbed energy can be rejected to the outside atmosphere if there is a free circulation of outside air through the space between the panes of the double window.

GLOSSARY

blank	Unfinished sheet of plate glass
devitrification	The change from a vitreous (glassy) condition to a crystalline condition
dielectric	Nonconducting
float bath	A large vat in which molten glass floats on molten metal
hermetically sealed	Sealed by fusion
jalousie	A window or shutter with movable horizontal slats
jeweler's rouge	A very fine abrasive powder containing ferric oxide
solar radiation	Energy radiating or traveling, as a wave motion, from the sun

REVIEW QUESTIONS

1   Explain why glass must be cooled slowly.
2   (a) Why is vision normally better through plate glass than through sheet glass?
     (b) How does the cost per square foot of plate glass compare with that of sheet glass of comparable thickness?
3   Explain why thick plate is often cast rather than drawn.
4   What is meant by the fire finish of sheet or float glass?
5   How would you compare float glass and plate glass from the standpoint of:
     (a) Production cost
     (b) Degree of light refraction
     (c) Thicknesses produced
6   What is the basic difference between modern rolled glass and plate glass?
7   (a) What is the advantage of wired glass?
     (b) Where does wired glass find extensive use in buildings?
8   (a) What is heat-absorbing plate glass?
     (b) Where is such glass used?
9   Explain how insulating glass restricts condensation.
10   What is the reason for the range of thicknesses in any grade of sheet glass?

11 (a) What is the reason for placing fibrous glass inserts in some glass blocks?

   (b) Where should such blocks be used?

12 During the spring, with the sun's rays having an angle of incidence of 55°, a single sheet of glass in a south wall, at about 45° latitude will:

   (a) Transmit about —— % of the radiant energy

   (b) Reflect about —— % of the energy

   (c) Absorb about —— % of the energy

SELECTED SOURCES OF INFORMATION

Belcana Glass, Ltd., Montreal, Que.
Canadian Pittsburgh Industries Ltd., Montreal, Que.
Libbey-Owens-Ford Glass Co., Toledo, O.
Mississippi Glass Co., St. Louis, Mo.
Owens-Illinois Glass Block, Toledo, O.
Pilkington Bros. Ltd., St. Helens, England
Pittsburgh Plate Glass Co., Pittsburgh, Pa.
Solarpane Manufacturing Co., Regina, Sask.

10

BITUMINOUS
MATERIALS

The term *bitumen* is a generic name applied to various mixtures of hydrocarbons. They may be gaseous, liquid, semisolid, or solid in nature and are completely soluble in carbon disulfide. The most common materials within this family of bitumens are tars, pitches, and asphalts.

When destructive distillation is carried out on such materials as wood, coal, shale, peat, or bone, the resulting condensate is tar. Partial evaporation or fractional distillation of tar produces the solid or semisolid residue known as pitch. The most common material of this kind used in construction is coal-tar pitch.

Asphalts are dark brown or black solids or semisolids which are found in the natural state and are also produced by the refining of petroleum. Some of the best known deposits of natural asphalt are found in Trinidad, in an asphalt lake, and in Kentucky, Utah, Colorado, and California, where it occurs in various forms. Some are semisolid and some, rock asphalt and Gilsonite, are very hard. Today, however, more than 95 percent of the asphaltic materials used in North America are derived from the refining of petroleum.

Bitumens have a number of properties which make them useful in the construction industry. One is the tendency to adhere to a solid surface. This adhesiveness will depend on the nature of the surface and the state of the bitumen. For an adhesive to act it must be able to wet a surface; bitumens have this ability in a fluid state, but the presence of water on the solid surface will prevent adhesion.

The water resistance of bitumens is important; in general it is very good. Under certain conditions water may be absorbed by minute quantities of inorganic salts in the bitumen or by fillers in it. There is very little difference in the absorption qualities of the pitches and the asphalts—both are very low.

The viscous or flow properties of bitumens are of importance, both at the high temperatures encountered in processing and application and at the low temperatures to which bitumens are subjected in service. Flow properties are very complex and as a result, tests have been formulated to measure the consistency of the materials at temperatures comparable to those encountered during the service life of the bitumen.

One of these tests is the penetration test, which measures the depth of penetration in tenths of millimeters of a weighted needle in a bitumen after a given time, at a known temperature. Commonly, a weight of 100 grams is applied for five seconds at a temperature of 77°F. The penetration is a measure of hardness; typical results are approximately 10 for hard coating-grade asphalts, 15 to 40 for roofing asphalts, and up to 100 or more for waterproofing bitumens.

Another common test is the softening-point test, which measures the temperature in degrees Fahrenheit at which a steel ball falls a known distance through the bitumen when the test assembly is heated at a known rate. Usually the test consists of a ⅜-in.-diameter steel ball, weighing 3.5 grams, which is allowed to sink 1 in. through a ⅝-in.-diameter, ¼-in.-thick disk of bitumen held in a brass ring. The whole assembly is heated at a rate of 9°F per minute. The softening point value is used to grade bitumens into groups. Typical values would be up to 240°F for coating-grade asphalts, from 140 to 220°F for roofing asphalts, and down to 115°F for bituminous waterproofing materials.

Ductility tests are conducted also to determine the amount a bitumen will stretch at temperatures below its softening point. A briquet having a cross-sectional area of 1 sq in. is placed in a tester and elongated at a rate of 5 cm per minute at a temperature of 77°F. Ductility values range from 0 to over 150 cm, depending on the type of bitumen.

Lack of compatibility between different bitumens is a factor which requires attention. Though these reactions do not always occur, sometimes if asphalt is applied over pitch it will soften and flow off, leaving the pitch exposed. If pitch is applied over asphalt, the pitch may harden and crack. It is therefore advisable to avoid using these two bitumens together, if possible.

TYPES OF BITUMENS

Tar and Pitch

Most of the tar and pitch used in construction is made by the distillation of coal. Tar is used to saturate felt paper and to coat kraft paper to render it waterproof. The coal-tar pitch is used in making pitch and gravel built-up roofs. Pitch will soften and flow at relatively low temperatures, so it should be applied only to roofs with a low slope. Coal-tar pitch oxidizes quite rapidly when exposed to ultraviolet rays of the sun and should always be protected by a coating of gravel or slag.

Asphalt

A large percentage of the asphalt used results from the refining of naphtha base crude oils, which produce aviation-grade gasoline, fuel oil, cold-test lubricating oils, and asphalt. The properties of this residual, known as straight-run asphalt, depend on the nature of the crude oil from which it was refined and the conditions of refining.

There are three main groups of asphalt products produced from straight-run asphalts: (1) hot asphalts, those softened by heat; (2) cutback asphalts, those dissolved in mineral solvents; and (3) emulsion asphalts, those dispersed or suspended in a water base.

Hot asphalt can be used directly or it can be processed further to produce a harder material. This can be done by a process in which air is blown through heated residual asphalt. Control of the process produces various degrees of hardness. Consistency can also be increased by using a pulverized mineral filler whose main purpose is to increase viscosity.

Hot asphalts have good resistance to the transmission of water and water vapor when they are applied to dry surfaces and the heating process is controlled.

Cold flow (the tendency for a piece of asphalt to flow, spread out, and lose its shape unless it is very cold) is inherent in all hot asphalts. Also, if stress is exerted on a piece of this type of asphalt, it will flow in a manner to relieve the stress.

Hot asphalts bond poorly to damp or wet surfaces, have relatively poor flexibility, oxidize under the sun's rays, and are brittle at low temperatures. As is the case with pitch, it is difficult to control the application thickness of hot asphalt.

Cutback asphalts are of three types: No. 1, straight-run asphalt and solvent, with or without a small amount of fiber added; No. 2, heavily filled cutback, made by adding a large amount of filler and fiber to asphalt cut with solvent; and No. 3, primer-type cutback asphalt in solution with no filler or fiber.

These asphalts have poor bonding power on wet surfaces but some of them have damp-bonding ability. No. 2 cutback generally has excellent vapor-barrier characteristics and increased weather resistance. Primer-type cutbacks are thin enough to penetrate the pores of masonry, wood, and paper to provide a firm bond for other bitumen applications. They are also used to wet surfaces such as metal for good adhesion. Primer-type cutbacks are made from soft, ductile asphalts as well as harder-base asphalts, depending on requirements. The thin, penetrating types are used on dense surfaces, the harder, enamel types on metal, and the more-viscous types on porous surfaces. None is intended to be used as a finish coating.

Emulsion asphalts are divided into three groups, depending on the type of emulsifier: (1) soap type, in which soap is used as the emulsifier; (2) clay-modified soap type, with a combination of soap and clay as emulsifier; and (3) clay-base type, with a mineral material, usually clay, as the emulsifier. The clay most commonly used for this purpose is bentonite.

The main advantage of emulsions over other bituminous products is that they are easy to handle; the addition of water is all that is necessary to decrease their viscosity. Drying involves, primarily, the loss of water by evaporation. No heating is required in their application and they have good bonding qualities, even to damp or wet surfaces. These asphalts, particularly the clay-base type, undergo less deterioration from weather exposure than other forms of bitumens.

USES OF BITUMENS

In general, the uses to which bitumens are put are controlled by their desirable qualities; their limitations control the methods of application and their performance. Adhesiveness and waterproofing qualities, along with low cost, make them useful as a protective agent in built-up roofing, prepared roofing, and prepared siding. They are used as waterproofing and dampproofing agents and as vapor barriers. In addition, they are widely used as adhesives and sealants.

The form in which bitumen is used for any of these purposes depends on the qualities and characteristics desired. Saturated felts—which are used in built-up roofing, as a base for prepared roofings and sidings, as a membrane for waterproofing, and as underlays for floors—require a particular grade of bitumen. It must have a low viscosity at the saturation temperature, with a flash point above that temperature. It should also be able to stand up under low temperatures reasonably well. The asphalt commonly used in the preparation of such felts has a softening point of approximately 140°F and a penetration value of 50.

Prepared roofing products are coated with asphalt after being saturated. The coating-grade asphalts used are usually No. 1 cutbacks with a softening point of from 200 to 240°F. They are normally air-blown products with low penetration values of 18 to 30 at 77°F and low temperature susceptibility. Saturating and coating asphalts must be compatible.

Bitumens are widely used to provide a waterproof coating for walls and to make waterproof membranes in buildings and other structures. When hot-applied bitumens are used below grade, where they are not subject to high temperatures, types are used which have a low softening point (115 to 145°F) and a high penetration value (up to 85). When the bitumens are to be used above grade on vertical surfaces subjected to direct sunlight, a type with a higher softening point (200 to 220°F) and a lower penetration value (15 to 25) should be used. Cutbacks and emulsions, applied cold, are being used much more extensively for this purpose, with or without a felt membrane.

Other uses of asphalts are in the manufacture of sealants, acoustical coatings, paints, floor tile, and mastic flooring. In most cases these asphalts are modified by the addition of mineral matter, the type of mineral depending on the product.

Asphaltic cutbacks and emulsions have their greatest use in road construction and maintenance. It accounts for about 85 percent of the asphalt produced in North America.

Asphalt in pavement acts as a binder for the aggregates; in this capacity as a cement, the asphalts are usually semi-solid. Before it can be mixed with the gravel, crushed stone, or sand, the asphalt must be made liquid by heating, by cutting with solvent, or by emulsifying with water.

Liquid Paving Asphalts

Most of the liquid asphalts used for paving are cutbacks; three common types are used, depending on the type of solvent used. When gasoline is used as a solvent, a rapid-curing liquid asphalt is the result; kerosine produces a medium-curing asphalt; heavier fuel oils produce a slow-curing asphalt.

These names refer to the rate at which solvent is lost, either during construction or after the pavement has been laid.

Each of these three types of asphalt is further subdivided into six grades (0 to 5) depending on differences in viscosity. Zero grade has the lowest viscosity in each case and runs freely at ordinary temperatures. Grade 5 material approaches semisolid consistency. The differences in viscosity are obtained by varying the amount of solvent added in each case. Slow-curing liquid asphalts are also produced by refining a fluid asphalt-base stock to the required consistency for each S.C. grade.

The liquid asphalt to be selected for any given project depends on the construction conditions. In general a rapid-curing grade can be used as a binder for open-graded aggregates that coat quickly during mixing or for surface treatments. Medium-curing grades are required for dense-graded aggregates, which require longer mixing time. Slow-curing grades are used with aggregates requiring a long mixing time and for projects where the pavement may have to be torn up and reworked from time to time.

Asphalt Paving Cements

The binders for the more expensive asphalt pavements are usually asphalt cements. These semisolid materials are also separated into grades having different ranges of hardness. To grade them, the penetration test is employed. The most common grades of asphalt cement in use are shown in Table 10·1. The 50 to 60 penetration grade is the hardest asphalt cement and the 150 to 200 grade is the softest.

Table 10 · 1
Grades of asphalt cement.

GRADE	PENETRATION
1	50 to 60
2	60 to 70
3	70 to 85
4	85 to 100
5	100 to 120
6	120 to 150
7	150 to 200

GLOSSARY

destructive distillation	The process of decomposing a substance and collecting the resulting by-products
emulsion asphalt	Asphalt suspended in a watery liquid
flash point	The temperature at which a flammable material will break into a sudden flame
viscosity	The physical property of a fluid or semifluid which allows it to offer continuous resistance to flow

REVIEW QUESTIONS

1 Outline the difference between coal tar and coal-tar pitch.
2 Describe briefly how the majority of the asphalt used today is produced.
3 Explain why it is important to know the flow properties of pitches and asphalts.
4 What are ductility tests designed to show?
5 Why should pitch be used only on roofs with very little slope?
6 What type of asphalt binds best to a damp or wet surface?
7 Explain what is meant by cutback asphalts.
8 Name two advantages of using emulsion asphalts.
9 What is meant by having a low viscosity at the saturation temperature?
10 What is the primary purpose of asphalt in a paving mix?

SELECTED SOURCES OF INFORMATION

Allied Materials Corporation, Oklahoma City, Okla.
American Bitumuls & Asphalt Co., San Francisco, Calif.
The Asphalt Institute, College Park, Md.
British American Oil Company, Toronto, Ont.
The Flintkote Company of Canada Limited, Toronto, Ont.
The Tremco Mfg. Co., Toronto, Ont.

11

BUILDING PAPERS

Paper is believed to have been used by the Chinese as early as 2000 B.C. Since that time great developments have taken place and are still taking place in the paper industry so that paper is a commonly used commodity in every facet of modern society, including the construction industry.

In building construction, paper is used for sheathing, roofing, and insulation; in making asphalt shingles, laminated and corrugated building products, and concrete-form materials; as a moisture and vapor barrier; as a cushioning material; as wallpaper; as an envelope or sheathe for other materials; and as a fireproofing material.

Most paper is made from cellulose fibers, although a certain amount is also produced from asbestos fiber. The largest source of cellulose fibers is wood pulp, but wastepaper, jute waste, manila hemp, rags, straw (particularly wheat straw), and bagasse (cane and corn stalks) are also utilized. Many building papers are made from coarse materials such as wastepaper and jute waste, but, depending on specific requirements, certain amounts of the better pulps are blended with these.

PULP

Three types of wood pulp are produced: mechanical, chemical, and semichemical. Mechanical pulp, sometimes referred to as *groundwood,* is produced by grinding blocks of wood against a revolving abrasive stone or by grinding steamed wood chips in a grinding mill. Chemical pulp is produced by digesting wood chips in various chemicals to free the cellulose fibers from the lignin binding. In the production of semichemical pulp, wood chips are first subjected to a mild chemical treatment and then mechanically disintegrated in rotating-disk refiners.

Pulp produced by the first mechanical method has almost identical composition to the original wood. It is the cheapest form of pulp produced because 90 percent or better of the original raw material is used, compared with 50 percent or more in the chemical process. No chemicals are required, and equipment for making this type of pulp is less expensive. However, because of the process involved, fibers produced by this system are shorter and weaker than those produced by other methods, so paper made from this pulp will not be as strong as that made from longer fibers. Also sunlight and atmosphere will act on the lignin in such paper, causing it to change color. Pulp produced by the grinding of steamed wood chips has different characteristics from that produced by the first method. Fibers are longer and softer and have a distinctive brown color.

Three basic types of chemical pulp are produced: sulfite, sulfate, and soda. Sulfite pulp is produced by cooking chips from low-resin-content coniferous trees under heat and pressure in a solution of calcium, magnesium, or ammonium bisulfite, containing sulfur dioxide. This type of pulp can be bleached very white and is practically pure cellulose. It is used in the production of the highest quality papers. Sulfate pulp, often called kraft paper, is produced by cooking chips of almost any kind of wood in a solution of about equal parts of caustic soda and sodium sulfide. The resulting fibers are strong but more difficult to bleach, and the pulp is often used only partially bleached. It is used in the manufacture of papers in which color is not a consideration. Soda pulp is produced by cooking chips, mainly from deciduous trees, in a caustic soda solution under pressure. The pulp is relatively pure cellulose, bleaches well, but produces paper of only medium strength. It is often used in combination with other types of chemical pulp.

Production of semichemical pulp is on the increase because there is a relatively high yield (up to 75 percent) and because a variety of woods, including hardwoods, can be used. This type of pulp is generally mixed with other fibers to produce various types of commonly used paper.

The production of pulp from material other than wood is carried out by various methods, depending on the material. Repulping of wastepaper, for example, includes a process for deinking.

Before the pulps made by the processes just described can be made into paper having desirable characteristics, they must be treated to improve their papermaking qualities. This process is known as beating and refining and varies somewhat, depending on the particular pulp being treated and the type of paper to be made.

Beating consists of passing pulp, suspended in water, under a heavy revolving drum studded with metal bars which rub the fibers against bars set in a bed plate. This rubbing and cutting action separates the fibers, reduces them to the proper length, and frays the ends and side walls. This fraying enables the fibers to mat together to form a uniform sheet of paper.

During the beating stage, various nonfibrous additives are introduced into the pulp. Depending on the additive used, these increase the resistance of paper to water penetration, increase the tensile strength and wet strength, help to increase absorbency and opacity, and help to decrease the tendency of fibers to collect in bundles. Rosin and wax emulsions are added to increase resistance of paper to water penetration. Mineral fillers such as clay and calcium carbonate are added to increase opacity and softness of the paper. The addition of starch increases bursting and tensile strength. Sodium silicate increases the firmness or stiffness of paper as well as its strength.

Most pulps which have been through the beater are passed through a final refining machine, called a Jordan, before they are ready to be made into paper. Pulp passes from the beaters to a vat where more water is added, and the mixture kept stirred to prevent fibers from settling out. From this vat the pulp is pumped to the Jordan, which consists of a cone-shaped shell fitted on the inside with a series of bars or ribs (Fig. 11·1) inside which a ribbed cone is rotated at high speed. The fibers are rubbed between the sets of bars, cutting them to length, further fraying the fiber walls and curling or crimpling them. The object is to create fibers with greater matting power.

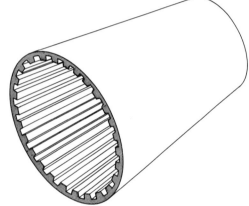

Figure 11·1
Inside of Jordan outer shell.

After passing through the Jordan, the pulp is further diluted with water and run through fine screens to separate dirt, sand, and fiber bundles. It is now ready for the paper machine where the paper is formed.

PAPERMAKING

There are two types of paper machine, the Fourdrinier and the cylinder. Most paper products, with the notable exception of paperboards, are made on a Fourdrinier machine. The papermaking process is begun on this machine by running very highly diluted pulp (97.5 to 99.5 percent water) known as paper stock onto an endless belt made of wire mesh containing 3,000 to 6,000 openings per sq in. Water drains away through the holes assisted by suction under the wire at certain points.

As a result, a film of interlaced fibers is deposited on the wire belt. Even distribution of fibers across the sheet is improved by a lateral shaking motion of the frame carrying the

211

belt. The thickness of the sheet of paper being formed, and hence its weight, is determined by the rate at which paper stock is allowed to flow onto the belt and the speed of belt travel. This may vary from 50 to 2,000 ft per minute. Various widths of sheet are made from 50 to over 300 in., while the weight of paper may vary from about 2 to 12 lb per 100 sq ft.

After it leaves the wire belt, the wet sheet of paper is picked up on an endless belt of woolen felt and carried to heavy rolls which press more water from it. It then passes through a long series of rotating heated rollers, supported by a layer of canvas which travels with the paper. Here practically all the remaining water is driven out and the paper is ready for the finishing that is required. When paper is required to be smooth and dense, it is passed through a series of polished steel rollers called *calender rolls*. The smoothness and density of the paper are controlled by the pressure on the rollers and the number of times the sheet is passed between them. For most building papers, smoothness is not a prime consideration and softness and absorbency, rather than density, are desirable qualities.

The cylinder machine has a cylinder mold, which is covered with fine wire cloth, revolving in a vat of paper stock. The pulp suspension is flowed onto the surface of the cylinder where fiber matting takes place and water is drained off. Altering the length of time that the mat remains on the cylinder controls the thickness of the paper sheet. From the point at which the sheet leaves the cylinder, the process is similar to the Fourdrinier process.

Paper from the paper machines or the calender rolls is

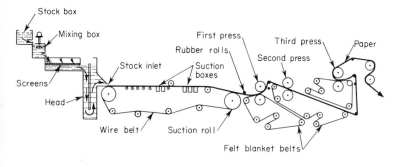

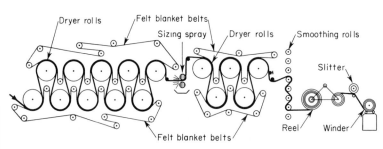

Figure 11 · 2
Diagrammatic illustration of papermaking process.

Figure 11 · 3
Rewound roll of building paper.
(Domtar Construction Materials Ltd.)

wound into large rolls. These may be later rewound into smaller rolls or cut into narrower widths as required for further processing (Fig. 11 · 3).

PAPER TREATMENT

Many building papers go through further processing to produce products designed for specific jobs. These processes include saturating the paper with asphalt or asphalt emulsion, coating the surface with a layer of asphalt, embedding crushed slate in an asphalt surface coating, coating the surface with wax, laminating two sheets of paper together with a layer of asphalt, and laminating a sheet of paper and a sheet of copper foil together with asphalt. Another process involves the forming of a corrugated sheet of paper and laminating it between two flat sheets. Figure 11 · 4 shows a roll of paper

Figure 11 · 4
Paper starting on the asphalting process.
(Domtar Construction Materials Ltd.)

213

Figure 11·5
Paper with first asphalt coat.

starting through an asphalting process. In Fig. 11·5, the paper has received its first asphalt treatment, while in Fig. 11·6, the paper is emerging after receiving its final asphalt coating.

TYPES OF PAPER

Sheathing Paper

Two types of sheathing paper are produced. One is a plain paper and the other an asphalt-impregnated or coated felt or kraft paper. Two kinds of plain sheathing are made, one a low-cost paper made from a mixture of semichemical pulp and wastepaper and the other a tough paper made from kraft pulp. The first is normally produced in 36-in.-wide rolls con-

Figure 11·6
Paper emerging from final asphalt treatment.

214

taining 400 sq ft and weighing about 3¾ lb per 100 sq ft. Kraft sheathing is produced in two widths and several weights. A strong, tough sheathing is made in widths of 36 and 72 in., in rolls of 400 and 800 sq ft weighing 10¾ lb per square. A lighter kraft, in 36-in. rolls of 400 sq ft weighing 4 lb per square, is also common.

Asphalt-impregnated and coated papers are made from felt and kraft papers. Various amounts of asphalt are used per hundred square feet of paper so that papers of various weights are made, from 4 to 10 lb per square. These are what are known as breather papers, impervious to water but not to water vapor. Rolls are generally 36 in. wide and contain 400 sq ft of paper.

Roofing Papers

Two types of roofing papers are made, those which are used in making a built-up roof, generally called *roofing felts,* and what is known as *rolled* roofing, a heavy, mineral-surfaced paper used as a final roof covering.

Both are made largely from mechanical pulp produced by grinding steamed wood chips in a grinding mill. The method yields long fibers which produce paper with good saturating properties. Generally rag pulp is added to give extra strength and absorbency.

Roofing felts are usually produced in 36-in.-wide rolls, in various weights from 3 to 20 lb per square. Rolled roofing is made 18 and 36 in. wide, in various weights from 45 to 120 lb per square.

Insulating Paper

The primary objective in the production of this type of paper is to secure bulk and entrapped air with as much strength as possible. Insulating papers are made both from wood pulp and from asbestos fiber.

Wood-fiber insulating paper is made from groundwood or bagasse with some wastepaper pulp added. The paper is usually gray, produced in 36-in.-wide rolls, weighing about 9 lb per square. It is used for insulating walls, ceilings, and floors.

Insulating paper made from asbestos fibers is a soft, pliable paper used for insulating pipes carrying steam, boilers, and other vessels with high temperatures. It is produced in various weights from 5 to 10 lb per square.

A heavier asbestos-felt paper is produced for use as a built-up roofing material. It is saturated with asphalt and produced in rolls 36 in. wide weighing approximately 15 lb per square.

Cushioning Paper

This is much the same as wood-fiber insulating paper, but less attention is paid to strength. Its chief use is for cushioning under linoleum, carpets, or slate roofing. Two grades are commonly made, 12-oz and 16-oz paper; 12-oz weighs about 8 lb per square, and 16-oz about 11 lb per square. Both are put up in rolls 36 in. wide.

Vapor-barrier Paper

These papers, which are intended to prevent the passage of moisture vapor through walls, ceilings, and floors, are made in three different types. One, a waxed paper, is made from strong, light kraft in three grades commonly known as X, XX, and XXX. X grade weighs about 2 lb per square, XX grade about 3 lb, and XXX grade about 4 lb. All are made up in rolls 36 in. wide.

The second type consists of two thicknesses of paper laminated together with a film of asphalt. Two kinds of paper are used—one is a kraft paper, the other a mixture of groundwood pulps treated by the sulfite and the kraft methods. Rolls are 36 in. wide, contain 400 sq ft, and weigh from 2 to 6½ lb per square.

The third type consists of a sheet of kraft paper laminated to copper foil by an asphalt film. This is a heavy-duty material used both for vapor barrier and for flashing. It is available in rolls from 6 to 60 in. wide, in weights of 1, 2, and 3 oz per sq ft.

Laminating Paper

This is a special, high-strength kraft paper made for use in the production of plastic laminates. The thin, strong paper is impregnated with liquid plastic resin and several sheets are laminated together under heat and pressure to form the base for the plastic sheet.

Concrete-form Paper

Two different types of concrete forms are made from paper. One is made from strong kraft paper in the form of a spiral tube. These are used as column forms and as ducts and core forms in concrete floors (Fig. 11·7).

The other type is a boxlike form made from corrugated container paper. This is unbleached kraft paper sized with rosin and coated with wax sizing and starch to make it abrasion-resistant. The boxes are approximately 16 × 32 in., of various depths, reinforced with a gridwork of the same type of paper. These forms are used in forming ribbed concrete slabs.

Figure 11 · 7
Paper tube core forms.

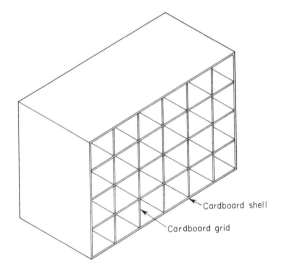

Cardboard shell

Cardboard grid

Figure 11 · 8
Paper box forms.

Wallpaper

Paper from which decorative wallpaper is made is produced in two grades, No. 1 Hanging and No. 2 Hanging. No. 1
Hanging is made from bleached sulfite or bleached soda pulp,
mixed with not more than 20 percent high-quality groundwood. Talc is used as a filler, rosin and sodium silicate as
sizing. The paper is coated with a clay film bound to the
paper with casein, and the design is printed over the clay
coating.

No. 2 Hanging is from 72 to 90 percent groundwood and the rest unbleached sulfite. Little filler is used, but the paper must be sufficiently sized to stand the application of water paste without wetting or breaking through.

Envelope Paper

Paper is used as an outer covering or envelope for a number of building materials. One of these is gypsum board, composed of a layer of calcined gypsum covered on both sides by a sheet of kraft paper. A number of insulating materials are enveloped in a kraft paper cover, sometimes plain, sometimes asphalted.

Fireproofing Paper

Paper to be used for fireproofing is made from asbestos fibers, since this is an incombustible material. The material may be in the form of a matted paper, similar to asbestos insulating or roofing paper, or it may be in the form of a cloth woven from thread spun from asbestos fibers.

GLOSSARY

asbestos	A mineral occurring in long, delicate fibers or in fibrous masses; it is incombustible, nonconducting, and chemically resistant
bagasse	Residue of cane or corn stalks after the juice has been extracted
calender rolls	Highly polished steel rollers used to smooth the surface of paper or plastics
deciduous tree	A tree which produces broad leaves
emulsion	A milky fluid made by suspending particles of material in a watery liquid
Fourdrinier	An endless-belt-type of papermaking machine
groundwood	Wood pulp made by grinding wood blocks against abrasive stones
Jordan	A final refining machine used in the processing of wood pulp
jute	Glossy fiber of the jute plant
kraft	A strong, usually brown paper made from sulfate pulp
rosin	The hard, amber-colored residue left after distilling off the volatile oil of turpentine
sheathing paper	Paper used to provide an airtight barrier over walls, floors, etc.

REVIEW QUESTIONS

1 (a) What is the basic material used in the manufacture of most commonly used papers?
   (b) What is the main source of this material?
   (c) How does paper made from asbestos fiber differ from most others?
2 (a) Explain what is meant by chemical pulp.
   (b) How does it differ from semichemical pulp?
3 (a) What type of tree is used in making sulfite pulp?
   (b) What is a major advantage of this type of pulp over the others?
   (c) Give two reasons why the production of semichemical pulp is increasing.
4 List five wood-pulp additives and give the purpose of each.
5 What is the basic purpose of a Jordan in the pulp-refining process?
6 Outline the major use of each of the following types of building paper:
   (a) Sheathing paper
   (b) Asphalt-impregnated paper
   (c) Waxed paper
7 Outline the basic features of roofing felt and rolled roofing.
8 Explain the difference between insulating paper made from wood fiber and that made from asbestos fiber.
9 Give three advantages gained by the use of fiber tubes for column forms.
10 Explain what is meant by envelope paper and give two examples of its use in construction materials.

SELECTED SOURCES OF INFORMATION

Allied Chemical Canada Ltd., Montreal, Que.
Atlas Asbestos Company Ltd., Montreal, Que.
Canadian Paper Company, Montreal, Que.
Canadian Pulp and Paper Association, Montreal, Que.
Crown Zellerbach Corporation, Seattle, Wash.
Johns-Manville Company, New York, N.Y.
The Phillip Carey Company Ltd., Montreal, Que.
Sidney Roofing & Paper Company, Vancouver, B.C.
The Sisalkraft Co., Chicago, Ill.
Sonoco Products Co., Hartsville, S.C., and Granby, Que.

12

BUILDING BOARDS

Some of the basic building materials, such as wood, stone, brick, and glass, have some inherent disadvantages in weight, flexibility, insulation value, etc. Some of them vary widely in size and strength from piece to piece. For many years much research in the building industry has been aimed at developing materials with more consistent quality in standard sizes.

Many new building products have been manufactured as a result of this research and prominent among them is a group that have at least one thing in common: they are all flat, relatively thin in section, and have been made to standard sizes —many of them to a common 4 × 8-ft dimension. These are *building boards,* which are made of several different materials and used for a variety of purposes.

Plywood is an outstanding example of such a board. It was designed to eliminate some of the inherent defects of sawed lumber and has gained tremendous popularity in the construction field because it has proved to be superior in several ways to sawed lumber. Its manufacture and uses have already been described in Chap. 1. Other common building boards include hardboard, insulating wood fiberboard, chipboard, gypsum board, strawboard, asbestos-cement board, corkboard, paperboard, mineral fiberboard, and plastic foam board.

HARDBOARD

Hardboard is made from processed wood chips. Chips of controlled size are subjected to high-pressure steam in pressure vessels. When the pressure is released the chips "explode" and the cellulose and lignin are separated from the unwanted elements. The cellulose fibers and lignin are then mixed into a homogeneous mass and formed into a continuous board which is cut up into convenient lengths. These pressed into uniform, hard, grainless sheets in heated presses.

Three grades of board are made: (1) Standard, (2) Tempered, and (3) Low Density. In each case the standard product is smooth on one side with a burlap-like impression on the other (screen side). It is also available smooth on both sides.

Standard hardboard has a density of about 60 lb/cu ft but is flexible enough to be quite easily bent. It is light brown and is produced in thicknesses of ⅛, 3/16, ¼, and 5/16 in. Boards are 4 ft wide and are available in lengths of 4, 6, 8, 10, 12, and 16 ft. This grade of hardboard is not suitable for exterior work.

Tempered hardboard is made by impregnating standard board with a tempering compound of oils and resin and baking it to polymerize the tempering material. The result is a board with a density of about 70 lb/cu ft which has considerably greater durability and strength than standard hardboard. It is also stiffer and more brittle but has improved machining qualities and much greater resistance to water penetration, making it suitable for exterior use. Tempered hardboard is dark brown and is available in the same thicknesses, widths, and lengths as standard hardboard.

Low-density hardboard weighs from 50 to 55 lb/cu ft and is not as strong or durable as standard hardboard. It is a pale brown and is made $\frac{3}{16}$ and $\frac{1}{4}$ in. thick; 4 ft wide; and 4, 6, 8, and 10 ft long.

Several special-purpose boards are made from this basic material. One is a tempered hardboard with score lines pressed into the surface forming 4-in. squares. Another is a tempered board with the surface treated to imitate leather. Another is treated with black dye during manufacture to produce a black hardboard. Still another is an untempered board with the smooth surface made to imitate wood grain and vertical grooves pressed into the surface to imitate random planking.

INSULATING FIBERBOARD

Insulating fiberboard is made from three types of fiber—wood, sugar cane, and asbestos.

Wood fibers are produced by two methods. One method consists of pressing logs against a grindstone which breaks down the wood into fibers by the shearing and rubbing action of the stone against the wood. About 45 percent of the wood fiber used is manufactured by this process.

In the second process, logs are first made into chips about $\frac{5}{8}$ in. long. The chips are charged into pressure vessels called digesters where they are softened with live steam. The softened chips are then fed between two disks, one stationary and one rotating, and the shearing action of the rotating disk breaks the chips down into fibers.

Fibers from both processes are mixed and diluted with water so that oversized fibers can be screened out and returned for further processing. The mixture is stored in tanks and fed to a forming machine, which consists of a vat and a rotating drum covered with stainless steel wire mesh. The drum picks up the fibers to form a sheet of uniform thickness. The surface of the drum, under the mesh, is lined with suction compartments under 15 in. of vacuum which draw the fibers firmly against the mesh and remove excess water. As the sheet is discharged from the drum it passes through several sets of press rolls, is cut into boards of the desired length, and is fed into drying kilns.

221

Two basic grades of board are made, insulating grade and sheathing grade. Insulating-grade board has a density of about 17.5 lb/cu ft, while sheathing grade weighs about 18.25 lb/cu ft. Two types of sheathing board are made, one having both surfaces and all edges coated with asphalt and the other with the fibers impregnated with asphalt during manufacture. Sheathing board is made 4 ft wide; $\frac{7}{16}$, $\frac{1}{2}$, and $\frac{5}{8}$ in. thick; and 8 and 9 ft long. This type of board is intended for exterior use over frame or masonry construction and for insulation and sound control where moisture is a factor.

Insulation-grade board is made up as insulating panels, decorative panels, decorative ceiling tile, V-notch plaster base, and roof insulation. Standard thicknesses of this type of board are $\frac{1}{2}$, $\frac{5}{8}$, $\frac{3}{4}$, and 1 in., but thicker boards for roof insulation are made by laminating two or more thin sheets with asphalt cement. As insulating panels, the board is made 4 ft wide and from 4 to 16 ft long. V-notch plaster base has V-shaped notches on three sides, as shown in Fig. 12·1. The standard thicknesses of this type of board are $\frac{1}{2}$ and 1 in.; panels are 16 × 48 in. One common type of decorative panel is $\frac{1}{2}$ in. thick; 12, 16, or 24 in. wide; and 8, 9, or 10 ft long. The edges are tongue-and-grooved, and the surface may be natural, white-coated, or white-finished. Ceiling tile are made various sizes, with tongue-and-groove edges and the same choices of finish as decorative panels. They are intended to be applied over strapping which is nailed at right angles to the ceiling joists, over solid backing, and in suspended ceiling systems.

A special insulating board is also manufactured which has a sheet of $\frac{1}{8}$-in. hardboard glued to one or both faces. It is intended for use where a hard, paintable surface is required.

Cane fiberboard is made by shredding cane and processing the fibers in much the same way as in the digesting process used with wood fibers. The same types of board are made as are made from wood fibers.

Mineral fiberboard is made from asbestos fibers mixed with a cementing agent. This type of board is used primarily for fireproofing and acoustical purposes.

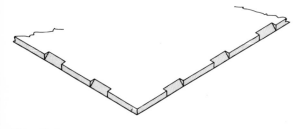

Figure 12 · 1
V-notch fiberboard plaster base.

Figure 12 · 2
Disk waferizer. (Dept. of
Industry and Information.
Regina, Sask.)

CHIPBOARD

Chipboard is made by binding wood chips with phenolic resin or urea formaldehyde glue in the form of a 4-ft-wide board. The chips are produced by feeding pieces of log into a disk waferizer, which cuts the pieces into thin wafers about 1½ in. square and from 0.010 to 0.050 in. thick. They are dried, separated according to thickness into core and face wafers (thick wafers form the core), and fed to the production line. Here they receive a coating of glue and are blown into a steel forming table, first a layer of face wafers, then two layers

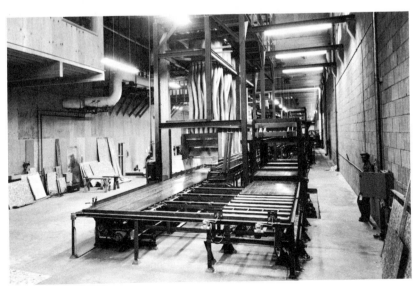

Figure 12 · 3
Head end of board-
forming line.
(Dept. of Industry
and Information. Regina,
Sask.)

223

Figure 12 · 4
Board-forming hot presses.
(Dept. of Industry and Information.
Regina, Sask.)

of core wafers, followed by a final layer of face wafers. The board passes through a hot press which heats the glue and polymerizes it, laminating the chips into a solid board.

Boards are made ¼, ½, and ¾ in. thick; 4 ft wide; and 8 to 16 ft long. They are intended for exterior sheathing as well as for various interior uses. Sometimes a ⅛-in. sheet of hardwood plywood is laminated to one face to produce a relatively inexpensive type of hardwood interior finishing material.

GYPSUM BOARD

A brief description of the manufacturing process employed in the making of gypsum board is given in Chap. 8. Thicknesses of board produced, widths, and common lengths are also discussed. In addition to the standard, ivory-colored interior board described in Chap. 8, gypsum board is also produced with a paper face having various wood grains printed on the surface. This treatment is normally used only on the ⅜- and ½-in. boards.

STRAWBOARD

As the name implies, strawboard is made of compressed wheat straw, processed at 350 to 400°F and covered with a tough kraft paper. Two grades are produced, structural board and insulating board. The insulating grade weighs 3 lb/sq ft in 2-in. thickness; the same thickness of structural board weighs 3.5 lb/sq ft. For exterior use, the paper used is impregnated with asphalt.

224

Structural-grade board is manufactured 2 in. thick, 4 ft wide, and 6, 7, 8, 9, and 10 ft long. It is used for nonbearing partitions, as a plaster base, for insulating purposes, exterior sheathing, roof decking, and as an inner form face for concrete basement wall forms.

Insulation grade is also 2 in. thick and 4 ft wide but comes in 5-ft lengths only. It is intended primarily for roof-deck insulation.

Plaster may be applied directly to the paper surface of strawboard. When stucco is to be applied to the exterior surface, the board should first be covered with stucco wire.

ASBESTOS-CEMENT BOARD

A paste of portland cement heavily reinforced with asbestos fibers is used in the manufacture of asbestos-cement board. To provide high strength in a short period of time the boards are steam-cured. The result is a hard, smooth, highly fire-resistant material that has many uses in the construction industry.

Flat boards are made ⅛, ¼, ⅜, and ½ in. thick; 4 ft wide; and from 6 to 12 ft long. Various types of corrugated sheets are made from the same material (Fig. 12·5). They are used for wall cladding, roof decks, and roofing. Curved corrugated sheets can be made on special order. In addition, insulating panels are made, using a core of asphalt-impregnated wood fibers, glass fiber, or expanded polystyrene, covered on one or both sides by flat sheets of asbestos-cement board. These panels are normally 4 ft wide and in various lengths up to 12 ft. The minimum thickness for panels faced on one side

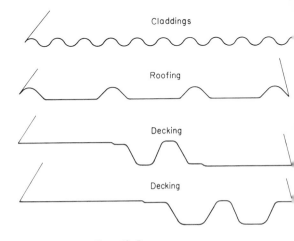

Figure 12·5
Corrugated asbestos-cement boards.

is generally $1\frac{7}{32}$ in. and for panels faced on both sides, $1\frac{1}{16}$ in. Thicker panels may be produced as specified.

This type of panel is also produced with one surface finished with a baked-on acrylic paint. They are used in curtain-wall construction, for partitions, and in many other interior and exterior applications.

All types of asbestos-cement boards must be drilled for the insertion of screws, bolts, or other fasteners. Hard-tipped bits should be used for this purpose. Figure 12·6 illustrates a number of fastening devices used with asbestos-cement products. Cutting should be done with carbide or diamond-tipped blades or with an abrasive disk.

CORKBOARD

Ground cork is mixed with synthetic resin, formed into sheets of from 1 to 6 in. thick, and baked under pressure into rigid boards. The standard board length is 36 in., and widths vary according to the thickness. Common widths are 12, 18, 24, and 36 in. Corkboard is used almost exclusively as an insulating material.

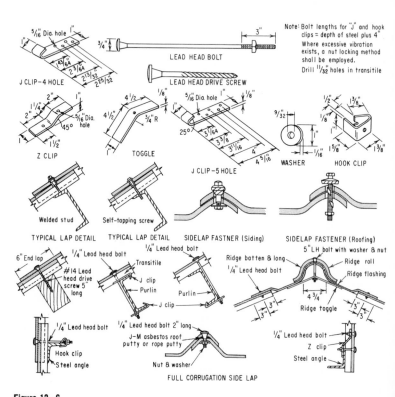

Figure 12·6
Asbestos-cement board fasteners.

PAPERBOARD

Two different types of board are made from paper. One consists of paper pulp pressed into boards ³⁄₁₆ or ¼ in. thick; 4 ft wide; and 6, 7, or 8 ft long. Usually one surface is primed for easier finishing.

The other type consists of a layer of stiff paper folded into corrugated form and faced on both sides with a thick paper backing, cemented to the core (Fig. 12·7).

Figure 12·7
Corrugated paperboard.

MINERAL FIBERBOARD

Thick mats of mineral fibers, usually glass or rock wool, are covered with a backing of stiff paper on one or both sides to form rigid boards, ranging in thickness from ½ to 2 in. The usual board size is 24 × 48 in. These units are used for roof-deck insulation and are cemented to the deck with asphalt adhesive.

PLASTIC FOAM BOARDS

Polystyrene and polyurethane plastics are foamed by a patented process to about 40 times their original volume. This foamed material is molded into boards from ½ to 3 in. thick, 12 or 24 in. wide, and from 4 to 12 ft long. This material is used for perimeter insulation for concrete floor slabs, for wall and roof-deck insulation, and for roof decks when properly supported (Fig. 12·8).

These plastic boards have high insulation value and relatively high compressive strength, and are flexible enough to fit over curved surfaces. They can be applied to walls, using

Figure 12·8
Polystyrene rigid slabs used as decking on a hyperbolic paraboloid roof.
(Dow Chemical Co.)

either cement mortar or a special plastic adhesive as the bonding agent. Boards to be used as roof-deck insulation are sometimes enclosed in a stiff paper sheath so that asphalt adhesive can be used to cement them in place.

The same type of board also forms the core of several types of sandwich panels used in curtain walls. Facing and backing for these panels can be wood, steel, or rigid plastic sheets. Bonding is done by special plastic adhesives. A more detailed description of some of these panels is given in Chap. 14.

GLOSSARY

homogeneous	Consisting of similar material throughout
impregnating	Saturating
polymerize	To change into another compound having the same elements but with more complex molecules and different physical properties

REVIEW QUESTIONS

1 List three advantages of plywood over sawed lumber.
2 How does the density of standard hardboard compare with:
  (a) tempered hardboard?
  (b) Douglas fir plywood?
3 Explain why tempered hardboard can be used for exterior use, while standard hardboard is not satisfactory for this purpose.
4 How does the k factor (thermal conductivity) of wood fiber insulating board compare with that of:
  (a) cane fiberboard?
  (b) asbestos fiberboard?
5 Outline two differences between insulation-grade fiberboard and sheathing-grade fiberboard.
6 What is the main advantage of gypsum board as a building board?
7 What special equipment is required for:
  (a) cutting asbestos-cement board?
  (b) drilling asbestos-cement board?
8 Give three common uses of foamed-plastic building boards.

SELECTED SOURCES OF INFORMATION

The Arborite Company, Montreal, Que.
Atlas Asbestos Co. Ltd., Montreal, Que.
Canadian Forest Products Ltd., New Westminster, B.C.
Canadian Johns-Manville Co., Ltd., Toronto, Ont.

The Celotex Corporation, Chicago, Ill.
Dow Chemical Co., Midland, Mich.
International Panel Boards Ltd., Montreal, Que.
Stramit Corporation Ltd., Innisfail, Alberta
Western Gypsum Products, Ltd., Winnipeg, Manitoba

13

PLASTICS

The term *plastics,* as it is commonly used today, refers to a group of synthetic materials which are made from a number of common substances. Chemists have taken coal, oil, salt, natural gas, cotton, wood, and water and made from them materials that never before existed.

TYPES

Many different plastics have been produced, but there are about 12 common and basic types. These fall into two general classifications, *thermoplastic* and *thermosetting* plastics. Thermoplastic plastics become soft when heated and harden when cooled regardless of the number of times the process is repeated. Thermosetting plastics set into a permanent shape when heat and pressure are applied to them during the form-ing stage. Reheating will not soften them again.

The chemical types belonging to the thermoplastic group include acrylics, cellulosics, polyethylene, styrene or poly-styrene, nylons (polymides), and the vinyls. The chemical types in the thermosetting group include phenolics, mela-mines, epoxy resins, ureas (amino plastics), polyesters, and silicones.

PRODUCTION

The production of plastic products is divided into three steps that sometimes overlap. The manufacturer converts raw materials into basic plastic compounds in the form of granules, powder, beads, or liquid resins. The processor takes these basic compounds and forms them by one method or another into sheets, films, tubing, rods, and other solid or semisolid shapes. During this process the plastics are usually combined with one or more other materials in order to achieve certain desired physical properties in the product. Some-times plasticizers are added for workability, fillers are added to produce bulk, fibers are added for strength and durability, or hardeners are used to induce setting. In addition, a plastic is sometimes combined with a conventional material to give it a special property. Finally, a fabricator makes finished plastic products.

Plastic products are formed by a number of methods in-cluding molding, extrusion, calendering and coating, lami-nating, reinforcing, and casting.

Thermosetting and thermoplastic plastics both can be molded. Thermosetting types are usually molded by the compression and transfer-molding process. The compression method simply involves placing the plastic in a mold of the desired size and shape and applying heat and pressure. This causes the plastic to flow and completely fill the cavity, after which it is allowed to cool and harden. Transfer molding involves heating the plastic at least to a semiliquid state before it reaches the mold and then forcing it into the closed mold by a hydraulic ram.

The principal molding methods used with thermoplastic plastics are injection and blow molding. Injection molding consists of forcing hot plastic at high pressure into a cool, closed mold. In blow molding, the plastic is forced against the inside surfaces of a mold by air pressure and hardened in that position.

Extrusion forming is done in two ways. The simplest is the forcing of semiliquid plastic through a die of the proper size and shape, in a manner similar to that used for forming brick by extrusion. Sheets (thicknesses of over 10 mils), films (thicknesses up to 10 mils), tubes, rods, and profile shapes are formed in this way. The other extrusion method involves forcing wire, cable, or cord through a die along with the plastic so that the material emerges with a plastic coating.

In the calendering process, plastic is fed to revolving rollers which turn out a thin sheet or film. The thickness of the product is determined by the roller spacing. The surface of the sheet may be smooth or matted, depending on the roller surface. In a somewhat similar process, paper, metal, wood, fabric, ceramics, or other plastics are passed between rollers which apply a plastic coating to one or both surfaces.

The first step in producing laminated plastics is to impregnate the layers of the base material—cloth, paper, sheets of glass fiber, or wood—with plastic. Then the layers are pressed together under high pressure and heat. Normally, thermosetting plastics are used in this process.

Thermosetting plastics are also used in the reinforcing method. A glass-fiber mat is heavily impregnated with plastic and shaped over a mold with little or no pressure involved. These reinforced products have exceptionally high strength and are light in weight, making it possible to produce fairly large units at relatively low cost.

The casting method can be employed with either thermoplastic or thermosetting plastics. A fluid plastic is poured into a mold or onto a wheel or belt and cured. No pressure is used.

USES IN CONSTRUCTION

Plastics are widely used in the construction field in several ways. Some plastic products are used as structural or semistructural components and some are used as auxiliary materials or as a part of another material.

One of the more common plastic products used for structural purposes is a glass-fiber-reinforced corrugated sheet, using acrylic, vinyl, or a polyester plastic. Such sheets are used for roofing, either by themselves or in conjunction with corrugated sheet metal or corrugated asbestos-cement roofing sheets. The same type of sheet also can be used as wall cladding, for making room dividers, or for skylights. They are made in a variety of colors, as well as white and translucent. Sheets are normally 18 or 24 in. wide and up to 14 ft long.

The same plastic materials are also used to produce flat sheets, also reinforced with glass fiber. In flat form, the sheets can be made in almost any size or shape desired, as, for example, in the church domes shown in Fig. 13·1. In this particular case a copper color has been incorporated into the plastic coating.

Plastics are being widely used in the manufacture of sandwich panels used in curtain-wall construction. In some cases only the sandwich core is a plastic material, while in others both the core and one or both faces are made of plastic. The panels in the building shown in Fig. 14·55, for example, are made entirely of plastic. Other sandwich panels are made by bonding glass-fiber-reinforced plastic sheets to an aluminum-grid core.

Curtain-wall panels can also be single sheets of reinforced plastic, like those shown in Fig. 14·54. There translucent plastic panels are being used to replace glass panels in a factory building. The main reason for the change is to reduce

Figure 13 · 1
Fiber-glass-reinforced plastic church domes.
[Fibreglass R.P. Report (Canada)]

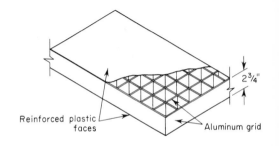

Figure 13 · 2
Section of plastic-faced sandwich panel with aluminum grid core.

breakage, since the plastic panels are slightly flexible. In addition, however, the dead load of the wall is reduced considerably, since the glass weighs almost seven times as much per linear foot as the plastic panels. Sheets of clear vinyl plastic are also substituted for glass in roofs and domes to allow the entrance of light.

Rigid slabs of foamed plastic are sometimes used for structural purposes. In Fig. 13·3, slabs of expanded polystyrene are being used to form the roof deck for a hyperbolic paraboloid roof. Because of their flexibility, the boards can readily be fitted to the contours of the roof. Later the deck will be covered with a layer of concrete. In Fig. 13·4, similar slabs

Figure 13 · 3
Rigid boards of polystyrene used as roof decking.
(Dow Chemical Co.)

Figure 13 · 4
Foamed plastic boards for decking over a steel cable frame.
(Dow Chemical Co.)

Figure 13 · 5
Plastic waffle pans.
[Fibreglass R.P. Report (Canada)]

are being used as decking but, in this case, over a steel-cable frame rather than a wood one.

Plastic is finding increasing use in making pans used for forming ribbed or waffle concrete floor slabs. In Fig. 13·5, glass-fiber-reinforced plastic waffle pans are shown in place, ready for the pouring of a concrete slab.

One of the greatest uses made of plastics is in the manufacture of insulation. Several plastic materials can be foamed in various ways, in the factory or on the site. In the factory the general practice is to make rigid slabs of foamed insulation. A standard slab size is 24 × 48 in. in various thicknesses; but slabs 1 and 2 ft wide, from 4 to 16 ft long, and from 1 to 12 in. thick are also commonly produced. Polystyrene and polyurethane are the two types of plastic used for this purpose, with the slabs being produced either by extrusion or by the molding process. Polystyrene has a k (thermal conductivity) factor of about 0.25 and a density of from 1.2 to 4.5 lb per cu ft. Polyurethane's k factor is about 0.15 and its density approximately 2 lb per cu ft.

On the site the insulating material is produced by foaming-in-place, using polyurethane or epoxy-resin plastics. The process consists of injecting controlled amounts of resin liquid and a foaming catalyst into an enclosed space. The two react to form a foam which expands and sets to fill a certain portion of the space. The process is repeated until the space is completely filled.

Constant research is being carried on into the possible

234

uses of plastics for structural purposes. In addition to exceptional strength and lightness, plastics have the added advantage of being able to be molded to almost any desired shape. This could mean a reduction in the number of component parts required to form a given structure. Also, many plastics are highly resistant to shattering, impact, weathering, and corrosion.

Plastics have a large place in the manufacture of nonstructural materials used in construction. Materials falling into this category include wall and floor coverings, vapor and moisture barriers, flashing material, water stops, expansion-joint material, pipe and conduit, and a wide variety of hardware products.

A considerable number of floor coverings, both resilient and rigid, involve the use of plastics. Vinyl and vinyl-asbestos tile are resilient-type floor coverings in common use (see Chap. 16). Several very resilient floor coverings in sheet form are made partially or wholly of plastic. One such product consists of a sponge vinyl backing covered with a closely woven layer of synthetic fiber. A layer of colored vinyl covers the fibers and binds them to the backing, and a clear vinyl coating provides a tough wearing surface. A somewhat similar product is made by covering a backing of matted jute fibers with a thick, patterned coating of colored vinyl.

Several hard-surface floor toppings involve the use of epoxy resins. A high-friction topping is made by applying a ⅛- to ¼-in. layer of the resin compound to a base floor and scattering sand or other abrasive material over the surface before curing takes place.

A smooth epoxy topping is produced by blending dry salt-free sand and white portland cement with the resin components. The mixture is troweled over a base floor primed with an epoxy-resin primer, to a depth of from ⅛ to ¼ in. The topping can be colored by adding pigmented bases to the resin portion of the mix.

A terrazzo topping can be produced by mixing small marble chips with the resin and spreading and leveling the mix with a trowel. After 24 hours curing, the surface can be ground and the final grouting and polishing done—in the next 48 hours.

Plastics are used in the manufacture of many different wall coverings. Plastic wall tiles, for example, usually made from molded styrene, are widely used. They are not as hard as ceramic tile but are easy to apply, come in a wide range of colors, and are relatively inexpensive.

Rigid panels or sheets in color and color patterns are made from styrene, acrylic, and vinyl plastic. Hardboard, plasterboard, and paperboard are plastic-coated or covered with a thin film of vinyl containing a printed pattern. Gypsum board and hardboard are also produced with one face clad in vinyl fabric.

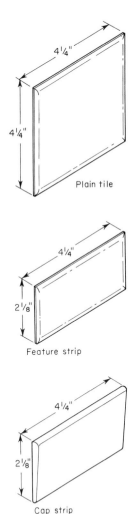

Figure 13·6
Plastic wall tile.

Flexible vinyl sheets with textured patterns are available as wall covering. These are applied like wallpaper and are useful where high resistance to damage and low maintenance costs are important. Steel- and aluminum-backed vinyl sheets are produced which can be formed and shaped without damaging the vinyl covering.

Plastic laminates have been a popular material for covering cabinet tops, table tops, etc., but they are also used as a wall covering. Plastic laminates are so called because they consist of three or four layers of material bonded or laminated under high pressure. The base (Fig. 13·7) is made up of a multiple layer of strong kraft paper impregnated with phenol-formaldehyde resin, a thermosetting plastic. This is covered with a printed pattern sheet saturated with melamine resin. A protective top sheet is also saturated with either melamine or phenolic resin. In some cases, a sheet of aluminum foil is inserted between the base and the decorative center layer. This is intended to dissipate heat and prevent marring of the surface from burns.

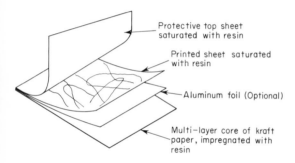

Protective top sheet saturated with resin

Printed sheet saturated with resin

Aluminum foil (Optional)

Multi-layer core of kraft paper, impregnated with resin

Figure 13·7
Build-up of plastic laminate.

These layers are bonded under pressure of about 4,000 tons, while passing through a heat cycle of 270 to 350°F. Common panel thicknesses are 1/16, 1/10, and 1/8 in., but panels can be made to order from 1/8 to 1 1/2 in. thick. Standard widths are 24, 30, 36, 48, and 60 in.; lengths range from 5 to 12 ft. A great many colors and patterns are available, including a wide range of wood-grain patterns. In addition, a number of metal moldings faced with plastic laminate are available as edge trim and for use in vertical applications.

Films used as moisture and vapor barriers are commonly made from polyethylene and polyvinyl chloride in thicknesses of 2, 4, and 6 mils. Both transparent and black film are made, in widths of from 3 to 20 ft. For use as flashing, polyvinyl chloride sheets are manufactured in 3 thicknesses, 0.020, 0.040, and 0.060 in., in standard rolls of 36 linear ft, 36 in. wide; widths of 9, 18, 27, and 54 in. are also available.

Water stops (strips placed across construction joints in concrete walls to prevent water passage) and strips to be used to form control joints in concrete block walls are made from polyvinyl chloride.

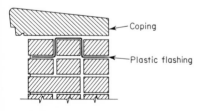

Coping

Plastic flashing

Figure 13·8
Parapet flashing.

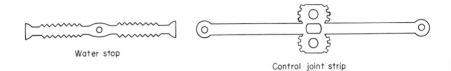

Water stop

Control joint strip

Figure 13 · 9
Typical control strips.

Several types of plastic material can be used to make pipe, but a great deal of the plastic piping at present on the market is made from polyethylene. Plastic pipe has some advantages over metal pipe because of its resistance to rust and corrosion; the ease and economy of installation; its flexibility, which may eliminate some fittings; and the long lengths in which it can be made. However, generally speaking, plastic pipe lacks high-temperature and pressure resistance, has poor mechanical strength, and is often higher in material cost. These disadvantages vary with the type of plastic used, the size of the pipe, and the thickness of the pipe wall.

AUXILIARY USES

Auxiliary uses of plastic in the manufacture and use of construction materials cover a wide field. These are uses in which the plastic involved plays a hidden or inconspicuous but important role. One of the best examples of this is the use of phenolic or urea formaldehyde thermosetting plastic resin for bonding layers in a sheet of plywood. Similar adhesives are extensively used in manufacturing glue-laminated wood beams and in the fabrication of wooden trusses.

Epoxy-resin adhesives are used for gluing where metal, concrete, glass, porcelain, or rigid plastics are involved. Epoxies can be formulated for compressive strengths up to 30,000 psi.

Another important auxiliary use of plastic is as a coating for another material. Plywood is produced which has a tough plastic exterior coating to render it more weatherproof and to produce a smooth, grainless paint surface. Plastic coatings are used to help protect concrete forms from damage and to prevent concrete from sticking to them.

Coatings of silicone are applied to exterior masonry to protect it from water penetration and to make it easier to clean. Vinyl- and epoxy-resin coatings are sprayed over the inside surface of metal pipes to render them more resistant to rust and corrosion.

Plastics form the basis of various paints, enamels, lacquers, and varnishes. Vinyl, polyurethane, acrylics, epoxies, and cellulose acetate all are used in the manufacture of coatings of this type.

Many of the caulking compounds, sealing compounds, glazing compounds, and expansion-joint fillers are manufactured from synthetic resins. Premolded, foam-rubberlike expansion-joint filler is made from expanded polyvinyl chloride and from expanded polyurethane. Sealing, glazing, and caulking compounds in paste form are made from acrylics, liquid polymer polysulfide, and butyl compounds. They are normally applied by a caulking gun. Polybutene-based glazing mastic is produced in ribbon form by extrusion. Other sealing compounds are made in two parts which are mixed on the job and poured as a liquid into the space to be sealed.

The foregoing examples do not constitute the entire list of uses for plastics in construction. However, they illustrate the adaptability of these materials and the wide range of products possible from one type of plastic.

GLOSSARY

acrylic	A glasslike thermoplastic resin made by polymerizing esters of acrylic acid
amino	A compound containing the group (NH_2)
calendering	Pressing between rollers
catalyst	A substance that speeds up a reaction without itself undergoing change
cellulosics	Substances containing cellulose
ceramic tile	Glazed clay tile
epoxy resin	A class of thermosetting resins derived from certain special types of organic chemicals; specifically, epichlorhydrin and a double phenol
ester	A compound formed by the substitution of a hydrocarbon radical for the acid hydrogen in an acid
ethylene	A colorless gaseous hydrocarbon product
extrusion	The forcing out of a material through an opening
hydraulic ram	A piston operated by liquid pressure
hyperbolic paraboloid	Basically, a warped parallelogram
impregnate	To soak or fill
melamine	A white crystalline compound made from calcium cyanamide
melamine resin	A synthetic resin made by combining melamine and formaldehyde
mil	One one-thousandth of an inch
nylon	A synthetic plastic made from coal, tar, and water
phenol	A crystalline compound made by the distillation of organic substances such as wood or coal
phenolic	A synthetic resin made by the reaction of a phenol with an aldehyde

238

plasticizer	An agent added to various plastics to make them softer and more flexible
polyethylene	A thermoplastic resin made by polymerizing ethylene
polymer	A compound consisting of the same elements, in the same proportions, as another, but with higher molecular weight
polymerize	To change into another compound with higher molecular weight and different physical properties, by the union of two or more molecules of the same kind
polystyrene	A clear, colorless, plastic resin made by polymerizing styrene
primer	A first coat used to prepare a surface for further treatment
resilient	Elastic, having the ability to regain its original shape after being deformed
resin	A solid, semisolid, or liquid substance that may be a natural or a synthetic organic material
sandwich panel	A panel made by enclosing a sheet or slab of material with facings of a different material
silicone	A synthetic resin made by polymerizing an organic silicon compound
styrene	A liquid hydrocarbon made from cinnamic acid
synthetic	A material formed by the artificial building up of simple compounds
terrazzo	A type of flooring in which the surface consists of marble chips in irregular pattern
thermal conductivity	Heat-transmitting ability
urea	A soluble crystalline compound made from carbon dioxide and ammonia and condensed with formaldehyde to produce urea-formaldehyde resin
vinyl	A thermoplastic resin made by the polymerization of a vinyl compound such as vinyl acetate

REVIEW QUESTIONS

1 (a) Name the two general classes of synthetic plastics.
   (b) Describe the primary difference between these two classes.

2 (a) List the three steps that are generally involved in the production of plastic products.
  (b) Explain why this system of production is usually employed.
3 Explain how transfer molding differs from compression molding.
4 (a) What is meant by extrusion forming?
  (b) What types of products are formed in this way?
  (c) How do you differentiate between plastic sheets and plastic films?
5 Name six uses made of plastic laminates in building construction.
6 (a) Outline the extent to which plastic products are used for structural purposes.
  (b) What do you consider to be the future of plastics in this field?
7 (a) Give three reasons why plastic material has become important in thermal insulation.
  (b) List three methods of using plastic materials as insulation.
8 Give three reasons why plastic films are so widely used as a moisture barrier.
9 (a) What is meant by auxiliary uses of plastics?
  (b) Name four common auxiliary uses of plastics in construction.

SELECTED SOURCES OF INFORMATION

The Arborite Company, Montreal, Que.
CIBA Products Company, Fairlawn, N.J.
Cyanamid of Canada Ltd., Montreal, Que.
Dow Chemical Co., Midland, Mich.
Electrovert Ltd., Toronto, Ont.
Monsanto Company, St. Louis, Mo.

14

EXTERIOR WALL MATERIALS

Walls of buildings serve one or more of three basic functions. One is to act as a load-bearing component of the structure, a second is to protect the interior from the elements, while the third function is to present an attractive exterior appearance.

Walls are constructed in several different ways, and the materials used to build them depend, to some extent at least, on the method of construction. The simplest type of wall is one made of a framework of studs and plates and having the upper-floor frame, the ceiling frame, and the roof frame attached to it. A second type consists of a framework of wooden or steel arches, rigid frames or A frames, which in fact constitutes both wall and roof framework. A third kind of wall is a solid unit consisting of some type of masonry. A fourth is that often found in large buildings, where the entire skeleton of the building is made from heavy timbers, steel, or reinforced concrete. The wall material simply fills in the spaces between those members. Such a skeleton frame is illustrated in Fig. 14·1.

Stud walls are normally covered first with some type of sheathing—boards, plywood, insulating fiberboard, or exterior gypsum board. This sheathing helps to give rigidity to the frame, provides one weather barrier, and acts as a base over

Figure 14·1
Steel building frame.
(Bethlehem Steel Co.)

which weatherproofing paper and exterior finish are applied. The method of application may vary somewhat with the material. Boards should be applied diagonally in order to provide the maximum rigidity. Plywood in 4×8 ft sheets, usually ½ in. thick, is also applied with the long edge horizontal. Blocking between studs should be supplied to support the long edges. Exterior gypsum board, which is covered with asphalt-impregnated paper, is made in 2×8 ft sheets, with the long edges V-jointed. These sheets are also applied horizontally.

Often this sheathing is covered with one or two layers of building paper. When two layers are used, the inner one may be an unsaturated felt or kraft paper and the outer one a waterproof paper. These should not be vapor-barrier type papers.

Over this is applied the exterior finishing material. For this type of wall it may be stucco, brick veneer, artificial stone veneer, natural stone veneer, terra-cotta facing, wood siding, boards and battens, aluminum siding, plywood, insulating fiberboard siding, rolled siding, wood shakes or shingles, hardboard siding, or asbestos-cement siding and siding shingles.

STUCCO

Stucco is a type of plaster made with portland cement which is applied to exterior surfaces to form a finish coating. It can be applied directly to masonry walls, but over wood sheathing some type of wire must be used to tie the sheathing and stucco together. Either a woven wire mesh (see Fig. 14·5) or expanded metal lath (Fig. 14·2) can be used. In either case, the openings should be large enough to permit the first coat to be forced through the openings to embed the wire completely. Wire should not be less than ¼ in. away from the sheathing and should be nailed every 8 or 9 in. When gypsum or fiberboard sheathings are used, girts should be placed between the studs to allow such nailing.

Stucco is applied in three coats, a base or scratch coat, a second or brown coat, and a final finish coat. All three coats are composed of 1 volume of portland cement to 3 to 5 volumes of clean, sharp sand. To this may be added ¼ volume of hydrated lime, hydrated-lime putty, slaked-lime putty, or 2 to 3 lb of diatomaceous earth to increase plasticity.

The scratch and brown coats should be applied about ⅜ in. thick with sufficient time between applications to allow for proper curing. Each coat should be kept moist for at least 48 hours. The finish coat should not be less than ⅛ in. thick and should be applied not sooner than seven days after application of the brown coat. Mineral color may be added to the finish coat, or prepared dry stucco already colored is available for finish coats.

A variety of treatments can be given to the finish coat to produce certain textures. Among those commonly used are

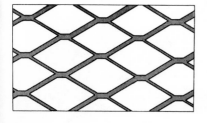

Figure 14 · 2
Expanded metal lath.

French trowel, Italian finish, Modern American, spatter dash, English cottage, and travertine. Consult a stucco manual for an illustration of these and other stucco textures. Coarse, colored pebbles may be sprayed against the newly applied finish coat to produce a pebble dash finish.

BRICK VENEER

Brick veneering over a light wood frame is done in two ways. One is to use regular brick laid up to produce a 4-in. thickness of veneer. The other method is to use thin slabs of brick (Fig. 14·3) manufactured for the purpose. There are two methods of using the 4-in. thickness. One is to lay up the brick over the sheathing, using metal ties nailed to the sheathing to hold the brick in place. The other is to cover the studs with paper-backed wire mesh, apply a 1-in.-thick layer of mortar, and set the brick with their backs in the mortar (Fig. 14·4). Any type of face brick can be used. When the thin veneer slabs are used, they are set in a mortar base which is applied over a stucco wire backing (Fig. 14·5).

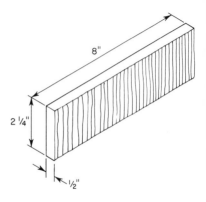

Figure 14·3
Thin brick veneer.

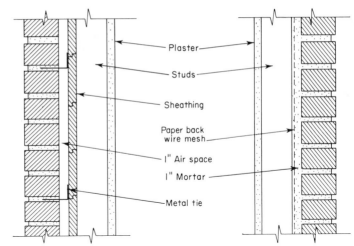

Figure 14·4
Four-inch brick veneer.

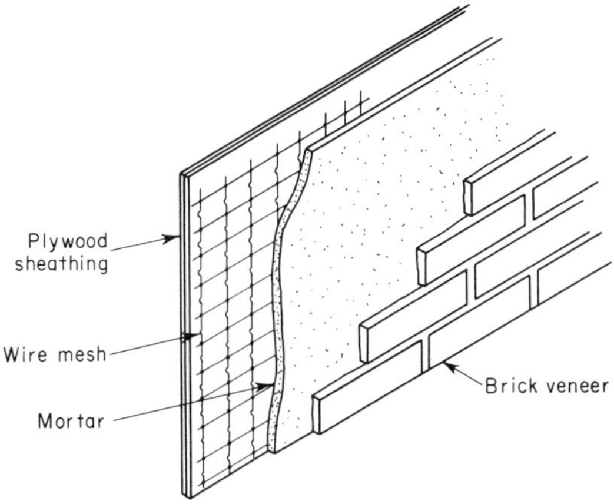

Figure 14·5
Brick veneer set in mortar backing.

ARTIFICIAL STONE VENEER

Artificial stone veneer, sometimes called cast stone, is made by casting colored mortar into molds which turn out units having faces resembling roughhewn stone. The units are about 1 in. thick and made in various sizes such as 2 × 8 in., 2 × 16 in., 4 × 4 in., 4 × 8 in., 4 × 16 in., 8 × 8 in., and 8 × 16 in. These units are set in a mortar bed which is applied over a stucco wire backing.

NATURAL STONE VENEER

Thin slabs of some natural stones such as sandstone, limestone, and slate with either regular or irregular dimensions are laid up in a mortar bed in the same way as artificial stone or brick.

TERRA-COTTA FACING

Many types of terra-cotta facing are made, but the one most commonly used for buildings with light frame walls is known as vitrolite. It is made from china clay in thin slabs $1\frac{1}{32}$, $\frac{7}{16}$, and $\frac{3}{4}$ in. thick. Units are made in 4- to 24-in. squares and 8 × 12 in., 8 × 16 in., 12 × 16 in., and up to 30 × 36 in. rectangles. Common colors include white, black, red, tan, blue, green, and gray. The face side is mechanically ground and polished to produce a bright, mirrorlike finish.

Asphaltic mastic is used to attach the vitrolite units to external surfaces, leaving joints of approximately $\frac{1}{16}$ in. These are later buttered with joint cement and painted. Direct contact with metal, concrete, or other hard substances should be avoided.

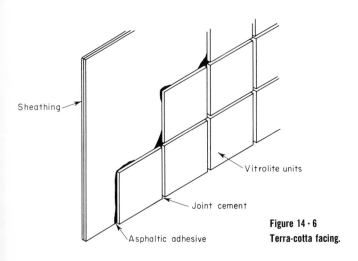

Sheathing

Vitrolite units

Joint cement

Asphaltic adhesive

Figure 14·6
Terra-cotta facing.

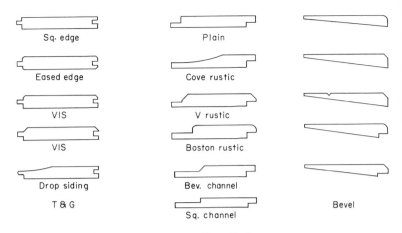

	Sq. edge		Plain		
	Eased edge		Cove rustic		
	VIS		V rustic		
	VIS		Boston rustic		
	Drop siding		Bev. channel		
	T & G		Sq. channel		Bevel

Figure 14 · 7

Redwood siding patterns.

WOOD SIDING

Several wood species are used in making siding, but the two most common ones are redwood and cedar.

Redwood siding is manufactured in three types: (1) tongue-and-groove, (2) shiplap siding, and (3) bevel siding. Each type is made in three or more patterns (Fig. 14·7). Tables 14·1, 14·2, and 14·3 give available sizes in the various types and patterns.

Redwood siding is classified in four grades: (1) Clear All Heart V.G., (2) Clear All Heart, (3) A-Grade V.G. (contains

Table 14 · 1

Sizes in tongue-and-groove siding patterns (redwood).

PATTERN	NOMINAL SIZE, IN.	THICKNESS, IN.	OVERALL WIDTH, IN.	EXPOSED WIDTH, IN.
Square edge	1 x 3	25/32	2½	2¼
	1 x 4	25/32	3½	3¼
	1 x 6	25/32	5½	5¼
	1¼ x 4	1¹/16	3½	3¼
	1¼ x 6	1¹/10	5½	5¼
Eased edge	1 x 4	25/32	3½	3¼
	1 x 6	25/32	5½	5¼
V one side	⅝ x 4	9/16	3⁷/16	3¼
	⅝ x 6	9/16	5⁷/16	5¼
	⅝ x 8	9/16	7⁷/16	7¼
	1 x 4	¾	3½	3¼
	1 x 6	¾	5½	5¼
	1 x 8	¾	7½	7¼
	1 x 10	¾	9½	9¼
	1 x 12	¾	11½	11¼
V and center V	1 x 6	¾	5½	5¼
	1 x 8	¾	7½	7¼
Drop siding	1 x 6	¾	5½	5¼

Table 14 · 2
Sizes in shiplap
siding patterns (redwood).

PATTERN	NOMINAL SIZE, IN.	THICKNESS, IN.	OVERALL WIDTH, IN.	EXPOSED WIDTH, IN.
Plain	1 x 6	$^{25}\!/_{32}$	5½	5
	1 x 8	$^{25}\!/_{32}$	7½	7
	1 x 10	$^{25}\!/_{32}$	9½	9
	1 x 12	$^{25}\!/_{32}$	11½	11
Cove rustic	1 x 6	¾	5½	5
	1 x 8	¾	7½	7
	1 x 10	¾	9½	9
V rustic	⅝ x 6	⁹/₁₆	5½	5
	⅝ x 8	⁹/₁₆	7½	7
	1 x 6	¾	5½	5
	1 x 8	¾	7½	7
	1 x 10	¾	9½	9
	1 x 12	¾	11½	11
Boston pattern rustic	1 x 6	¾	5½	5
	1 x 8	¾	7½	7
	1 x 10	¾	9½	9
	1 x 12	¾	11½	11
Beveled channel	1 x 10	¾	9½	9
Square channel	1 x 6	¾	5½	5
	1 x 8	¾	7½	7
	1 x 10	¾	9½	9
	1 x 12	¾	11½	11

clear sapwood), and (4) A Grade (contains clear sapwood and flat grain).

Cedar siding is manufactured in five styles: (1) bevel siding, (2) California rustic, (3) drop siding, (4) log cabin siding, and (5) channel siding. Figure 14·8 illustrates the shape of each style. Tables 14·4 and 14·5 give the various sizes in each style.

Cedar siding is divided into five grades: (1) Clear, (2) "A," (3) "B," (4) "Rustic," and (5) "C." Specifications for each grade are given in standard grading and dressing rules published by lumber manufacturers.

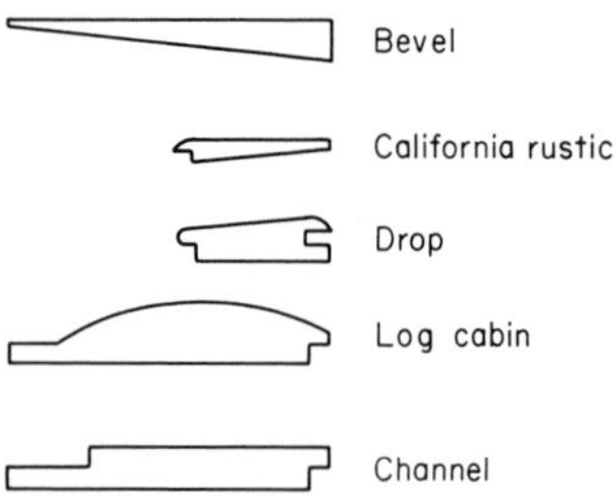

Bevel

California rustic

Drop

Log cabin

Channel

Figure 14 · 8
Cedar siding patterns.

BOARDS AND BATTENS

A board-and-batten exterior finish is one in which boards of various kinds—redwood, cedar, cypress, fir—rough-sawed or planed, are applied to a wall vertically, with narrow strips of the same material nailed over the vertical joints. A variation of this system is the use of vertical plank siding. This is 1- and 2-in. material, usually cedar or redwood, with tongue-and-groove edges and various arrangements of molding cuts

PATTERN	NOMINAL SIZE, IN.	THICKNESS, IN.		OVERALL WIDTH, IN.	EXPOSED WIDTH, IN.
		THIN EDGE	THICK EDGE		
Anzac	1 x 8	$\frac{3}{8}$	$\frac{25}{32}$	7½	6¼
	1 x 10	$\frac{3}{8}$	$\frac{25}{32}$	9½	8¼
	1 x 12	$\frac{3}{8}$	$\frac{25}{32}$	11½	10¼
Plain bevel	½ x 4	$\frac{3}{16}$	$\frac{15}{32}$	3½	2½
	½ x 5	$\frac{3}{16}$	$\frac{15}{32}$	4½	3½
	½ x 6	$\frac{3}{16}$	$\frac{15}{32}$	5½	4½
	½ x 8	$\frac{3}{16}$	$\frac{15}{32}$	7½	6½
	⅝ x 6	$\frac{3}{16}$	$\frac{9}{10}$	5½	4½
	⅝ x 8	$\frac{3}{16}$	$\frac{9}{10}$	7½	6½
	⅝ x 10	$\frac{3}{16}$	$\frac{9}{10}$	9½	8½
	¾ x 6	$\frac{3}{16}$	¾	5½	4½
	¾ x 8	$\frac{3}{16}$	¾	7½	6½
	¾ x 10	$\frac{3}{16}$	¾	9½	8½
	¾ x 12	$\frac{3}{16}$	¾	11½	10½
Rabbeted bevel	⅝ x 4	$\frac{3}{16}$	$\frac{9}{16}$	3½	3
	⅝ x 6	$\frac{3}{16}$	$\frac{9}{16}$	5½	5
	⅝ x 8	$\frac{3}{16}$	$\frac{9}{16}$	7½	7
	½ x 4	$\frac{3}{16}$	½	3½	3
	½ x 6	$\frac{3}{16}$	½	5½	5
	½ x 8	$\frac{3}{16}$	½	7½	7
	¾ x 6	$\frac{9}{32}$	$\frac{11}{16}$	5½	5
	¾ x 8	$\frac{9}{32}$	$\frac{11}{16}$	7½	7
	¾ x 10	$\frac{9}{32}$	$\frac{11}{16}$	9½	9
	¾ x 12	$\frac{9}{32}$	$\frac{11}{16}$	11½	11

Table 14 · 3
Sizes in bevel
siding patterns (redwood).

NOMINAL SIZE, IN.	THICKNESS, IN.		OVERALL WIDTH, IN.	EXPOSED WIDTH
	THIN EDGE	THICK EDGE		
½ x 4	$\frac{3}{16}$	$\frac{15}{32}$	3½	Variable
½ x 5	$\frac{3}{16}$	$\frac{15}{32}$	4½	
½ x 6	$\frac{3}{16}$	$\frac{15}{32}$	5½	
½ x 8	$\frac{3}{16}$	$\frac{15}{32}$	7½	
¾ x 8	$\frac{3}{16}$	¾	7½	
¾ x 10	$\frac{3}{16}$	¾	9½	
¾ x 12	$\frac{3}{16}$	¾	11½	

Table 14 · 4
Sizes in cedar bevel siding.

PATTERN	NOMINAL SIZE, IN.	THICKNESS, IN.	OVERALL WIDTH, IN.	EXPOSED WIDTH, IN.
California rustic	½ x 4	½ to $\frac{5}{32}$	3½	3
Drop siding	1 x 4	¾ to $\frac{15}{32}$	3½	3¼
Log cabin	2 x 8	1½	$7\frac{9}{10}$	$6\frac{11}{16}$
	1¼ x 6	1¼	5⅜	5
Channel	1 x 8	¾	7½	7
	1 x 10	¾	9½	9

Table 14 · 5
Sizes in common cedar siding patterns.

247

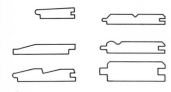

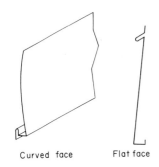

Figure 14·9
Wall plank patterns.

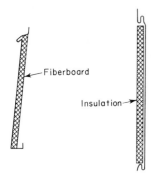

Curved face   Flat face

Figure 14·10
Sheet aluminum siding.

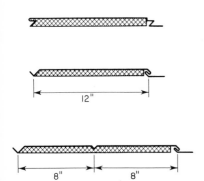

Fiberboard

Insulation

Figure 14·11
Insulated aluminum siding.

12"

8"   8"

Figure 14·12
Vertical wall panels of aluminum.

on the face (Fig. 14·9). Plank for this purpose is manufactured in both clear and knotty grades.

ALUMINUM SIDING

A number of types of siding are made from aluminum sheet. Some consist of a single thickness of metal formed into the required shape (Fig. 14·10), while others have a rigid insulation backing. In addition, a baked-on vinyl enamel is used to produce siding with a permanently colored surface in a wide range of colors. Vertical paneling is also made in similar style. Aluminum sheet for siding and paneling is from 0.02 to 0.025 in. thick. Siding is made 9 and 12 in. wide in sections 12 ft long, while vertical panels are made 12 and 16 in. wide and 8, 9, 10, 11, and 12 ft long.

PLYWOOD EXTERIOR FINISH

Any exterior grade of plywood can be used for siding purposes. It can be applied in 4 × 8 ft sheets with the long edge vertical and the joints covered by battens, or it can be cut in strips and applied horizontally like bevel siding. However, several types of plywood are made particularly for exterior finishing. One type, with a striated surface, is usually applied horizontally in 16-in.-wide overlapping strips with the striations vertical (Fig. 14·13). Another is ¾-in. plywood with one surface coated with a plastic resin film. It is normally applied in 12- or 16-in. horizontal overlapping strips (Fig. 14·14). The plastic coating provides a very smooth, grainless paint surface. Still another type has deep vertical grooves 2 or 4

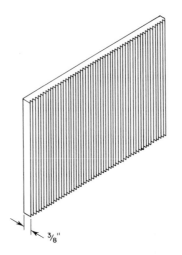

³⁄₈"

Figure 14·13
Striated plywood.

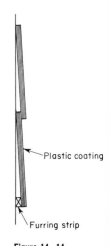

Plastic coating

Furring strip

Figure 14·14
Resin-coated plywood.

in. o.c. The long edges are shiplapped to provide the continuous groove pattern. It is generally applied vertically but can be installed horizontally for special effects.

INSULATING FIBERBOARD SIDING

This material is made from ½-in. wood fiberboard with one face covered with a heavy coating of asphalt. Finely crushed slate is embedded in the asphalt in patterns imitating brick, stone, and wood grain. The board is produced in strips 8 to 16 in. wide and 24 to 96 in. long, with shiplap edges (Fig. 14·15).

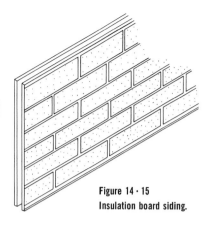

Figure 14·15
Insulation board siding.

ROLLED SIDING

Rolled siding is similar in appearance to fiberboard siding but is produced on heavy paper and packed in rolls—hence the name "rolled" siding. It is applied in horizontal courses over solid sheathing.

WOOD SHAKES AND SHINGLES

Red cedar shingles and shakes, very well known roofing materials, are also used for exterior wall finish. (See Chap. 17 for sizes, grades, etc., of shingles and shakes.)

Either the single- or the double-course method can be used in applying shingles or shakes to sidewalls. Single coursing is similar to roof shingling except that recommended exposures are greater. The maximum recommended exposure for 16-in. shingles on sidewalls is 7½ in.; for 18-in. shingles it is 8½ in.; and for 24-in. shingles it is 11½ in. Maximum recommended weather exposure for shakes, single coursed for wall construction, is: for 18-in. shakes, 8½ in.; for 24-in. shakes, 11½ in.; and for 32-in. shakes, 15 in. Figure 14·16 illustrates shingles single coursed on a sidewall. At outside corners shingles can be lapped, mitered, or butted to corner boards.

Double coursing involves applying two courses of shingles or a course of shingles and a course of shakes directly on top of one another. This provides a heavy shadow line at the butts (Fig. 14·17) and allows for still wider exposure. The recommended exposure for 16-in. double-coursed shingles is 10 in.; for 18-in. shingles, 11 in.; and for 24-in. shingles, 14 in. When double coursed, 18-in. shakes can be exposed 14 in., and 24-in. shakes up to 20 in.

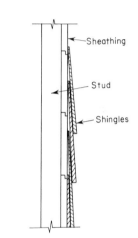

Figure 14·16
Single-coursed sidewall shingles.

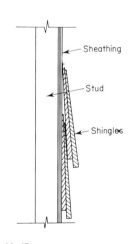

Figure 14·17
Double-coursed sidewall shingles.

HARDBOARD SIDING

Tempered hardboard cut in 12- and 16-in. strips 4, 8, and 12 ft long is often used as siding. Three methods of applica-

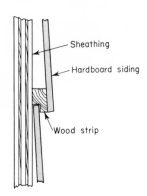

Figure 14 · 18
Hardboard lap siding.

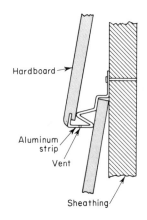

Figure 14 · 19
Hardboard vented siding.

tion are used. One consists of applying the strips in the same way that bevel siding is applied. Another method involves using a rabbeted wood strip at the bottom of each course to accentuate the shadow line (Fig. 14·18). In the third method, preformed metal strips hold the siding in place and give a deep shadow line. These metal strips have holes drilled in their bottom surface to provide ventilation behind the board.

ASBESTOS-CEMENT SIDING AND SIDING SHINGLES

Asbestos-cement siding boards are made in strips 12 in. wide, 48 in. long, and ³⁄₁₆ in. thick with a smooth face and straight edges. The shingles are 12 × 24 in. with deep vertical wood-grain pattern on the face and a wavy bottom edge. Both siding and shingles are prepunched for application on 16-in. centers. Walls are usually strapped on 12-in. centers, and the shingles are fastened with soft-headed nails, which will not crack the material. Figure 14·20 illustrates the application over strapping.

Buildings consisting of a framework of arches or prefabricated frames of any type are generally covered with some type of cladding. In the case of curved wooden arches, this cladding is generally in the form of thick, double tongue-and-groove wood decking. Over it some type of roofing is applied —shingles, metal roofing sheets, etc. Other types of cladding include plywood sheets, corrugated asbestos-cement sheets, corrugated sheet metal, corrugated plastic sheets, and corrugated galbestos. The latter consists of a core of sheet steel which is first dipped in a bath of molten zinc. Immediately a layer of asbestos felt is applied under great pressure and is bonded to the zinc coat. The felt is then impregnated with

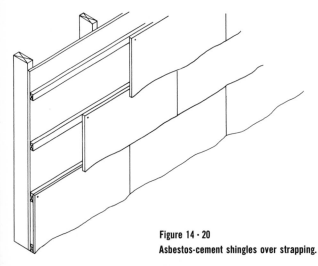

Figure 14 · 20
Asbestos-cement shingles over strapping.

asphalt, and finally a tough, waterproof colored coating is applied to both sides. Galbestos sheets are available in widths of 30 and 33 in. in lengths up to 12 ft.

The building shown in Fig. 14·21 consists of a steel framework and floor decks and is clad with materials which are fastened to the frame and carry no structural loads themselves. Such walls are known as curtain walls.

Masonry has been the traditional material for load-bearing exterior walls, and with the advent of skeleton-frame construction, masonry products have continued to play a part in the design of curtain walls. Other well-known materials such as wood, glass, concrete, and steel are used for curtain wall, and a great many new products have been designed and manufactured specifically for this purpose.

BRICK

Brick curtain walls may be formed in several different ways, in conjunction with steel or reinforced-concrete frame buildings. The wall can be made of face brick over a backup wall of common brick, clay tile, or concrete block. Figure 14·22 illustrates each combination. It can be in the form of a brick cavity wall composed of two wythes of brick separated by a 2-in. air space. The inner wythe can be face brick or common brick with some type of interior finish applied. S.C.R. brick in a single wythe also can be used. In some cases an 8-in. brick curtain wall can be used as a backup for other facing materials such as stone or terra-cotta.

Various methods are used to attach the brick curtain wall to the skeleton. If the frame is of reinforced concrete, metal ties are usually employed to anchor the ends of the curtain-wall sections to columns. These consist of flat metal straps, one end of which can be anchored to the column, while the

Figure 14 · 21
Curtain-wall construction.
(Columbia Acoustics &
Fireproofing Co.)

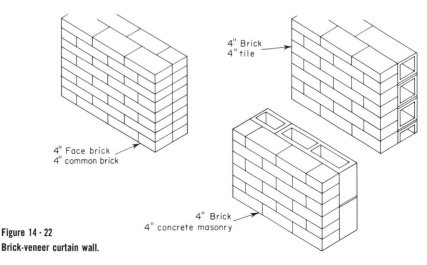

4" Brick
4" tile

4" Face brick
4" common brick

4" Brick
4" concrete masonry

Figure 14 · 22
Brick-veneer curtain wall.

251

Figure 14·23
Metal masonry anchors.

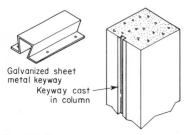

Galvanized sheet
metal keyway
Keyway cast
in column

Figure 14·24
Anchor key way.

other end is laid into a mortar joint between courses of brick (Fig. 14·23). A metal keyway, shaped like the one shown in Fig. 14·24, is cast into the sides of the column. The same system can be used with a steel frame with fireproofing concrete (Fig. 14·32). Brick and spandrel beam can be bonded simply by a mortar joint between them, or a keying system such as that illustrated in Fig. 14·25 can be used.

When the building has a steel frame, the brick curtain wall can be laid so as to enclose the frame (Fig. 14·26), or the frame can be left exposed (Fig. 14·27). Cavity walls often conceal the columns (Fig. 14·28). In such cases the brick is carried over the spandrel beams by steel lintel angles.

TILE, CERAMIC VENEER, AND TERRA-COTTA

Structural tile and facing tile are used in various ways in the construction of curtain walls. Structural tile is used as a

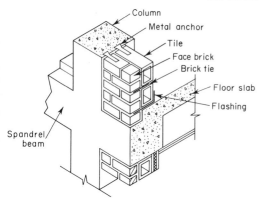

Column
Metal anchor
Tile
Face brick
Brick tie
Floor slab
Flashing
Spandrel beam

Figure 14·25
Brick keyed to spandrel beam.

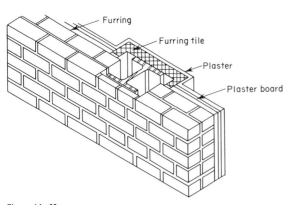

Furring
Furring tile
Plaster
Plaster board

Figure 14·26
Curtain wall conceals steel frame.

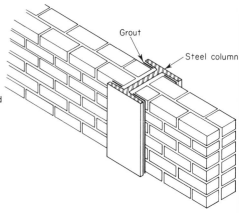

Grout
Steel column

Figure 14·27
Exposed steel frame.

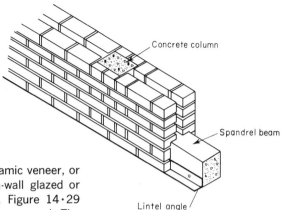

Figure 14 · 28
Cavity curtain wall, concealed frame.

backup for face brick, facing tile, stone, ceramic veneer, or architectural terra-cotta. Eight-inch through-wall glazed or textured structural tile can be used alone. Figure 14·29 illustrates some of the combinations which are used. The same methods are used for tying tile to columns and bonding them to spandrel beams as are used for brick.

Terra-cotta is a term used to describe a material consisting of a burned clay body with some decorative type of face, produced in slab form. There are two general types, ceramic veneer and architectural terra-cotta. Ceramic veneer in general is a flat slab, while architectural terra-cotta usually has some sort of sculptured face.

Two kinds of ceramic veneer are produced, adhesion type and anchor type. Adhesion-type ceramic veneer is set on the wall in mortar bond only. Slab thickness is limited to a maximum of 1¼ in., and the face area, which is normally glazed

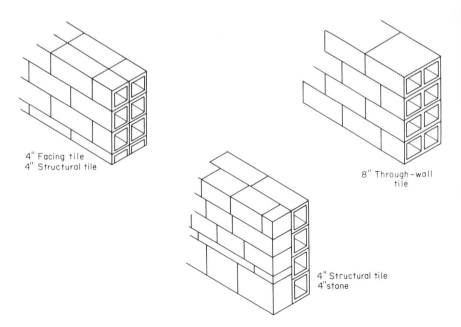

Figure 14 · 29
Structural-tile curtain wall.

253

with ceramic colors, is limited to 600 sq in. Figure 14·30 illustrates some typical applications. Many building codes require that a unit shearing strength of not less than 50 psi be developed between the backing and the facing.

Anchor type ceramic veneer is fastened to the backup wall by some type of metal anchor and supported at intervals by steel angles. Figure 14·31 shows some typical anchoring methods. Thicknesses vary from 1½ to 3 in., and units are produced in maximum width of 24 in. and maximum length of 36 in. Within these limits, units can be made any size to suit a particular design. The majority of mass-produced units have a maximum size of 18 × 24 in.

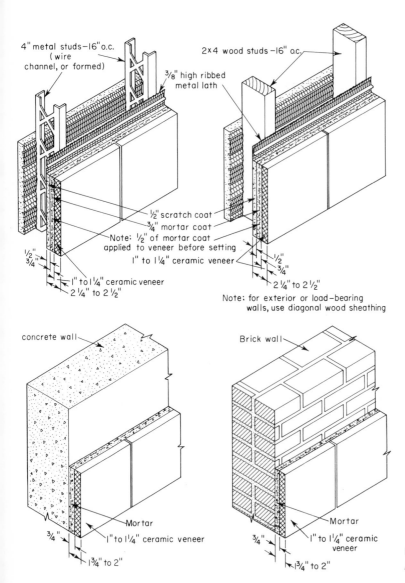

4" metal studs—16" o.c.
(wire channel, or formed)

2x4 wood studs —16" o.c.

3/8" high ribbed metal lath

1/2" scratch coat
3/4" mortar coat
Note: 1/2" of mortar coat applied to veneer before setting
1" to 1¼" ceramic veneer

1/2"
3/4"

1" to 1¼" ceramic veneer
2¼" to 2½"

1/2"
3/4"
2¼" to 2½"

Note: for exterior or load–bearing walls, use diagonal wood sheathing

concrete wall

Brick wall

Mortar
3/4"
1" to 1¼" ceramic veneer
1¾" to 2"

Mortar
3/4"
1" to 1¼" ceramic veneer
1¾" to 2"

Figure 14 · 30
Adhesion-type ceramic veneer.

254

Figure 14 · 31
Anchoring ceramic veneer.

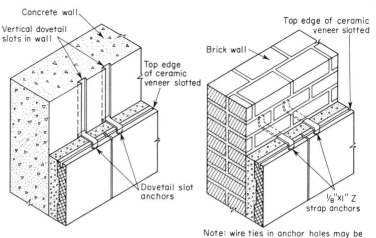

Note: wire ties in anchor holes may be used in lieu of strap anchors

¼" diameter pencil rods are passed through loops of loop dowel anchors. Dowel ends are bent down and under pencil rods to hold rods at least 1" out from structural concrete.

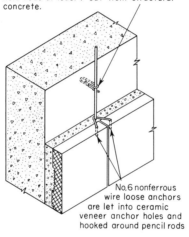

No. 6 nonferrous wire loose anchors are let into ceramic veneer anchor holes and hooked around pencil rods

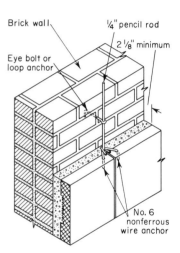

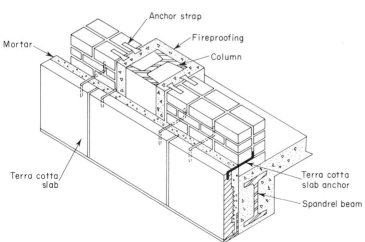

Figure 14 · 32
Terra-cotta-faced curtain wall.

255

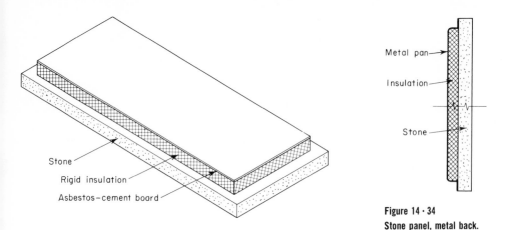

Figure 14 · 33
Stone sandwich panel.

Stone
Rigid insulation
Asbestos–cement board

Metal pan
Insulation
Stone

Figure 14 · 34
Stone panel, metal back.

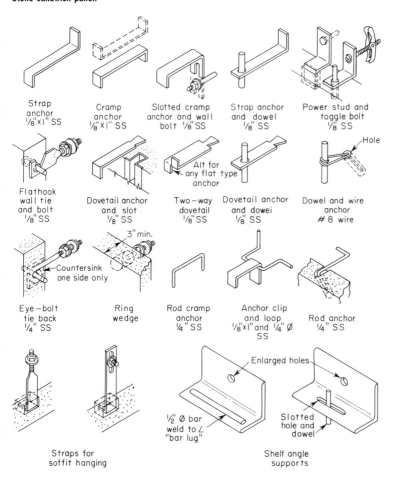

Strap
anchor
1/8"x1" SS

Cramp
anchor
1/8"x1" SS

Slotted cramp
anchor and wall
bolt 1/8"SS

Strap anchor
and dowel
1/8" SS

Power stud and
toggle bolt
1/8" SS

Flathook
wall tie
and bolt
1/8" SS

Dovetail anchor
and slot
1/8" SS

Two–way
dovetail
1/8" SS

Alt for
any flat type
anchor

Dovetail anchor
and dowei
1/8" SS

Hole

Dowel and wire
anchor
8 wire

Eye–bolt
tie back
1/4" SS

Countersink
one side only

3"min.

Ring
wedge

Rod cramp
anchor
1/4" SS

Anchor clip
and loop
1/8"x1"and 1/4" Ø
SS

Rod anchor
1/4" SS

Straps for
soffit hanging

Enlarged holes

1/2" Ø bar
weld to ∠
"bar lug"

Slotted
hole and
dowel

Shelf angle
supports

Figure 14 · 35
Typical stone anchors.
(Indiana Limestone Co.)

256

STONE

Stone facing can be used either over a backup wall of masonry or supported by a subframe of aluminum or steel. Two types of facing panel are available, solid stone slabs and insulated sandwich panels. Solid stone slabs will vary in thickness from 1 to 5 in., with bond stones (Fig. 14·36) up to 8 in. thick. The face area will also vary according to the type of stone, the quarry from which it is produced, and the slab thickness. In general maximum size will be about 9 × 13 ft × 5 in., but the actual size will depend on the specifications for the particular job.

Stone sandwich panels can have a facing of limestone, granite, or marble and are made in two ways. One is to bond 2 in. of rigid insulation, such as expanded polystyrene or mineral fiberboard, to 2 in. of stone. The back may or may not be covered with a rigid board such as hardboard or asbestos-cement board. Such panels are made to order, but the practical maximum size would be 4 ft wide with a maximum area of about 25 sq ft. The other type of stone sandwich panel consists of 2 in. of glass-fiber insulation between a 2-in. slab of stone and a thin metal pan.

Stone facing slabs over a masonry backup wall are held in place by metal anchors and supported by bond stones or shelf angles. The metal anchors are embedded in the stone and in the backup wall; Fig. 14·35 shows some of the types of anchors used. Figure 14·36 illustrates the support of stone facings by bond stones or shelf angles. No anchors are required in bond stones. Stones under 30 in. in height require two anchors per stone in the top bed only; two anchors top and bottom should be provided for stones over 30 in. in height. If the stone is less than 24 in. wide, one anchor per bed is sufficient. A steel-frame building can also be faced with stone slabs, using a system of shelf angles and rod ties.

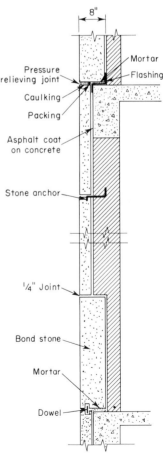

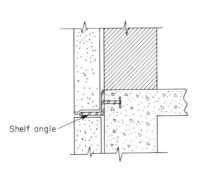

Figure 14 · 36
Stone facing on masonry backup.

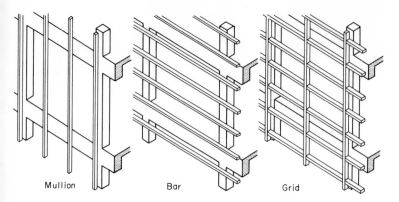

Figure 14 · 37
Curtain wall subframes.

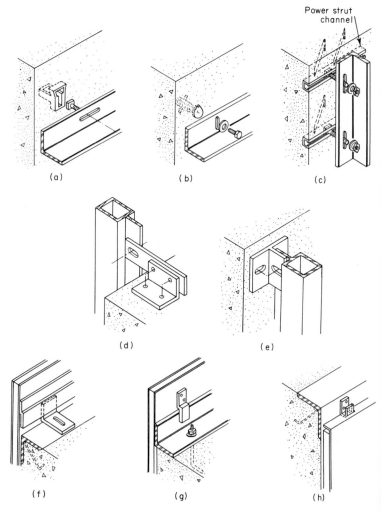

Figure 14 · 38
Anchoring subframes to concrete.

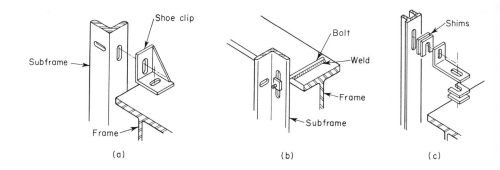

(a) (b) (c)

Figure 14 · 39
Anchoring subframe to steel.

Stone sandwich panels are usually supported by some type of subframe (Fig. 14·37) which, in turn, is attached to the building frame. Some of the methods used to attach subframes to a concrete building are shown in Fig. 14·38, while some methods of attaching to a steel frame appear in Fig. 14·39.

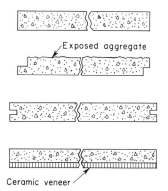

Figure 14 · 40
Solid concrete panels.

CONCRETE

Concrete is used in several ways to produce materials for curtain walls. Concrete blocks are used in much the same way as structural tile or brick, and similar methods are used to anchor them. Precast concrete slabs are made up as curtain-wall panels, using both standard and lightweight concrete. They are made in a number of shapes, plain and insulated, and in a variety of surface finishes. Blocks may have a smooth, plain concrete surface, plain concrete with textured surface, or an exposed aggregate surface. A layer of colored aggregates and white cement is sometimes used on the surface of the panel to produce a terrazzo-like finish, or colored mineral oxides may be used to produce colored panels. Slabs may also be faced with a layer of ceramic veneer. Various styles of insulated concrete panels are also produced (Fig. 14·41).

Any of the anchoring methods used to fasten stone panels in place also can be used with concrete panels. Edges of panels can be placed against the face of steel columns and a

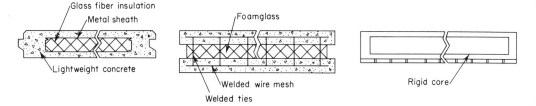

Figure 14 · 41
Insulated concrete panels.

259

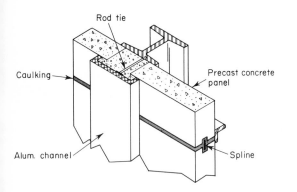

Figure 14 · 42
Concrete facing slab supported by channel.

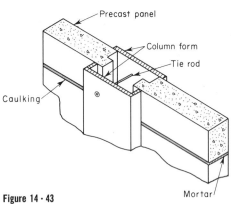

Figure 14 · 43
Forming columns around panel edges.

steel or aluminum cover channel used to hold them in place (Fig. 14·42), or panels can be erected and braced in place and the column cast around their edges afterward.

WOOD

Wood can be used as curtain-wall material in two ways. In heavy timber frame buildings, light wood framing can be used to form a single panel the size of a bay (Fig. 14·44). This framing may be covered with stucco, plywood, planking, sheet metal, asbestos-cement board, etc. Plywood can be used as a skin to form insulated sandwich panels which are then used as curtain-wall material.

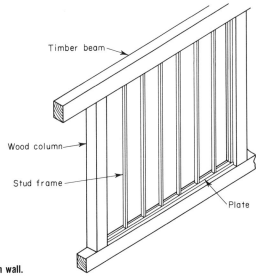

Figure 14 · 44
Wood-frame curtain wall.

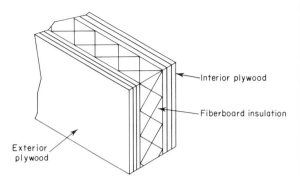

Figure 14 · 45
Plywood sandwich panel.

Interior plywood

Fiberboard insulation

Exterior plywood

GLASS

Glass is used in curtain-wall construction in sheet, block, and tile form. Glass blocks are standardized units produced in sizes of 6 × 6 in., 8 × 8 in., 12 × 12 in., and 4 × 12 in.— all 4 in. thick. They are laid in mortar in stack bond, in much the same way as unit masonry. Figure 14·47 illustrates several methods of anchoring glass blocks to a masonry wall. Notice in every case the fiber-glass padding between the ends of the blocks and the wall and the cushion between the blocks and the edges of the jamb. The entire panel must rest on a resilient pad of some kind so that blocks do not come in contact with the structural frame.

Glass tile are units similar to glass block but only 2 in. thick with a 1⅛-in. air space. They are often made up into modular panels 4 and 5 ft long and 1 and 2 ft high. These panels are complete with an aluminum perimeter frame and neoprene gasket. The frames are made so that panels can be joined easily, with aluminum batten strips to cover the joints. These glass tile may be either light-transmitting or ceramic-faced.

Figure 14 · 46
Glass blocks.

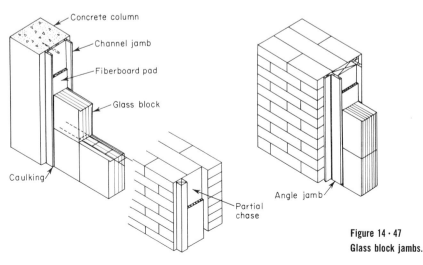

Concrete column

Channel jamb

Fiberboard pad

Glass block

Caulking

Partial chase

Angle jamb

Figure 14 · 47
Glass block jambs.

A similar product is made by laminating two sheets of glass or a sheet of glass and a sheet of porcelain enameled steel to a foam-glass or styrofoam core, to form a 2-in.-thick sandwich panel. Colored or ceramic glazed glass is used. These units can be made any practical size to suit a particular design.

Glass sheets are used in several ways. One is in the form of plate glass usually ¼ in. thick. Sizes produced vary with different manufacturers, but the general maximum is 72 × 144 in., and the minimum area is 12 × 25 in. Panels may be clear (Fig. 14·48) or have a clear polished face with ceramic enamel fired on the back. Plate is also produced with clear or patterned face and aluminized back.

These panels are usually supported by extruded aluminum frames of many designs. Figure 14·49 illustrates some typical aluminum units in use.

Figure 14 · 48
Clear plate-glass panels.
(Alliance Wall Corp.)

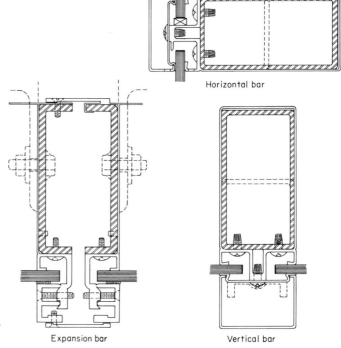

Horizontal bar

Figure 14 · 49
Typical aluminum subframes.
(Pittsburgh Plate Glass Co.)

Expansion bar

Vertical bar

Figure 14 · 50
Glass block and plate-glass curtain wall.
(Pittsburgh Corning Corporation)

Insulating glass panels are made by sealing two sheets of plate glass together, with an air space between them. They are supported by similar methods to those used for single units.

Another method of using glass is in the form of window walls. These are simply windows with wood or metal sash, combined in groups to form large panels. There are innumerable sizes and combinations possible, and any manufacturer of such products will furnish literature on request giving details of sizes, etc., made by that company.

METAL

Metals are widely used in the manufacture of curtain-wall panels. Steel, stainless steel, and aluminum are the metals most commonly used, and from them a great variety of panels are made, as skin facings and as insulated sandwich panels. Steel skin facings are generally made by forming (bending) a flat sheet to the desired shape. Stainless steel facings are normally rolled, while many aluminum facings are extruded. Figure 14·51 illustrates some of the shapes available in single-skin facings.

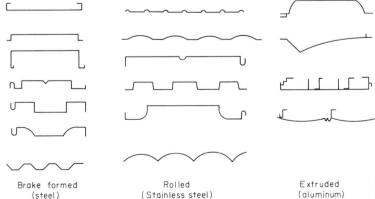

| Brake formed (steel) | Rolled (Stainless steel) | Extruded (aluminum) |

Figure 14 · 51
Single-skin facings.

Two types of sandwich panel are made, open end and closed sandwich. In one case the core insulation is completely surrounded by metal, while in the other, only the front and back are covered. Figure 14·52 illustrates the construction of a typical sandwich panel of each type.

In addition to insulation, sandwich panel cores often contain a stabilizing core member in the form of a sheet of hardboard, asbestos-cement board, or other rigid material. Many of the panels made from steel have an exterior finish of porcelain enamel. For some uses, galvanized steel is provided. Sometimes aluminum facings are used. They may be plain, etched, or anodized.

Sizes vary widely from one manufacturer to another. Panel thicknesses range from ¾ to 4 in., widths from 12 to 36 in.; lengths of up to 60 ft are available in some types. Figure 14·53 illustrates a few of the many shapes in open and closed panels.

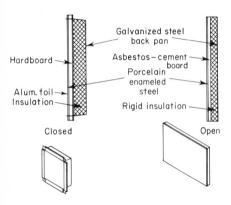

Figure 14 · 52
Typical sandwich panels.

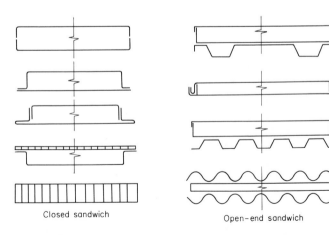

Closed sandwich

Open-end sandwich

Figure 14 · 53
Typical sandwich-panel shapes.

264

PLASTIC

Plastic panels are produced in flat and corrugated sheets and in sandwich panels. Many of the sheet-type panels are made from fiber-glass-reinforced polyester plastic. They may be clear, translucent, or colored. In Fig. 14·54, fiber-glass-reinforced sheets are being installed in a factory building.

Plastic sandwich panels are made in several ways. One method involves the use of an aluminum grid faced on both sides with a sheet of fiber-glass-reinforced plastic. Foamed polystyrene, foam glass, asbestos-cement board, and plywood are all used as core material to be faced with plastic. The panels shown in Fig. 14·55 are of reinforced plastic over a rigid insulation core 2½ in. thick. Another type of plastic

Figure 14 · 54
Plastic sheet panels.
[Fibreglass R.P. Report (Canada)]

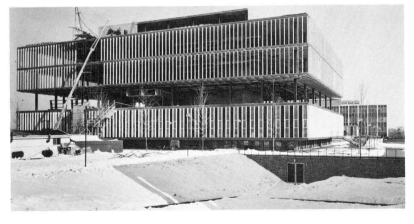

Figure 14 · 55
Plastic sandwich panels.
[Fibreglass R.P. Report (Canada)]

sandwich panel consists of a core of ⅜-in. chipboard coated on both sides with a 3/16-in. layer of phenolic-resin plastic. A thin layer of polyvinyl plastic imprinted with a stone pattern and color is bonded to one face and a sheet of kraft paper to the other.

Plastic curtain-wall panels of all types are usually mounted in some type of subframe, similar to those shown in Figs. 14·37 and 14·49.

ASBESTOS CEMENT

See Chap. 12 for a description of sandwich panels of asbestos-cement board laminated to a rigid insulation core.

GLOSSARY

cladding	External covering of a building
curtain wall	An exterior wall covering which carries no structural load
diatomaceous earth	Earth containing silica formed from the skeletons of one-celled animals
insulated sandwich	A wall unit consisting of two outer skins enclosing a core of insulation
neoprene	A type of synthetic rubber
S.C.R. brick	Brick with a nominal 6-in. width
shelf angle	A metal angle projecting from a backup wall which acts as a shelf to support a facing material
spandrel beam	A beam occupying the space over an opening or series of openings in a wall
stabilizing core	A central stiffener
striated	Marked with small grooves or channels
subframe	A light frame attached to the structural frame for the purpose of carrying a curtain wall
tempered hardboard	Hardboard that has its density and its resistance to water penetration increased
translucent	Admitting diffused light

REVIEW QUESTIONS

1 (a) What is a curtain wall?
   (b) Give two reasons why curtain-wall construction is so widely used.
2 Explain why paper used over exterior sheathing should not be a vapor barrier.
3 Give two reasons for using wire with a stucco exterior finish.

4 Explain why redwood and cedar are the most popular woods for making siding.
5 Outline the advantages of using aluminum products as exterior siding.
6 By means of careful diagrams, illustrate how brick curtain wall can be tied to spandrel beams and columns of a reinforced-concrete skeleton frame.
7 (a) What is a bond stone?
   (b) What is a stone anchor?
8 What are some advantages of using precast concrete slabs as curtain-wall panels?
9 Outline the differences between glass block and glass tile.
10 (a) List some of the factors to be considered when planning to use glass sheets as curtain-wall material.
   (b) Explain what is meant by window walls.
11 What is the difference between an open-end and a closed-sandwich curtain-wall panel?

SELECTED SOURCES OF INFORMATION

Alliance Wall Corp., Alliance, O.
Aluminum Company of Canada Ltd., Montreal, Que.
American Iron & Steel Institute, New York, N.Y.
American Plywood Association, Tacoma, Wash.
Atlas Asbestos Company Ltd., Toronto, Ont.
Building Products of Canada Ltd., Halifax, Nova Scotia
California Redwood Association, San Francisco, Calif.
Facing Tile Institute, Washington, D.C.
Federal Seaboard Terra Cotta Corporation, New York, N.Y.
International Panel Boards Ltd., Gatineau, Que.
Minnesota & Ontario Paper Co., Minneapolis, Minn.
National Gypsum Company, Buffalo, N.Y.
Southern Pine Association, New Orleans, La.
Stark Ceramics, Inc., Canton, O.
The Steel Co. of Canada, Limited, Hamilton, Ont.
Structural Clay Products Institute, Washington, D.C.
Western Gypsum Products, Limited, Winnipeg, Manitoba

15

INSULATING MATERIALS

THERMAL INSULATION

In cold weather we are interested in transferring heat from furnaces, radiators, heating panels, etc., into the various rooms of our buildings. At the same time we are interested in preventing that heat from being transferred from the interior of the building to the outside. During the summer it is important that we prevent the transfer of hot outside temperatures to the working and living space within our buildings. All this is done by the judicious use of materials which best prevent the transfer of heat. Such material we call thermal insulation.

There are three methods for the transfer of heat—conduction, convection, and radiation. The inside of a concrete wall which has one side exposed to outside winter temperatures feels cold to the touch. Heat is being conducted from the side of higher temperature to that of lower temperature. From there it is transferred to the outside air by radiation. When air is heated it expands and begins to circulate. During the circulation, if it comes in contact with cooler surfaces, some of its heat is given up to them. It is therefore important to try to prevent air currents (convection currents) from being set up in the walls and ceilings of our buildings. This can be done by keeping the layer of air relatively thin—not over 1 in.—and by dividing the space into small enclosed compartments. The convection currents set up in the confined spaces are insignificant and can cause little heat transfer. To prevent heat loss by conduction we must use the materials that are poor conductors; to prevent loss by radiation, materials must be used which will reflect rather than radiate heat.

KINDS OF THERMAL INSULATION

All the materials used to prevent heat losses are known as thermal insulation; there are nine basic kinds: loose fill; blankets; batts; structural insulation board; slab or block insulation; reflective insulation; foamed-in-place, sprayed-on, and corrugated insulations.

Loose-fill insulation is generally bulky and can be divided into two main types: (1) fibrous and (2) granular. The fibrous type is made from mineral wool—rock wool, glass wool, or

268

slag wool—or vegetable fiber—usually wood fiber. Granular insulations are made from expanded minerals such as perlite and vermiculite or from ground vegetable matter such as granulated cork.

Blanket insulation is made from some fibrous material, such as mineral wool, wood fiber, cotton fiber, or animal hair, manufactured in the form of a mat. Mats are made in various thicknesses and cut in a variety of widths, sometimes with a paper cover (Fig. 15·1).

Figure 15·1
Rolled blanket insulation.

Batts are similar in basic manufacture to blankets, but they are restricted as to length, are always covered with paper, and are made especially for installation between stud spacings. Batts usually have paper tabs along the edges for easier attachment to the frame.

Structural insulation board is made from a variety of substances such as cane, wood, and other vegetable fibers. It is used for various purposes such as exterior or interior sheathing, insulating roof decking, roof insulation board, interior finishing board, shingle backer, and insulating form board.

Slab or block insulation is made in rigid units, normally smaller in area than insulation board, though some of them may be made from two or more pieces of insulation board cemented together to make a thick slab. This type of insulation is also made from cork, shredded wood and cement, mineral wool with binder, vermiculite and asphalt, cellular glass, foamed concrete, foamed plastic, cellular hard rubber, or from concrete made with perlite, vermiculite, or expanded clay as aggregate.

Reflective insulations are composed of metallic or other special surfaces with or without some type of backing. Unlike all others, reflective insulations rely on their surface characteristics, thickness of air space, temperature difference, etc., for their insulating value. It is important that reflective insulations be installed so that the reflective surface faces an air space of at least ¾ in. Properly installed, they also act as a vapor barrier.

Sprayed-on insulations are produced by mixing some fibrous or cellular material with an adhesive and blowing the mixture onto the surface to be insulated. Areas that are otherwise difficult to insulate because of their shape, location, etc., are treated in this manner.

Cellular mass insulation is made from liquid resin. Two ingredients are used which, when mixed, foam up and solidify to fill the space into which they were introduced.

Corrugated insulation is made from paper, corrugated and cemented into multiple layers. Some types are sprayed with an adhesive which hardens to give the product extra stiffness, while others are faced with foil to provide extra insulative value.

DESCRIPTION, USES, AND APPLICATION OF THERMAL INSULATIONS

Loose-fill Insulations

Fibrous loose-fill insulation is made by passing a stream of molten rock, glass, or slag through a jet of air. The jet blows the material into long, thin threads which solidify into a wool-like mass. This is packed into bags, ready for application. In some cases it is poured from bags into spaces between framing members, but more often it is blown into open and concealed spaces by compressed air. This will produce a more uniform and more compact job than can be obtained by hand methods. Mineral wool fill insulation does not support combustion, repels vermin, and does not absorb moisture. Mineral-wool-filled partitions have been accorded a 1½-hour fire rating when faced with metal lath and plaster.

Vegetable fiber loose fill is usually made from wood shredded into a lightweight, fleecy insulating material. This is generally treated to make it moisture-resistant, fire-resistant, and vermin-repellent. Like mineral wool, this material can be placed by hand or blown into place.

Fibrous loose fill normally is applied over horizontal surfaces. In vertical spaces it may have a tendency to settle over a period of time, leaving an uninsulated space at the top. However, it is used to insulate walls of buildings that have been built without insulation. In such cases, holes are drilled in the wall between each pair of studs, a hose inserted, and the insulation blown in until the space is filled.

Mineral-type granular loose fill is made from either perlite or vermiculite. Perlite is a nonmetallic mineral, a siliceous volcanic rock containing combined water. The rock is crushed and heated quickly to above 1500°F, which causes the crude perlite particles to expand and turn white. The combined water vaporizes to form microscopic cells in the heat-softened particles. The result is a honeycomb structure containing a great many sealed cells which give it strength, lightness, and resistance to water penetration. The material, which weighs from 7½ to 15 lb per cu ft, is screened into various sizes for use as loose fill, plaster aggregate, or concrete aggregate and packed in bags containing 4 cu ft.

Vermiculite is a mica-like mineral chemically known as hydrated magnesium-aluminum-iron silicate. It is made up of many very thin layers with a minute amount of water between each pair. The crude ore is crushed to controlled sizes and heated in a furnace to about 2000°F. The water is turned to steam, forcing the layers apart and expanding the individual granules to at least twelve times their original size (Fig. 15·2). As each granule expands it traps within

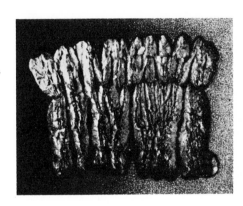

Figure 15 · 2
Magnified view of vermiculite granule after expansion. (Vermiculite Institute)

itself thousands of dead air cells. These provide a large part of the insulation value of the material. The rest comes from the shiny surfaces of the individual layers, which act as reflective insulation.

The granules are graded into four sizes. Size 1 ranges from ⅜ in. to No 16 sieve, Size 2 from No. 4 to No. 30 sieve, Size 3 from No. 8 to No. 100 sieve, and Size 4 from No.16 to No. 100 sieve. Sizes 1 and 2 are generally used as loose-fill insulation for sidewalls and ceilings, over suspended ceilings, between wood sleepers over a concrete floor slab, as a fill for the cores of concrete blocks, and many other similar uses.

Blanket Insulations

Blanket insulations are made of felted fiber, usually of a mineral nature, manufactured to controlled thicknesses of 1, 1½, 2, 3, and 4 in. A variety of blanket insulation widths are made; some to fit between studs 16, 20, or 24 in. o.c., others are wider. The wider units are often used to wrap pipe but can be used in other applications as well. Some blankets are made in 8-ft lengths; others are put up in rolls of from 40 to 100 linear feet, depending on the thickness. Some are made with no covering at all; some with a paper back on one side only; some with vinyl, cardboard, or wire mesh on one side; while others are completely enclosed in an envelope.

Those with backing or envelopes are usually provided with a stapling flange so that they can be stapled to the sides or edges of studs and joists (Fig. 15·3). Blankets are used where large areas must be insulated. These include such places as sidewalls in new construction, overhead in floored attics, between joists in unfloored attics, in crawl spaces, and over suspended ceilings.

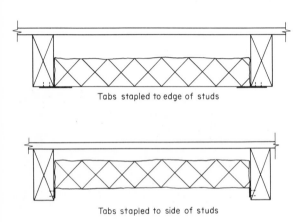

Tabs stapled to edge of studs

Tabs stapled to side of studs

Figure 15 · 3
Installing blanket insulation.

Batt Insulation

Batts are similar to blankets in many respects except that they are 48 in. long or less. They may have backing on one side or be completely enveloped and are used for the same purposes and in the same manner as blankets.

Structural Insulation Board

Structural insulation boards are made primarily from organic fiber—wood, cane, straw, or cork. In the case of wood and cane the raw material is first pulped, after which it is treated with waterproofing chemicals. The fibers are then formed into sheets of various thicknesses in a continuous process and cut into standard lengths. Some boards are impregnated with asphalt during the manufacturing process, while others are given a coat of asphalt after they are made.

Strawboard is made from carefully selected straw, fused under heat and pressure into a panel 2 in. thick and 4 ft wide. Boards are completely sealed in paper covers of various types to provide the proper surface for painting, papering, plastering, stucco, or roofing.

Corkboard is made from granulated cork mixed with resin and pressed into sheets of several thicknesses, depending on the use to which they will be put. A common thickness is 3 in., the board being used for roof insulation.

Structural insulation board is used in a variety of ways, including exterior wall sheathing, roof decking (Fig. 15·5) roof insulation under built-up roofing, shingle backer, interior finish board, insulating form board.

Insulation board used as exterior sheathing is normally supplied in ½-in.-thick square-edged sheets 4 ft wide and from 6 to 12 ft long, impregnated with asphalt. For shingle backer it is made ⁵⁄₁₆ or ⅜ in. thick in strips 11¾, 13½, 15, and 15½ in. wide and 48 in. long. For roof insulation, insulating fiberboard is made from ½ to 3 in. thick in single or multiple layers and in several dimensions. Interior wallboard is made ⁵⁄₁₆, ⅜, and ½ inch thick, in sheets 4 × 8 and 4 × 10 ft.

Figure 15 · 4
Straw panel board.
(Stramit Corporation Ltd., Edmonton, Alberta)

Figure 15 · 5
Straw board roof deck.
(Stramit Corporation Ltd., Edmonton, Alberta)

Rigid Slab Insulation

This type of thermal insulation is so called because the units are relatively stiff and inelastic. In most cases inorganic materials are used in their manufacture. Insulations falling into this category include mineral wool with binder, foamed plastic, cellular glass, foamed concrete, cellular hard rubber, shredded wood and cement. The insulative value of these materials lies in the fact that the basic material is a nonconductor and that the finished product contains millions of isolated air cells, ideal insulation.

Mineral wool has been described previously under blanket and batt insulation. When this material has been mixed with a binder and processed or fixed to a rigid back, sheets are produced which are suitable for roof-deck insulation and similar applications.

Foamed plastic insulation is made from expanded polystyrene and expanded polyurethane formed into slabs of various dimensions and thicknesses. Millions of tiny noninterconnecting air cells effectively resist the passage of heat and water vapor. For some applications such as insulation under built-up roofing, the slabs may be wrapped with asphalt-impregnated kraft paper.

Cellular glass insulation is made from expanded molten glass cast into block form and cut to various sizes and shapes. Thicknesses of 2, 2½, 3, and 4 in. are available in 12 × 18 in. blocks. A 1¾-in. thickness is available in 12 × 18 in. blocks, and a 1½-in. thickness is produced in 24 × 48 in. slabs.

It is a strong, rigid material with a compressive strength of about 100 psi and a density of 9 lb per cu ft. Its k factor is 0.38 at 50°F and 0.40 at 75°F. The usual method of application on flat surfaces is in hot asphalt or asphalt emulsion, as illustrated in Fig. 15·6. One method of applying blocks to vertical surfaces is with mastic. Another method is illustrated in Fig. 15·7, where the insulation was pressed in place over

Figure 15 · 6
Two-inch cellular glass insulation being applied to terrace area of new building. (Pittsburgh Corning Corporation)

pins spot-welded to the sheet-metal skin of the penthouse. Because of its rigidity, it is readily precut to shapes which will fit around steam or water pipes to insulate them (Fig. 15·8).

The manufacture of foamed concrete was described in Chap. 3. Because of its closed-cell construction, it is an important insulating material; walls made from blocks of this material, in its normal thickness, usually do not require any additional insulation. Foamed concrete of this type has a density of from 32 to 41 lb per cu ft with a k factor of from 0.82 to 1.09 Btu/(sq ft)(hour)(°F)(in.). Foamed concrete precast roof slabs are used for insulative as well as structural purposes and can have a built-up roof applied without further roof insulation.

Cellular hard rubber is a synthetic material containing cells filled with nitrogen. It is formed into slabs of varying sizes and thicknesses which are used in a similar manner to other kinds of rigid slab insulation.

Shredded wood or wood fiber by itself is a form of blanket insulation, but when portland cement slurry or special cements are added it sets up into a rigid block with similar insulating qualities.

Rigid slab insulations are particularly useful for such applications as roof-deck insulation, perimeter insulation, pipe insulation, cold-storage work, and cavity-wall insulation; it also can insulate masonry walls without furring.

Those rigid insulations which are impervious to moisture penetration resulting from continuous contact with the earth and moisture are particularly useful as perimeter insulation (Fig. 15·9).

A satisfactory method of insulating cavity walls is illustrated in Fig. 15·10. Here the required thickness of insulation is fixed to the backup wall with mortar or adhesive. Then the facing (brick, tile, stone) is laid up using metal ties to

Figure 15 · 7
Applying cellular glass insulation to a vertical surface. (Pittsburgh Corning Corporation)

Figure 15 · 8
Cellular glass insulation being secured to steam pipes by aluminum straps. (Pittsburgh Corning Corporation)

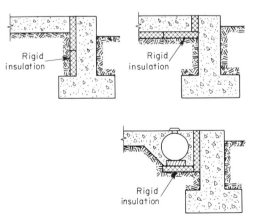

Figure 15 · 9
Perimeter insulation.

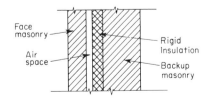

Figure 15 · 10
Insulated cavity wall.

anchor it to the backup wall and preferably leaving an air space between the face and the insulation.

Two methods are used to apply rigid insulation directly to masonry walls. One is to use portland cement mortar or a suitable adhesive to fix the slabs to the masonry. Then plaster can be applied directly to the inside face of the insulation. Mortar can be applied to the slabs by the use of a push box (Fig. 15·11).

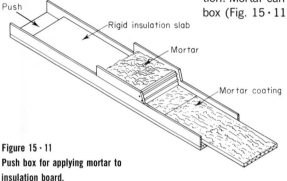

Figure 15·11
Push box for applying mortar to insulation board.

The other method mentioned above can be used if the wall is poured-in-place concrete. In such a case the inside face of the inner walls of the forms is lined with slab insulation. Strawboard can be used very well for such a purpose because the large size of the sheets facilitates the lining of the forms. When concrete is poured the insulation adheres to it, and when the forms are removed the inside of the concrete wall is left with an insulated surface to which plaster can be applied directly.

Concrete using as aggregate such lightweight materials as vermiculite, perlite, or expanded clay is useful as an insulation because of the cellular structure of the aggregates. Poured in place, it becomes a rigid slab that possesses structural strength as well as insulation value. This type of concrete is widely used as the base portion of a concrete slab-on-grade floor and as an insulating roof deck.

It is particularly important to incorporate insulating concrete in the floor slab when hot-water heating pipes are cast into the floor. Figure 15·12 illustrates a typical case.

Reflective Insulation

Reflective insulation is made from such materials as aluminum or copper foil or sheet metal, with bright surfaces that reflect heat rather than absorbing it.

Aluminum foil is produced in sheets or rolls and made up into blankets (Fig. 15·13). Other types of blankets consist of multiple-layer or accordion-style formations of paper covered with foil. Several companies supply gypsum lath and wallboard with one surface foil-covered. Some mineral-wool blanket insulations have a foil cover on one side.

276

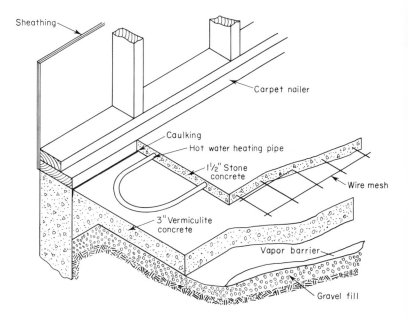

Figure 15 · 12
Insulating concrete for floors.

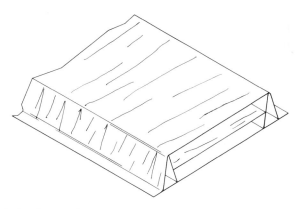

Figure 15 · 13
Aluminum-foil blanket.

Special papers coated with a polished-aluminum pigmented heat-reflective coating are produced as reflective insulation. These are supplied either in single sheets or with two sheets laminated by an asphalt adhesive. This material can be used as one side of a mineral-wool blanket.

Copper-foil insulation is commonly made in the form of a thin paper core covered on one or both sides with copper.

Reflective insulation can be used in stud, rafter, and joist spaces; to insulate walls, roofs, ceilings, and floors; and for cold-storage work.

As mentioned previously, it is necessary to install reflective insulation so that the reflective surface faces an air space of at least ¾ in. In ceilings, air spaces of at least 1½ in. are more effective.

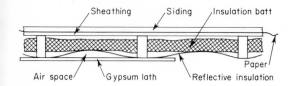

Figure 15 · 14
Reflective insulation draped between studs.

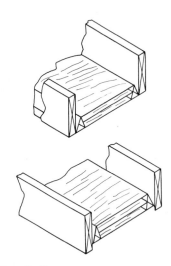

Figure 15 · 15
Foil blanket ceiling installation.

Sheet foil is commonly made 36 in. wide and on stud walls should be installed vertically for maximum benefit. A 36-in. width will span two 16-in. stud spaces and drape back between each pair of studs to form an air space between it and the inside finish (Fig. 15 · 14). For ceiling or floor insulation a foil blanket should be installed as shown in Fig. 15 · 15.

Foamed-in-place Insulation

This is a polyurethane product, made by combining a polyisocyanate and a polyester resin. Trichlorofluoromethane also can be used as a blowing agent in some cases, depending on the foam properties required.

This type of insulation can be applied either by pouring or by spraying. In either case, the two basic ingredients are drawn from their containers, measured, and mixed by machine. When the pouring system is being used, a carefully measured amount of the mixture is deposited in an existing cavity. The mixture reacts and foams up to fill a predetermined portion of the space to be filled. This volume of foam is called a "lift" and normally is limited to a height of about 14 in. When the foam has set, a new lift is poured and this process is repeated until the space is completely filled. The average density of this material when set is about 2 lb per cu ft.

The same materials are used for the spray application. A number of thin coats of foam are applied, one over the other, with sufficient time being left between each application for the foam to set up. By this system, any desired thickness of insulation can be applied, according to specifications.

Sprayed-on Insulations

Several materials are used in this type of application, one of them being the polyurethane foam described above. Other common ones are asbestos fiber mixed with inorganic binders, vermiculite aggregate with a binder such as portland cement or gypsum, and perlite aggregate using gypsum as a binder. Machines are used for blowing these insulations into place; as a result, the shape or irregularity of the surface being insulated is of little consequence.

Asbestos-fiber insulation is usually applied over a base coat of some adhesive, often a latex-type water emulsion. The primer should be applied to only as much of the surface as can be sprayed with fiber while the adhesive is still tacky. Application direct to metal lath does not require the priming adhesive.

This type of insulation also seals cracks and crevices to prevent dust from sifting through and eliminates joint and lap problems common to corrugated building materials. It also tends to protect metal from corrosive action.

The other two insulations in this group mentioned above can be sprayed over a base of gypsum lath, base coat plaster, masonry surface, or metal lath.

Figure 15 · 16
Sprayed-on asbestos-fiber insulation.
(Columbia Acoustics & Fireproofing Co.)

Corrugated Insulation

Corrugated insulation is usually made from paper formed into shapes that produce enclosed air pockets. One type is produced by shaping heavy paper into a series of small regular semicircular corrugations and covering both sides with a sheet of flat paper to give strength and produce the air pockets. This can be done using either single or multiple layers of corrugated paper (Fig. 15 · 17). This type of insulation is produced either in sheets or rolls, depending on the thickness of the mat, and is applied in strips fitting between studs or in large sheets cemented to a flat surface.

A more rigid type of corrugated insulation is made by forming a honeycomb-shaped mat with paper and covering both sides with a flat paper sheet. The whole thing is given its rigidity by spraying with a thin coating of portland cement slurry or other type of stiffener. The resulting paper mat, from 1 to 4 in. thick, is quite strong and may be used for

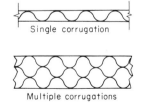

Figure 15 · 17
Corrugated paper insulation.

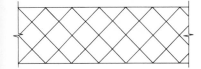

Figure 15 · 18
Paper honeycomb insulation.

nonbearing partitions, without further support, plastered on both sides. Figure 15 · 18 illustrates a cross section of this type of product.

DETERMINING HEAT LOSSES

Having studied the various ways by which heat is transferred and the materials which most effectively prevent heat loss or gain, we should now try to understand the common terms used in insulation engineering. This understanding will help you to be informed on the amount of heat that may be transferred by various kinds and thicknesses of insulation. This knowledge, in turn, will help you to select the most effective insulation for a specific situation.

Calculations of heat losses involve the use of five commonly used coefficients. They are: Btu, k, C, R, and U. Btu is the abbreviation for British thermal unit, the amount of heat required to raise the temperature of 1 lb of water 1°F. It is used to measure the amount of heat in the same way as an inch is used to measure distance and a second to measure time. For example, there are approximately 1,000 Btu in a cubic foot of natural gas, 535 Btu in a cubic foot of manufactured gas, 13,000 Btu in 1 lb of coal and 141,000 Btu in 1 gallon of fuel oil.

Thermal conductivity is another common term. It describes the number of Btu transferred in one hour, through 1 sq ft of homogeneous material 1 in. thick for a temperature difference of 1°F between the two surfaces of the material; it is designated by k. For example, the average k value for cellular glass is 0.40. This means that for a 1-in. thickness, 0.40 Btu of heat is transferred in one hour through 1 sq ft for every 1°F difference in temperature between the two surfaces of the material.

When we speak of the amount of heat transferred through a homogeneous or nonhomogeneous material under consideration without regard to thickness, we use the term conductance C. This means the number of Btu of heat transferred by 1 sq ft of a particular material in one hour for 1°F difference in temperature between the two surfaces. Insulation-grade strawboard, for example, made in the standard 2-in. thickness, has a C value of 0.17.

The resistance of a material to heat flow R is the reciprocal of k or C. Therefore $R = 1/k$ or $1/C$. Rock-wool insulation batts have an average k value of 0.27; consequently the R value of this material $= 1/0.27 = 3.7$.

We are most interested in the total transmission U of heat from one surface to the other of a complete structure such as a wall, ceiling, or floor. U is the number of Btu transmitted in one hour per square foot of structure surface for each 1°F difference in the temperature between the two surfaces. The U value of an uninsulated wood frame wall with wood sheathing and siding on the outside and gypsum lath and plaster on the inside is 0.24 Btu. If a 2-in. blanket insulation is inserted in the frame, the U value becomes 0.087 Btu and if the thickness of the insulation is increased to 3 in., the value becomes 0.065 Btu. Table 15·1 lists a number of common insulations and the average accepted k or C and R values for each.

Table 15·1

Heat loss coefficients (average).

MATERIAL	DESCRIPTION	CONDUCTIVITY OR CONDUCTANCE		RESISTANCE, R	
				PER IN. THICKNESS, $\dfrac{1}{k}$	PER THICKNESS LISTED, IN., $\dfrac{1}{C}$
		k	C		
Air spaces	Vertical		1.03		0.97
¾-in. or more thick, bounded	Horizontal—heat flow down		0.80		1.25
by ordinary materials	Horizontal—heat flow up		1.18		0.85
Air surfaces	Vertical		1.46		0.68
Still air	Horizontal—heat flow down		1.08		0.92
	Horizontal—heat flow up		1.63		0.61
Loose fills	Expanded vermiculite	0.50		2.00	
	Mineral wool (rock, slag, glass)	0.30		3.33	
	Wood fiber	0.30		3.33	
Batts or blankets	Mineral wool (rock, slag, glass)	0.27		3.70	
	Wood fiber	0.25		4.00	
Insulation boards	Wood or cane sheathing	0.38		2.63	
	Corkboard (without binder)	0.27		3.70	
	Wood or cane roof deck				
	1½ in.		0.24		4.17
	2 in.		0.18		5.56
	3 in.		0.12		8.33
	Strawboard normal, 2 in. thick				
	Insulation grade		0.17		5.88
	Structural grade		0.22		4.54
Rigid slabs	Foamed plastic	0.29		3.45	
	Cellular glass	0.40		2.50	
	Shredded wood and cement	0.55		1.82	
	Ytong 0.5 density	0.82		1.22	
	Ytong 0.65 density	1.09		0.91	
Foamed-in-place insulation	Polyurethane	0.19		5.26	
Cellular mass	Perlite concrete (1-to-7 mix)	0.53		1.89	
	Vermiculite concrete				
	(1-to-4 mix)	0.97		1.03	
	(1-to-6 mix)	0.76		1.31	
	Expanded clay concrete—3 in.		0.22		4.54
Sprayed-on	Perlite plaster				
	(2 cu ft/100 lb gypsum)	1.42		0.70	
	Vermiculite aggregate gypsum				
	plaster	0.95		1.05	
	Asbestos fiber with binder	0.26		3.84	

In order to determine the U value of a wall, ceiling, or floor, you must know the k or C value of each of the elements making up the structure. It must be remembered in this connection that the surfaces themselves have resistance values, depending on whether the surface is vertical or horizontal, whether or not the air at the surface is still or moving, and whether the heat flow at the surface is up or down.

When the conductivity or conductance values are all known, each must be converted to an R value, $1/k$ or $1/C$. All R values are then added and the U value of the complete structure will be the reciprocal of this total; that is $1/\text{sum of}$ R values.

Let us take a simple example. Find the U value of a frame wall consisting of 2 × 4 in. studs, ⅜-in. plywood sheathing, asphalt insulating siding, ⅜-in. gypsum lath, and ½-in. plaster inside finish. Resistance values are given in Table 15·2.

Table 15·2

ELEMENTS OF WALL	RESISTANCE
Outside surface	0.17
⅜-in. plywood sheathing	0.59
Asphalt insulating siding	1.45
Air space	0.97
Lath and plaster	0.41
Inside surface	0.68
Total R	4.27

$$U = \frac{1}{R} = \frac{1}{4.27} = 0.234$$

Now suppose that 2-in.-thick rock-wool batts had been installed between the studs as insulation. To the total R of 4.27 must be added the R for the batt (7.4) for a total R of 11.67. Now U will be $1/R = 1/11.67 = 0.085$. Going one step further, for a 40°F difference in temperature between inside and outside, in one hour each square foot of wall would transmit $40 \times 0.085 = 3.4$ Btu of heat. This compares with 9.36 Btu transmitted by the wall without insulation.

VAPOR INSULATION

The dampness that sometimes occurs inside buildings can be caused by penetration of moisture from the outside or by condensation of water vapor generated on the inside.

Protecting the interior of buildings against moisture penetration from outside involves well-known procedures. Protection against condensation of water vapor produced on the inside is a different matter and is perhaps not so well understood. Protection from the outside is provided by water-repellent materials which turn water aside and force it to return to the earth down the outside of the building. Moisture vapor, on the other hand, can permeate most ordinary building materials such as wood, paper, lath, plaster, untreated brick, etc.

In addition, this moisture vapor will condense into water when its temperature is reduced by contact with a cool surface or cool air. Hence, high humidity in a building may result in condensation of water not only on the inside of walls and windows but also on the outside or within the exterior walls, ceiling, or roof.

Moisture vapor is inevitable in a building. Occupants, cooking, laundering, unvented fuel-burning devices, humidifiers, and evaporation from basement floors or earth in crawl spaces all produce moisture vapor. Some moisture can be eliminated at its source, and adequate ventilation will help carry it away. But this does not provide the answer to the problem of condensation on the inside of buildings or within the walls. If the inside surfaces of walls and windows are kept warm enough, condensation will not take place on them. Vapor can be kept from penetrating the exterior walls from the inside by an effective vapor barrier—vapor insulation—on the inside of exterior walls.

VAPOR BARRIERS

Vapor barriers are materials which effectively retard or stop the flow of water vapor and normally are produced in sheets or thin layers. An acceptable vapor barrier is one that has a moisture-vapor permeance of not more than one *perm*. A perm is one grain of vapor transmission per square foot, per hour, per inch of mercury vapor pressure difference between the two surfaces.

Vapor barriers should be installed on the warm side of the insulation (Fig. 15·19). They should be continuous surfaces

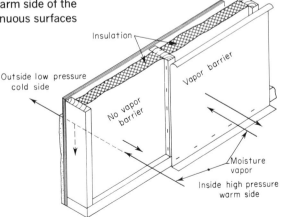

Figure 15 · 19
Vapor barrier on warm side of wall prevents moisture vapor from penetrating wall.

of asphalt or wax-coated paper, aluminum- or other metal-foil sheets, or polyethylene film. They can be attached to the insulation as part of the manufactured product or installed separately in or on the warm side of the wall, floor, or ceiling. For greatest effectiveness, they must be continuous and allow no openings through which vapor may pass. Asphalt-saturated felt paper is *not* a vapor barrier—it *is* a good moisture barrier and should be used on the outside of a building for that purpose.

Materials Used as Vapor Barriers

One effective vapor-barrier material is polyethylene film. It is a chemically inert plastic, unaffected by acids, alkalis, and caustics, produced in rolls 3 to 20 ft wide. Common thicknesses are 2, 3, 4, and 6 mil (1 mil = 0.001 in.). This film is useful not only as a vapor barrier for walls, ceilings, and floors, where the thinner grades are most often used, but also as a barrier to prevent the passage of moisture from the earth upward through a concrete slab laid on the ground.

Polyethylene film can be applied vertically in 36-in.-wide strips to studding on 16-in. centers with a full overlap on alternate studs, or sheets wide enough to cover the wall from top to bottom with an overlap on both floor and ceiling can be applied horizontally. The film is stapled to studs. Film should be applied lengthwise to ceiling joists with a lap of at least the full width of the joists. A full 6-in. overlap onto walls should be allowed. For floors, the film should be applied over subflooring in as full widths as possible with a 6-in. lap up the sidewalls.

The important thing in any such application as those described is to see that the film is not punctured. In cases where it must be cut around openings, electrical-outlet boxes, etc., care should be taken to see that it fits as snugly as possible around the opening.

Aluminum foil is used as a vapor barrier in several forms. One is the foil as a single sheet. Another is a thin layer of foil laminated to a heavy backing of asphalt-impregnated kraft paper. Still another consists of two layers of foil laminated with asphalt cement.

Kraft paper coated with asphalt or wax also acts as a vapor barrier. Sometimes two layers of paper are cemented with a continuous layer of asphalt. Whatever the material used, the same rule applies: the application should be continuous.

Moisture from the earth can enter a building through a concrete slab on grade by traveling upward through the concrete slab; when it reaches the warm inner surface it evaporates and becomes water vapor. To prevent this, a moisture barrier should be laid between the earth and the concrete. Polyethylene film is an excellent material for this purpose because it is impervious to the action of alkalis, decay, etc.

A 2-in. layer of sand should be laid over the grade to provide a cushion for the film. Then the film is laid over the sand
to form a continuous barrier to moisture. Material as wide as
possible should be used; where joints have to be made a wide
overlap is necessary for complete protection. Four- or six-mil
film should be used for this purpose because of its greater
resistance to tearing and puncturing. If wire mesh reinforcement is being used, it is laid over the film before the slab is
poured. In any case, great care must be taken to see that the
barrier is not broken during the preparation for the concrete
pour.

Care must be taken in insulating existing buildings where
no vapor barrier can be installed with the insulation. Where
there is a likelihood of too much moisture vapor being generated in the building, a good vapor barrier can be provided
by painting inside surfaces with two coats of lead and oil,
rubber emulsion, or aluminum paint.

In order to help control the moisture-vapor problem, the
indoor relative humidity should be kept within the limits
shown in the Table 15·3. If no method of measuring humidity
or automatically controlling humidities within given limits is
available, the formation of moisture on windows may be
taken as evidence of excessive humidity.

OUTSIDE TEMPERATURE, °F	MAX INSIDE RELATIVE HUMIDITY, %
Below 0	20
0 to 20	30
20 and over	40

Table 15 · 3
Relative humidity level needed
to control moisture buildup.

GLOSSARY

closed cells	Spaces which are completely separated from one another
convection	Transfer of heat by moving masses of matter
k factor	The unit rate of heat transmission
perimeter insulation	Insulation installed around the outer walls or foundations of a building
structural insulation board	A building board with structural strength as well as insulation value

REVIEW QUESTIONS

1. Give a concise definition of thermal insulation.
2. Give an example, other than the ones mentioned in the chapter, of each of the three methods of heat transfer.

285

3. Make a list of the nine basic kinds of thermal insulation and beside each write the name of two products that fall into that category of insulation.
4. What is the difference between batt and blanket insulation?
5. Explain why it is important that a reflective type insulation should face an air space of at least ¾ in.
6. What is one disadvantage of using loose-fill insulation in a vertical space?
7. Calculate the amount of heat transmitted by 1 sq ft of cellular glass insulation 3 in. thick, if the temperature at the inner surface is 50°F and at the outer surface it is 25°F.
8. Give two advantages of sprayed-on thermal insulation.
9. Explain why it is necessary to prevent the penetration of moisture vapor into the walls of a building.
10. Why should vapor barriers be installed on the warm side of the insulation?

SELECTED SOURCES OF INFORMATION

Aluminum Company of Canada, Ltd., Montreal, Que.
Atlas Asbestos Company Ltd., Toronto, Ont.
Cape Asbestos (Canada) Ltd., Toronto, Ont.
Dominion Rubber, Textile Division, Kitchener, Ont.
Dow Chemical Co., Midland, Mich.
Dow Chemical of Canada, Ltd., Sarnia, Ont.
National Cellulose Insulation Manufacturers Assn., Delphos, O.
Pal-O-Pak Insulation Company Inc., Hartland, Wis.
Pittsburgh Corning Corporation, Pittsburgh, Pa.
United States Mineral Wool Company, Stanhope, N.J.
Vermiculite Institute, Chicago, Ill.
Zonolite Company, Chicago, Ill.

16

FLOORING MATERIALS

This chapter deals with the final wearing surface which is applied over the subfloor. A great many materials are used as flooring. The choice of material for any particular room or area depends on a number of factors. One is the type of building involved—residential, industrial, or commercial— and the type of floor frame and subfloor. Another is the type of usage to which the floor will be subjected—light foot traffic, heavy foot traffic, wheeled traffic. Still another has to do with special requirements such as sound-absorption qualities, resilience, color, smoothness, resistance to chemicals, resistance to abrasion, or ease of maintenance. Cost is also important. This includes both the cost of the material and the labor involved in laying the floor. Flooring materials include wood, concrete, clay, asphalt, terrazzo, plastics, magnesite, rubber, and cork.

WOOD FLOORING

Wood flooring is made from both hardwood and softwood, in *strip, parquet,* and *block* form, with both *flat-grain* and *edge-grain* surface.

Softwood Strip Flooring

Softwood strip flooring is manufactured in two types, standard and heavy. Standard flooring is normally used in residences, offices, and schools; heavy flooring is intended for industrial uses, bowling alleys, and dance floors. Fig. 16·1 shows common widths and thicknesses of standard softwood flooring. Notice that the tongue and groove are located below

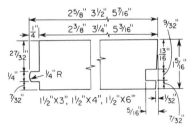

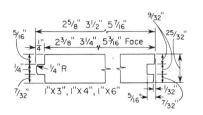

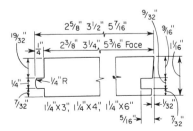

Figure 16·1
Standard softwood flooring.

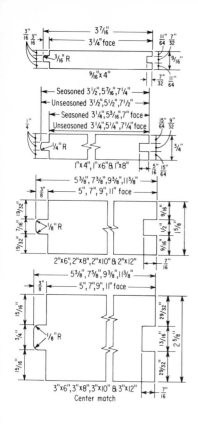

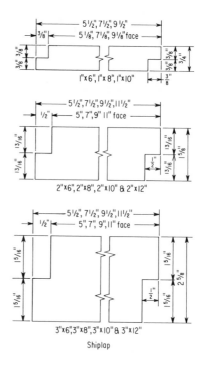

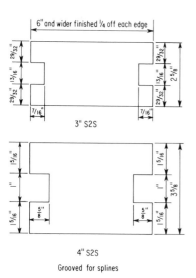

Shiplap

Figure 16·2
Heavy softwood flooring.

the center of the strip. Heavy softwood flooring is made in three styles, *center matched, grooved,* and *shiplap.* Fig. 16·2 illustrates the three styles and gives the common widths and thicknesses made. Southern pine and Douglas fir are commonly used for making softwood flooring because of their toughness and strength, but softwood flooring is also manufactured from hemlock, Sitka spruce, and red and white pine.

Grading rules vary somewhat from species to species but apply generally over the whole range of softwood flooring. Using Douglas fir flooring as an example, the first division is made into vertical-grain and flat-grain or angle-grain grades. Thus V.G. Flooring, K.D., means "vertical-grain flooring, kiln-dried." Vertical-grain flooring is then divided into three grades, "B and Better," "C," and "D." Specifications for each grade are outlined in grading rules published by manufacturers and lumbermen's associations and include permissible torn grain, pitch pockets, knots, and other defects as well as the minimum number of annual rings allowed per inch. Flat-grain flooring, which also contains angle-grain pieces, is also divided into three grades, "C and Better," "D," and "E." Again, grading rules specify the allowable defects.

Hardwood Strip Flooring

Many hardwood species are used to manufacture strip flooring, but the more common ones are maple, birch, beech, red and white oak, and walnut. The material is kiln-dried and made with tongue-and-groove edges and ends (end-matched) and usually has a channeled or grooved bottom surface. (Fig. 16·3). The purpose of the single or double channel or groove is to equalize moisture absorption and reduce cupping.

A variety of flooring thicknesses and face widths are made. The standard thicknesses and common uses are given in Table 16·1. In addition to these, extra-thick narrow flooring is made for bowling alleys.

The face widths in which each of the thicknesses listed above is made are given in Table 16·2.

Birch, maple, and beech flooring have similar grading standards and are available in First, Second, Third, and Fourth grades; quality shorts; and combination grades. Shorts consist of First- and Second-grade material in 9- and 18-in. lengths. There are two combination grades, prime and mill run. Prime combination grade consists of 60 percent First and 40 percent Second grade. Mill run is a combination of First, Second, and Third grades. Specifications for all grades are described in grading rules for hardwood flooring.

Oak flooring is first divided into two types, quartersawed and plain sawed and each type has its own grades. Quartersawed flooring is available in three grades, first grade, sap clear first grade, and second grade. In sap clear first grade, the face must be practically free of defects, but unlimited bright sapwood is allowed. The details of specifications for each grade are listed in grading rules for hardwood flooring.

Plain-sawed oak flooring grades are: first grade, second grade, No. 1 Common, No. 2 Common, prime-quality shorts,

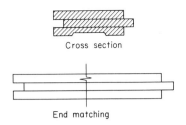

Cross section

End matching

Figure 16·3
Matched hardwood flooring.

Table 16·1
Hardwood strip flooring thicknesses.

THICKNESS, IN.		USES
NOMINAL	ACTUAL	
$\frac{3}{8}$	$\frac{11}{32}$	Residential, office floors
$\frac{1}{2}$	$\frac{15}{32}$	
$\frac{13}{16}$	$\frac{25}{32}$	
$1\frac{1}{16}$	$\frac{33}{32}$	Dance floors, gymnasiums, skating rinks, schools, churches
$1\frac{5}{16}$	$\frac{41}{32}$	
$1\frac{11}{16}$	$\frac{53}{32}$	

Table 16·2
Face widths of hardwood flooring.

THICKNESS, IN.	FACE WIDTHS, IN.
$\frac{3}{8}$	1½, 1¾, 2
$\frac{1}{2}$	1½, 1¾, 2
$\frac{13}{16}$	1½, 1¾, 2, 2¼, 2½, 2¾, 3¼
$1\frac{1}{16}$	2, 2¼, 2½, 2¾, 3¼
$1\frac{5}{16}$	2, 2¼, 3¼
$1\frac{11}{16}$	2, 2¼, 3¼

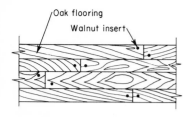

Figure 16 · 4
Colonial plank flooring.

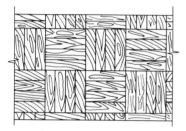

Figure 16 · 5
Parquet flooring.

mill-run grade, and No. 1 Common and Better shorts. Detailed specifications are given for each.

Strip flooring is also available in what is known as Colonial Plank, strips of various widths with round inserts of some contrasting wood (Fig. 16·4). Usual thickness is $2\frac{5}{32}$ in.; widths range from 3 to 8 in. Edges are tongue-and-grooved and the ends are grooved with splines supplied.

Parquet Flooring

Parquet flooring consists of blocks of hardwood of various sizes which can be laid in a number of patterns such as herringbone, basket weave, and squares. Common thickness is $2\frac{5}{32}$ in., and dimensions are $2\frac{1}{4} \times 6\frac{3}{4}$ in., 9, $11\frac{1}{4}$, $13\frac{1}{2}$, $15\frac{3}{4}$, and 18 in.; or 18×18 in. Small blocks approximately 1 in. square are also assembled in groups and held together with a paper backing to form parquet flooring. Blocks are designed both for blind nailing and for fastening to the subfloor with mastic. Fig. 16·5 shows parquet flooring laid in a square pattern.

Grading rules formulated for parquet flooring made from various hardwoods are available from national lumbermen's associations.

Block Flooring

Floor blocks are individual pieces of wood with edge-grain face made in a number of sizes; a common one is $2 \times 2 \times 3\frac{1}{2}$ in. They may be made with square edges (Fig. 16·6a) to be laid in mastic or with dovetailed bottom (Fig. 16·6b) to be attached to a base strip. In the latter case the blocks are grooved on their sides for splines and are held down by nailing the base strip to the subfloor.

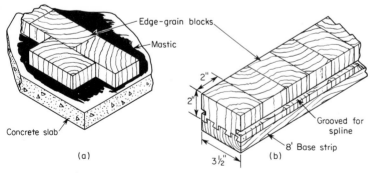

Figure 16 · 6
Edge-grain floor blocks.

CONCRETE FLOORING

Concrete is used for flooring in a wide variety of situations, ranging from basement play and recreation areas to buildings housing heavy industry. As a result they are subjected to every kind of wear and abuse, such as impact, abrasion, and attack by salts and aggressive liquids. In view of this, it is important that the best materials and workmanship go into the making of concrete floors.

Floors that are subject to light duty should have a strength of approximately 3,500 psi, whereas the strength of floors subjected to medium and heavy duty (foot or truck traffic) should range from 4,500 to 7,000 psi or more. A very important fact to consider in the construction of exposed concrete floors is that it is the aggregate that must withstand the bulk of the wear and tear of traffic. Even cement paste with very high compressive strength has poor abrasion resistance. It is the aggregate which lies at the surface of the floor that absorbs abrasion and impact.

For floors subjected to light traffic, a well-washed, graded, sound quartz or crystalline granite aggregrate will usually suffice. For heavier-duty floors, traprock, silica, and emery are desirable as aggregates, while for floors subjected to heavy traffic it is often preferable to use specially quarried or manufactured aggregates made from metallic and nonmetallic materials. Traprock and emery offer reasonably good abrasion resistance but are somewhat lacking in impact strength. They are quite satisfactory for foot traffic. If hard-wheeled or heavy vehicular traffic is expected, one of the metallic aggregates, specially manufactured for the purpose, will provide considerably greater wear resistance.

In any case it is important that the concrete be thoroughly mixed to ensure an even distribution of aggregates throughout the mix and a thorough coating of each particle of aggregate by cement paste. It is also important that the slump be kept as low as possible. This lessens the possibility of water bleeding to the surface and bringing with it a layer of cement paste which will provide a smooth but poor-wearing surface. Good curing procedures are also essential in the production of a strong concrete floor.

Floors may be poured as single monolithic slabs or they may be composed of a base slab covered by a topping. In the latter case, the base slab should be left with a well-roughened surface to provide a good bonding surface for the topping mix. The two-course floor makes it possible to use any one of a number of types of topping mix in order to achieve some desired result.

A particularly hard surface can be achieved by introducing metallic aggregates into the topping. These consist of specially processed, size-graded, iron particles, with often a

cement dispersal agent added. Fig. 16·7 illustrates the difference in wearing ability between floors made with and without metallic aggregates. The regular concrete floor surface on the right has deteriorated badly after five years of usage, while the adjoining floor section on the left, subject to the same traffic but made with metallic aggregate, is still in good condition.

Metallic aggregates are normally applied to the freshly poured surface as a shake and worked into the top by float and trowel. Various amounts can be used, depending on the type of use. Recommendations on the amount of metallic aggregate to be applied per square foot under various conditions of usage are given in Table 16·3.

Table 16·3
Amount of metallic aggregate for various types of use.
(Master Builders Co.)

TYPE OF TRAFFIC	AMOUNT, LB/SQ FT
Heavy foot traffic	0.5
Light wheel traffic	0.75
Medium wheel traffic	1.00
Heavy wheel traffic	1.25
Extra-heavy wheel loads	10
Extra-heavy impact	20

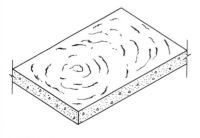

Figure 16·8
Nonskid concrete floor surface.

Metallic-aggregate topping can be finished to produce a nonskid surface. Finishing with a wooden or cork float produces a surface like that shown in Fig. 16·8. Nonskid surfaces can also be produced by using abrasive-type aggregates, such as aluminum oxide and silicon carbide, in the floor topping.

Colored concrete floors are produced by adding some type of inorganic coloring agent to the topping mix or by shaking it over the surface and floating it into the top. One type of coloring agent consists of mineral oxides in powder form. They are mixed with the topping mix at the recommended rate of not more than 10 lb per bag of cement. A general guide to the selection of coloring materials is given in Table 16·4.

Another coloring agent consists of a fine grade of silica aggregate, synthetic inorganic pigment, and a water-reducing agent, thoroughly mixed together. This is applied as a shake

COLOR REQUIRED	COLORING AGENT
Blues	Cobalt oxide
Browns	Brown oxide of iron
Buffs	Synthetic yellow oxide of iron
Greens	Chromium oxide
Reds	Red oxide of iron
Grays, blacks	Black iron oxide

Table 16·4
Mineral oxide coloring agents.

over the freshly finished floor top at the rate of ½ lb per square foot and floated into the surface. Final troweling produces a smooth surface.

Metallic aggregates are produced which have a coloring agent added. It is a synthetic, inorganic metallic oxide. This type of metallic aggregate is applied in a similar manner to others and can be given a float or a trowel finish. Fig. 16·9 shows a colored metallic aggregate topping applied to a single-course concrete floor.

The use of metallic aggregates also results in the production of floors that are nonsparking. Frictional sparks resulting from the striking of metal on stone are eliminated, and by having the right degree of conductivity metallic aggregate floors overcome the hazard of static sparks.

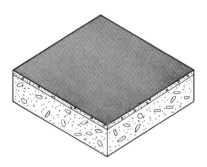

Figure 16·9
Colored metallic aggregate topping.

Concrete is also used to make floor tile by forcing the concrete into molds by hydraulic pressure and by allowing it to set and cure. Sometimes tile are made in two layers, the upper one being made of mortar with white cement and marble chips as aggregate. The upper layer also can be made of colored mortar. After curing, the tiles are surface-ground to produce a smooth finish.

CLAY-TILE FLOORING

Clay tile are made by a process similar to that used in manufacturing brick; both glazed and unglazed units are made. A number of general types of tile are produced, including quarry tile, pavers, packing-house tile, galley tile, faience, ceramic mosaic, and glazed interior tile.

Quarry tile are hard dense unglazed tile made either by the dry-press or extrusion method. Usually clays are used which, when burned, produce red, brown, and buff colors. They are made in square and oblong shapes, from ½ to ¾ in. thick. Square sizes are 2¾, 4, 6, 8, and 9 in., while oblong tile are 2¾ × 6 in., 3¾ × 8 in., 4 × 8 in., and 6 × 9 in. In conjunction with these a number of shapes of trim tile are made, including straight base, cove base, internal- and external-angle base, and double bullnose.

Paver tile are similar to quarry tile but with a thickness of from ⅜ to ⅝ in. Square pavers are 3, 4, 4¼, and 6 in. square, and oblong ones are 3 × 6 in. They are intended for a little lighter duty than quarry tile.

Packing-house tile are intended for heavy, industrial uses, with a thickness of from 1¼ to 1⅝ in. and 4 x 8 in. dimensions.

Galley tile are a special quarry tile with an indented pattern on the surface. Their thickness is from ⅝ to ¾ in.; usual face dimensions are 6 x 6 in.

Faience is a hard, durable glazed tile made with a comparatively uneven surface. Thicknesses vary from ½ to ⅝ in., and face dimensions are 4¼ × 4¼ in. to 6 × 6 in. They are intended both for interior use and for exterior use if they pass the Standard Weather Test.

Ceramic mosaic consists of small pieces of glazed or unglazed tile arranged in patterns (Fig. 16·10) in a standard sheet unit. In some cases a paper backing is used to hold the pieces together, while in others they are bonded to a preformed rubber grid. The latter sheet units are 9 x 9 in., while the ones on a paper back are approximately 1 x 2 ft. All have a nominal thickness of ¼ in.

These small tiles are made in a variety of shapes, with a

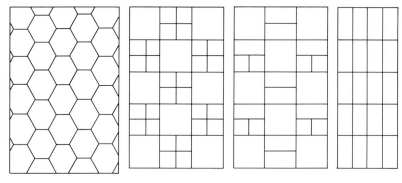

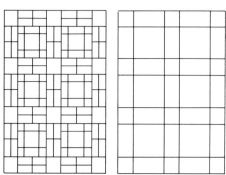

Figure 16 · 10
Ceramic mosaic patterns.

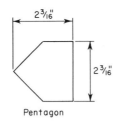

Pentagon

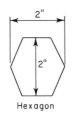

Hexagon

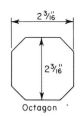

Octagon

Figure 16·11
Ceramic mosaic sizes.

number of sizes available in each shape. Square tile are made ½, ¾, 1, 1¹⁄₁₆, 1⁹⁄₁₆, and 2³⁄₁₆ in. square. Oblong sizes include ½ × 1¹⁄₁₆ in., ¾ × 1⁹⁄₁₆ in., and 1¹⁄₁₆ × 2³⁄₁₆ in. Sizes of other shapes are as follows: pentagon, 2³⁄₁₆ in.; hexagon, 1, 1¼, and 2 in.; octagon, 2³⁄₁₆ in. (Fig. 16·11).

Glazed interior tile have a glasslike finish, a hard mat glaze that is produced in a wide variety of colors. The nominal thickness is ⅜ in., and tile are made 3, 4¼, and 6 in. square; 2¹⁄₁₆ × 4¼ in. oblong; 3 in. hexagonal; and 4¼ in. octagonal.

Several methods are used to bond tile to the base floor. When the base is concrete, one common method is to lay them in Type A cement mortar. In this case grout is poured on the surface and rubbed into the joints after the tile have been laid. Organic adhesives or inorganic bonding coats are used when the tile are laid over a wood or asphaltic surface.

ASPHALT FLOORING

Asphalt is the basic ingredient in two types of flooring, asphalt mastic flooring and asphalt tile.

Asphalt mastic flooring is made by mixing an emulsified asphalt with portland cement, sand and gravel, or crushed stone to form a plastic mixture. This is spread over the floor, screeded, compacted, and floated to a depth of ½ in.

The emulsified asphalt is a clay type—a dispersion of asphalt in water, held in suspension by a mineral colloid. It has resiliency, adhesion, and masticity but does not flow under heat and is not toxic or flammable. The mix is usually made in the following proportions: 1 cu ft (1 bag) portland cement, 2 cu ft (12½ gal) emulsified asphalt, 2 cu ft clean sharp sand, and 4 cu ft hard washed gravel chips.

This asphaltic mastic flooring can be applied over a wood, concrete, or steel base. In each case the base must be primed with the proper type of asphaltic primer. In addition, in the case of a wood base, a tack coat of asphalt emulsion should be applied over the primer.

This mastic flooring also can be molded in forms to make sections of precast asphalt flooring, called asphalt planks. These are laid on a solid level base and cemented down with an asphaltic bonding preparation.

Asphaltic tiles are composed of asbestos fibers bound

together by a blend of selected asphaltic binders. Pigments are added for color and in some cases polystyrene plastic is added to produce a stronger tile. The ingredients are machine-mixed and formed into sheets ⅛ or ³⁄₁₆ in. thick under pressure. The sheets are then precision-cut into tiles of several sizes—9 × 9 in., 12 × 12 in., and 18 × 24 in. Feature strips 1 or 2 in. wide and 18 in. long are also produced.

A great range of colors and designs is produced, including a large number of insert designs. This makes possible an almost unlimited number of floor patterns possible with this type of tile. Asphalt tile can be laid over a wood, asphaltic mastic, or concrete base (including a concrete slab on grade) using an asphaltic adhesive. The surface must be smooth and even, since the asphalt tile tend to be brittle and may crack on an uneven surface. These tiles are highly resistant to water but are not resistant to organic acids or petroleum solvents. Hence they are not satisfactory for many industrial uses.

TERRAZZO FLOORING

Terrazzo is the name given to a type of ground concrete floor finish which results in a surface with a mottled appearance (Fig. 16·12). It is widely used in public buildings and makes a durable and attractive wearing surface.

A base slab is poured first, reinforced with wire mesh to reduce shrinkage and settlement cracks. Next, a layer of cement and sand, mixed very dry, is spread over the base, worked flat, and compacted. This forms a cushion on which the terrazzo topping is placed.

A gridwork, consisting of thin strips of brass, bronze, aluminum, or plastic, is laid on the sand-cement cushion, bedded in, and leveled. The grid stands up approximately 1 in. above the sand-cement layer and is so arranged that the floor area is divided into a number of squares or rectangles of equal size. Grids should be so arranged that a strip will run above and parallel to each floor beam and completely circle each column rising from the floor.

Terrazzo surface

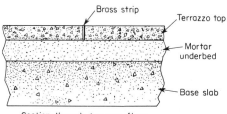

Section through terrazzo floor

Figure 16 · 12
Terrazzo floor.

The topping mix is then made up, consisting of cement, sand, and marble chips or an abrasive material as coarse aggregate. It is mixed as dry as is practical for placing. This topping is spread over the floor and compacted until it is level with the top of the grid strips. After the topping has cured sufficiently, the surface is ground and polished by machine.

Terrazzo has a tendency to be slippery, so on ramps, elevator entrances, and other locations where nonslip surface is required, abrasive aggregates such as aluminum oxide should be used. By the use of white cement, colored pigments, and carefully chosen marble chips of one or more colors, a great variety of effects can be produced.

PLASTIC FLOORING

Plastics are used in several types of flooring, including plastic terrazzo, vinyl-plastic tiles, vinyl-asbestos tiles, and vinyl-cushioned flooring.

In plastic terrazzo an epoxy resin is used instead of portland cement paste as a binder for marble chips. A mixture of a liquid epoxy resin, inert filler pigment, and color pigment is used as the resin component. A typical formulation consists of 100 lb of epoxy resin, 50 lb of fine calcium silicate, 2¼ lb of titanium dioxide, and ¾ lb of a mineral pigment. To this is added 10 lb of a hardening and curing agent, an aliphatic polymine. In this amount of binder 450 lb of small marble chips can be used.

This plastic mixture is spread over the floor about ¼ in. thick. After hardening (one to two days after application) the topping can be ground smooth and polished. This type of topping can be applied over a wood, concrete, or old terrazzo base. Mixes should be limited to about 100 lb total, because the plastic has a limited pot life, about 1 to 1½ hours at 75°F. Metal grid strips can be secured to the subfloor with an epoxy-resin adhesive. This topping weighs about 3 lb per sq ft, ¼ in. thick.

Vinyl tile is made of a layer of vinyl plastic bonded to a flexible backing. Tiles are 6 × 9 in. and 9 × 9 in. in thicknesses of ³⁄₃₂, ⅛, and ⁹⁄₁₀₀ in. Feature strips 1 × 36 in. and rolls 54, 45, and 27 in. wide are also made. Vinyl tiles can be applied to floors on or above grade and are laid in vinyl cement. For concrete floors on grade a special waterproof cement is used. Vinyl is highly resistant to fats and oils, most acids, alkalies, and petroleum derivatives. A wide range of colors and designs are available.

Vinyl-asbestos tiles are made of a composition of thermoplastic vinyl resin and plasticizer, asbestos fibers, pigments, and filler. These are mixed hot and formed into sheets ¹⁄₁₆ or ⅛ in. thick under pressure. Tiles 9 × 9 in. and feature strips 1 or 2 × 18 in. are cut from these sheets. The same general range of colors is found as in asphalt and vinyl tile.

This type of tile is suitable for floors on and above grade

and is laid in an asphaltic base cement. Vinyl-asbestos is highly resistant to grease, acids, and alkalies.

Vinyl-cushioned flooring is composed of a thick sponge vinyl backing covered with a layer of closely woven fiber glass fabric to provide strength and stability. Over this is laid a layer of vinyl plastic imprinted with the color or colors desired, and finally a surface of clear vinyl is applied. These layers are bonded together by heat and result in a flexible flooring material of approximately 0.15 in. thick.

The flooring is produced in rolls 54 and 72 in. wide and is laid in a special cement made for the purpose. Adjoining edges are joined with a special cement. Strong solvents should not be used for cleaning, and varnishes, shellacs, or lacquers should not be applied to the surface.

MAGNESITE FLOORING

Magnesite flooring compound is made from calcined magnesium oxide and magnesium chloride. These materials are mixed into a plastic state and applied to the floor in two separate coats, totaling from ½ to ¾ in. thick. A considerable quantity of coarse, fibrous filler is mixed with the first coat to give it strength and flexibility. The second coat has no fiber, but color pigment is mixed with it to produce any color or colors required.

Magnesite flooring is applied over either a wood or concrete base. Sometimes metal lath is laid over a wood base to produce a better bond. Marble chips may be added to the freshly poured surface and rolled in to produce magnesite terrazzo. Such flooring is quiet, resilient, nonslip, and fireproof but not completely water-resistant.

RUBBER FLOORING

Rubber is used for flooring in the form of tiles. Synthetic rubber is used since it has less tendency to oxidize than natural rubber. Pigments and plasticizers are mixed with the liquid rubber and the mixture is rolled into sheets under pressure and cut into 6-, 9-, and 12-in. squares and 18×36 in. rectangles, in thicknesses of $\frac{3}{32}$, $\frac{1}{8}$, and $\frac{3}{16}$ in.

Rubber tile is suitable for floors above grade and is laid in a rubber-base cement. It is very pliable and provides good resilience and relatively good sound absorption.

CORK FLOORING

Cork is used as a basic ingredient in two types of flooring, linoleum and cork tile.

Linseed oil is used as the binder in the manufacture of linoleum. It is oxidized by air treatment until it becomes a tough plastic substance somewhat like rubber. Powdered cork, resin gum, wood flour, and color pigments are then mixed with it and the resulting mixture is spread over a burlap backing and rolled into sheets. Three thicknesses are made— $3/32$ in. ("A" grade), $1/8$ in. ("AA" grade), and $1/4$ in. ("AAA" grade). It is produced in rolls 6 ft wide and as 9×9 in. and 12×12 in. linoleum tiles. Two types of roll linoleum are made, plain or battleship linoleum and inlaid linoleum. Plain linoleum is one single color while inlaid linoleum is made up of several colors which extend through to the burlap backing.

Linoleum can be laid on any wood floor above grade and can be laid over suspended concrete floors, providing they are dry. Two types of linoleum cement are used, plain for ordinary installations and waterproof cement for such locations as kitchens and bathrooms. Linoleum and linoleum tile should be laid over a thick felt paper base, which can be bonded to the subfloor with the same cement.

Cork tile is made by mixing cork shavings with resin and compressing the plastic mixture into molds. Tiles are baked to set the resin. Two thicknesses of tile are produced, $3/16$ and $5/16$ in.; sizes include 6-, 9-, and 12-in. squares and 6×12 in. and 12×24 in. rectangles.

They are laid on floors above grade in a special adhesive and rolled down with a heavy roller. The surface is sanded and given a coat of filler and finally waxed.

Cork tile are warm, quiet, and resilient but not as durable as many others. They resist water but not oils and grease.

The group of flooring materials which includes asphalt, vinyl, vinyl-asbestos, cork, rubber and linoleum tile, roll linoleum, and cushioned flooring are known as resilient floorings.

When preparing a subfloor to receive one of these resilient floorings and when laying the flooring material, manufacturers' instructions should be followed exactly. The same is true when applying cleaners, waxes, and polishes. A cleaning material which is satisfactory for one may cause permanent damage to another. Attention must also be paid to the recommended temperatures for laying these floorings and, in the case of many of them, to the temperature of the floor itself. For example, it is recommended that for concrete floors heated by radiant heating coils, the floor temperature should not exceed 85°F. If instructions such as the aforementioned are complied with, all these materials will give satisfactory service, and the choice of which one to use in a specific situation will depend on location, use, color desired, resiliency required, cost, and permanency.

GLOSSARY

abrasive aggregates   Concrete aggregates in which the particles have abrasive qualities

aliphatic polymine	A polymerized compound containing a fatty substance
asphalt mastic	A plastic flooring material containing asphalt
colloid	A substance in a state of fine division
faience	Terra-cotta tile with an indented or raised decorative surface
feature strip	A contrasting strip, usually in a floor
monolithic slab	A floor slab having the entire thickness poured at one time
mosaic	A surface decoration made by inlaying small pieces of material in patterns
parquet	Pieces of wood forming a geometric pattern
plasticizer	A material added to increase the plasticity of a product
pot life	The length of time during which a material will remain in a plastic, workable state in its container
primer	A first coat over a surface
shake	Material applied to a floor by sprinkling over the surface

REVIEW QUESTIONS

1 List 10 factors which may be taken into consideration when deciding on the material to be used as flooring for a particular area.
2 List three situations in which you would choose heavy edge-grain softwood flooring as the proper material for the floor.
3 What is mill-run hardwood flooring?
4 What are the advantages of block flooring?
5 Outline three advantages of a two-course concrete floor over a single-course floor.
6 List three reasons for using metallic aggregate in a concrete floor topping.
7 Draw a vertical section through a floor with terrazzo topping, showing all the parts of the floor.
8 (a) What is resilient-tile flooring?
   (b) List five flooring materials which fall into this category
9 Outline the differences between battleship linoleum and inlaid linoleum.

SELECTED SOURCES OF INFORMATION

Armstrong Cork Co., Lancaster, Pa.
Building Products of Canada Limited, Vancouver, B.C.
Canadian General-Tower Ltd., Galt, Ont.
Canadian Lumbermen's Association, Ottawa, Ont.
CIBA Products Company, Plastics Dept., Toronto, Ont.
Dominion Oilcloth & Linoleum Company Ltd., Montreal, Que.
Evertex Co. Ltd., Granby, Que.
Harris Mfg. Co., Johnson City, Tenn.
Ludowici-Celadon Co., Chicago, Ill.
Master Builders, Cleveland, O.
Mastic Tile Corporation of America, Joliet, Ill.
Portland Cement Association, Chicago, Ill.
Southern Pine Association, New Orleans, La.
Tremco Mfg. Co., Toronto, Ont.

17

ROOFING MATERIALS

The roof of a building is actually made up of three components: (1) the frame or skeleton, (2) the rigid inner layer or skin which is fastened to the frame and supports the outer skin, and (3) the exposed outer layer.

When the roof is flat, the material used to form the inner layer is usually referred to as decking. If it is sloped, the inner skin material is called the roof sheathing. Roof decks or sheathing may be boards, plywood, concrete, steel, gypsum, rigid insulation boards, strawboard, or tile, all of which have been discussed elsewhere in this book.

The exposed outer, waterproof layer of the roof is known as the roofing. Roofing materials include shingles of all kinds, wooden shakes, various kinds of roofing tile, slate, sheet metal, asbestos-cement sheet roofing, asphalt roofing, glass, and plastics.

SHINGLES

A common method of weatherproofing a sloping roof is to cover it with shingles or shakes. While originally both were made exclusively from wood, shingles are now made from asphalt-impregnated felt paper, from asbestos-cement, and from sheet aluminum.

Wood Shingles

Several species of wood are used to make wood shingles, including some pines, redwood, and red cedar; but by far the largest proportion of wood shingles on the market are made from western red cedar. There are a number of reasons for this choice. In proportion to its weight, which is quite light when dry, cedar has unusually high crushing strength. The trees grow slowly, and as a result the wood has narrow annual rings. This, in turn, results in a fine, evenly grained wood with uniform texture. Cedar trees grow very large, with relatively few knots, so that shingles free from blemishes and distorted grain can be produced in large quantities. Most important is the fact that cedar has a low coefficient of expansion and contraction due to changes in moisture conditions. This means that cedar shingles, in changing from a wet to an air-dry condition, are less likely to split or check than most wood.

Figure 17 · 1
Cutting up cedar log.
(Consolidated Red Shingle Assn. of B.C.)

In manufacturing cedar shingles, carefully chosen logs are first sawed into 16-, 18-, or 24-in. lengths. Because of the large diameter of many of these pieces, they must be split or cut into blocks of proper size for the shingle machines. To do this they are quartered, split, and requartered until they are of a convenient size. Every effort is made to produce blocks which have an edge-grain face (Fig.17 · 2).

Upright machines then saw these blocks into shingles, alternating the feed so that a tapered shingle with the butt either up or down is cut at each stroke. The operator also clips the edges of each shingle at right angles to the butt and cuts out defects, if any, during this clipping operation. He

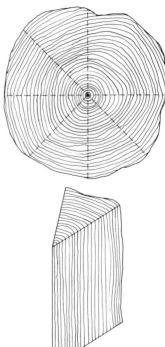

Figure 17 · 2
How shingle blocks are cut up.

Figure 17 · 3
Sawing and clipping cedar shingles.
(Consolidated Red Cedar Shingle Assn. of B.C.)

then drops the shingles into one of three chutes, depending on the grade, which carry them to the packing bins.

Here they are regraded and packed into bundles containing enough shingles to cover approximately 25 sq ft when properly applied at the recommended exposure. Shingles are packed green and may be shipped green or stacked and air dried or kiln-dried.

Most shingles are manufactured in random widths, but no shingle is allowed to be wider than 14 in. in any grade or less than 3 in. in most grades. Three standard lengths of shingle

Figure 17 · 4
Packing cedar shingles.
(Consolidated Red Cedar Shingle Assn. of B.C.)

Figure 17 · 5
Shingles going into dry kiln.
(Consolidated Red Cedar Shingle Assn. of B.C.)

are made—24, 18, and 16 in.; but 10 percent of the shingles in any shipment may be over or under the specified length.

Twenty-four-in. shingles are packed in bundles containing 13 courses on one side of the band sticks and 14 courses on the other. Eighteen-in. bundles contain 18 courses on each side, and sixteen-in. bundles are packed 20 courses to each side. Twenty-four-in. shingles are cut so that four butts measure 2 in. thick when green. This is designated as 4/2 in. With 18-in. shingles 5 butt thicknesses total 2¼ in., while with 16-in. shingles 5 butts total 2 in.

All lengths of shingles are divided into three grades: No 1, No. 2, and No. 3. The No. 1 grade of 16-in. shingles are commonly known as "5x," written as xxxxx.

No. 1 grade shingles are all edge-grain, strictly clear from butt to tip, and contain no sapwood. Cross-grain and diagonal grain may be considered defects, depending on the degree and location on the shingle. The sides of the shingle must be parallel within tolerance of ¼ in., and not more than 10 percent of the shingles in any shipment may be less than 4 in. wide.

No. 2 grade shingles must have 12 in. clear, measured from the butt in the 16- and 18-in. lengths, and 16 in. clear in the 24-in. length. Knots or knotholes not more than 2 in. wide for 16 in. and not more than 3 in. wide for 18- and 24-in. shingles are permitted. The total amount of sapwood within 10 in. of the butts must not exceed 1 in., but sapwood above that point is not considered a defect. The sides of 16- and 18-in. shingles must be parallel within a tolerance of ¼ in., while 24-in. shingles are allowed a tolerance of ⅜ in. Not more than 20 percent of the shingles in any shipment may be less than 4 in. wide.

No. 3 grade shingles may have sapwood in the butts but otherwise 16- and 18-in.-long shingles must have 6 in. clear, and 24-in. shingles 10 in. clear. Shingles 2½ in. wide are allowed in the 16-in. length, but not more than 30 percent of the shingles in any shipment may be less than 4 in. wide. A specifications manual should be consulted for a complete description of each grade in each length. Table 17·1 gives a brief summary of sizes, packing rules, running inches, and shipping weights for cedar shingles.

The amount that a roof shingle should be exposed to the weather depends on the pitch of the roof and the length of shingle used. The maximum exposure on ⅛ and ⅙ pitches should be 3¾ in. for 16-in. shingles, 4¼ in. for 18-in. shingles and 5¾ in. for 24-in. shingles. For roofs with a pitch steeper than ⅙, the maximum exposure for 16-in. shingles should be 5 in., for 18-in. shingles 5½ in., and for 24-in. shingles 7½ in.

The covering capacity in square feet of one bundle of shingles, with various exposures, in each of the three shingle lengths is given in Table 17·2.

Table 17 · 1

Summary of sizes, packing rules, running inches, and shipping weights of shingles. (Canadian Standards Association)

GRADES	SHINGLE THICKNESSES, GREEN, IN.	APPROXIMATE BUNDLE THICKNESS, IN.		NUMBER OF COURSES PER BUNDLE	NUMBER RUNNING INCHES PER 4-BUNDLE SQUARE		SHIPPING WEIGHTS PER SQUARE
		GREEN	DRY		GREEN	DRY	ROOF—4 BUNDLES
No. 1—24-in. (Royals)	4 butts = 2	6½/7	6⅓/6¾	13/14	1998	1920	192
No. 1—18-in. (Perfections)	5 butts = 2¼	8⅛	7⅞	18/18	2664	2620	158
No. 1—16-in. (XXXXX)	5 butts = 2	8	7¾	20/20	2960	2880	144
No. 2—24-in. (16-in. clear)	4 butts = 2	6½/7	6⅓/6¾	13/14	1998	1920	192
No. 2—18-in. (12-in. clear)	5 butts = 2¼	8⅛	7⅞	18/18	2664	2620	158
No. 2—16-in. (12-in. clear)	5 butts = 2	8	7¾	20/20	2960	2880	144
No. 3—24-in. (10-in. clear)	4 butts = 2	6¼/6¾	6/6½	13/14	1998	1920	192
No. 3—18-in. (6-in. clear)	5 butts = 2¼	7⅞	7⅝	18/18	2664	2620	158
No. 3—16-in. (6-in. clear)	5 butts = 2	7¾	7½	20/20	2960	2880	144

Table 17 · 2

Covering capacities per bundle of the various sized shingles, sq ft. (Canadian Standards Association)

EXPOSURE IN.	16-IN. SHINGLES 20/20 PACK	18-IN. SHINGLES 18/18 PACK	24-IN. SHINGLES 13/14 PACK	EXPOSURE IN.	16-IN. SHINGLES 20/20 PACK	18-IN. SHINGLES 18/18 PACK	24-IN. SHINGLES 13/14 PACK	EXPOSURE IN.	16-IN. SHINGLES 20/20 PACK	18-IN. SHINGLES 18/18 PACK	24-IN. SHINGLES 13/14 PACK
3½	17½	15½	—	7½	37½	34	25	11½	57½	52	38
4	20	18	—	8	40	36	26½	12	60	54½	40
4½	22½	20	—	8½	42½	38½	28	12½	—	56½	41½
5	25	22½	—	9	45	40½	30	13	—	59	43
5½	27½	25	—	9½	47½	43	31½	13½	—	61	45
6	30	27	20	10	50	45	33	14	—	63½	46½
6½	32½	29½	21½	10½	52½	47½	35	14½	—	—	48
7	35	31½	23	11	55	50	36½	15	—	—	50

Figure 17 · 6
Sawing blocks for shakes.
(Consolidated Red Cedar Shingle Assn. of B.C.)

Figure 17 · 7
Cutting resawed shake blanks.
(Consolidated Red Cedar Shingle Assn. of B.C.)

Wood Shakes

Shakes are used for the same purpose as shingles but are split rather than sawed from the cedar blocks. This produces a much rougher face than is the case with shingles.

Three types of shakes are made: (1) hand-split and re-sawed, (2) taper-split, and (3) straight-split. Hand-split and resawed shakes are made by cutting blanks of proper thickness from the block and running them through a band saw diagonally. This produces two tapered shakes with a split face and sawed back from each blank (Fig. 17 · 8). Taper-split shakes are produced by hand-splitting. A shingle like taper is achieved by reversing the block end-for-end with each split. Straight-split shakes are made in the same manner as taper-split, except that splitting is done from one end of the block only. This produces shakes which are the same thickness from end to end.

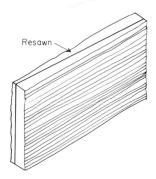

Resawn

Figure 17 · 8
Hand-split and resawed shakes.

Figure 17 · 9
Taper-splitting shake blanks.
(Consolidated Red Cedar
Shingle Assn. of B.C.)

Hand-split and resawed shakes are made in three lengths, 18, 24, and 32 in. The 18- and 24-in. shakes are made in two thicknesses, ½ to ¾ in. and ¾ to 1¼ in. The 32-in. shakes are made in the ¾ to 1¼ in. thickness only. Taper-split shakes are normally 24 in. long, tapering from ½ to ⅝ in. Straight-split shakes are made in two lengths, 18 and 24 in., both ⅜ in. thick.

Shakes are made from clear, 100 percent heartwood; taper-split and straight-split shakes must be 100 percent edge grain. Hand-split and resawed shakes may contain up to 10 percent flat grain in the total running inches of any bundle. Complete grading specifications are given in grading manuals.

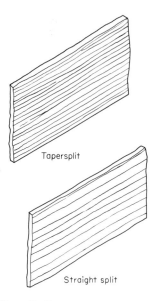

Tapersplit

Straight split

Figure 17 · 10
Split shakes.

Figure 17 · 11
Applying resawed cedar shakes.
(Consolidated Red Cedar Shingle Assn. of B.C.)

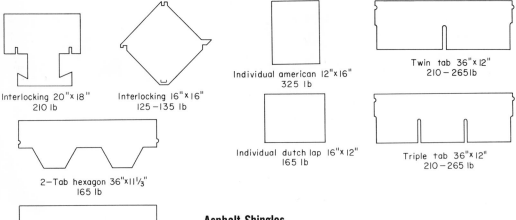

Interlocking 20"x18"
210 lb

Interlocking 16"x16"
125 – 135 lb

Individual american 12"x16"
325 lb

Twin tab 36"x12"
210 – 265 lb

Individual dutch lap 16"x12"
165 lb

Triple tab 36"x12"
210 – 265 lb

2 – Tab hexagon 36"x11⅓"
165 lb

3 – Tab hexagon 36"x 11⅓"
165 lb

Figure 17 · 12
Asphalt shingle shapes.

Figure 17 · 13
Asbestos-cement shingle shapes.

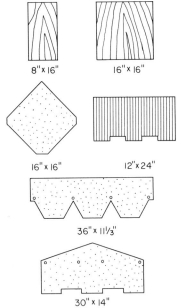

8"x16"

16"x16"

16"x16"

12"x24"

36"x 11⅓"

30"x 14"

24"x 15⅓"

24"x 15⅜"

Hexagonal starter

Eave starter

16" Ridge roll

Asphalt Shingles

Asphalt shingles are made from heavy rag felt, saturated with asphalt and coated with high-melting-point flexible asphalt. Ceramic-coated mineral granules are pressed into the asphalt coating on the exposed face to provide a fire-resistant surface. A number of weights and styles of shingles are made, each in a wide variety of colors. The weights refer to the weight of the quantity of shingles required to cover 100 sq ft, usually referred to as a *square* of shingles. This weight varies from 135 lb for light shingles to 325 lb for very heavy ones. Weights are varied by altering the thickness of the felt used, the amount of asphalt absorbed by the felt, the thickness of asphalt coating, and the amount of mineral used on the surface. Shingle styles include a number of individual shapes, as well as a number of double-and triple-tab multiple shingles. Most types of asphalt shingles can be used for re-roofing over old shingles as well as for new applications. Roof slopes should be at least 4 in 12 for shingles of this type to give satisfactory service. Broad-headed roofing nails or staples are used to fasten them down, and manufacturers' instructions should be followed when shingles are being applied. To prevent damage by wind, the corners of exposed tabs should be cemented down with asphalt roofing gum.

Asbestos-cement Shingles

Asbestos-cement shingles are made from a combination of asbestos fibers in portland cement paste. To this mix is added quantities of small, colored ceramic granules to produce permanent colors. The material is rolled into sheets ⁵⁄₃₂ in. thick, often with a wood-grain textured surface. Sheets are cut into shingles of various sizes and shapes (Fig. 17·13) with nail holes predrilled. Because this type of shingle is hard and brittle, heavy felt underlay is required and soft nails of copper or aluminum should be used. Cutting is done with a special shear. Ridge rolls, hexagonal starters, and 4 × 16 in. eave starters of the same material are available for use with this type of shingle.

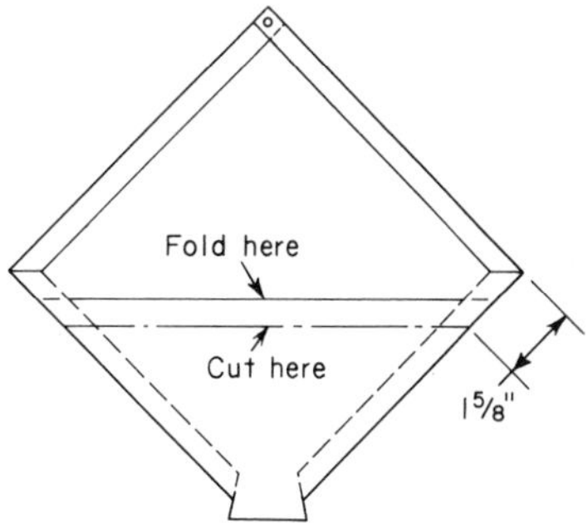

Aluminum Shingles

Aluminum shingles are made from sheet aluminum approximately 0.020 in. thick in the form of a 9-in. square. They are folded on all edges with reversed folds, as shown in Fig. 17·14, so that adjacent shingles will interlock. Starters are made by cutting a shingle as shown in Fig. 17·14; each shingle is fastened down with a single nail. This type of shingle may be used on roofs with a slope of 3 in 12 or steeper. They are manufactured with a plain aluminum surface, with an anodized finish, or with a baked-on vinyl-enamel finish in a variety of colors.

Figure 17·14
Aluminum shingle.

ROOFING TILE

Roofing tiles are basically a terra-cotta product, designed to be applied to a roof in a similar manner to shingles. But because of their weight—900 to 1,325 lb per square—wood sheathing and strong well-braced roof frames are necessary.

The tiles are made in a variety of styles, including French tile, Spanish tile, Roman tile, English tile, Mission tile, and shingle tile. Dimensions vary from one style to another and

Figure 17·15
Aluminum shingled roof.
(McReady Products Ltd.)

Figure 17·16
Clay tile shapes.

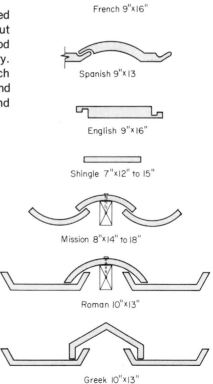

French 9"x16"

Spanish 9"x13

English 9"x16"

Shingle 7"x12" to 15"

Mission 8"x14" to 18"

Roman 10"x13"

Greek 10"x13"

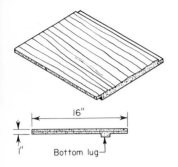

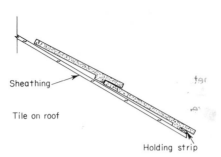

Figure 17·17
Concrete roofing tile.

range from 12 to 16 in. long and 9 to 12 in. wide. Glazed and unglazed tile are available in the colors normally associated with burned clay products.

All clay tile should be laid over an asphalt felt base and are fastened with copper nails. Elastic cement is used to caulk joints that are otherwise not watertight.

Concrete roofing tile are similar to English tile but have a lug across the underside about 3 in. from one end (Fig. 17·17). They are laid without nails and rely on their weight to hold them in place. The first course is supported by a horizontal furring strip nailed along the eave and each succeeding course is supported by the one below.

SLATE

Because of its structure, slate rock is easily split into thin slabs suitable for roofing. Usual thicknesses are ¼, ⅜, and ½ in., but slates up to 2 in. thick may be produced on special order. Slabs are cut into slates of various lengths from 10 to 24 in. Each length is produced in several widths so that a more or less random style of laying may be used with any length. For example, slates 10 in. long are made 6, 7, and 8 in. wide; 18-in. slates are made 9, 10, 11, and 12 in. wide; while 24-in. slates are produced 12 and 14 in. wide. The surface of the slates may be left in its rough textured state or ground to produce a smooth surface. Slate colors include black, gray, brown, purple, green, red, blue-black, mottled purple and green and purple variegated. Holes for nails are usually drilled at the quarry.

Slate may be laid over a nailing concrete surface, over gypsum or terra-cotta tile, or over a wood deck. Heavy felt paper, from 15 to 65 lb depending on the thickness of the slate, is laid over the surface and slates laid with 3-in. lap. Slates are held in place with copper nails. Slate also can be laid over a roof frame of steel purlins by wiring the slates to the purlins. Roof frames must be strong and well-braced, for slate roofing is very heavy; ¼-in. slate in place weighs about 1,000 lb per square, ⅜-in. slate about 1,500 lb, and ½-in. slate about 2,000 lb.

SHEET-METAL ROOFING

Sheet metal used for roofing includes steel, stainless steel, copper, lead, zinc, aluminum, and galbestos. The size of sheets varies with the different types of metal, and joints are necessary between sheets to produce a waterproof skin. In the case of the softer metals, joints between sheets are generally fabricated on the job, whereas with the hard metals, joints are usually prefabricated or the material is produced in a corrugated form and joints are made by lapping.

Fabricated joints in metal sheets, or seams, as they are called, can be any one of three different types, flat, standing, or ribbed. Flat seams are used when the roof is flat, or nearly so, since they can be readily soldered for additional seal. Roofs with a slope over 4 in 12 may have unsoldered standing seams. Ribbed seams are used with heavier metal for appearance or where expansion of the roofing material becomes a significant factor in the roof design.

Steel

Steel strip (described in Chap. 7) is coated with zinc, tin, lead, or combinations of two of these to produce steel roofing. Steel coated with zinc is commonly known as *galvanized* steel; coated with tin, it is called *bright plate,* while when coated with a mixture of 75 percent lead and 25 percent tin, it is known as *terneplate.*

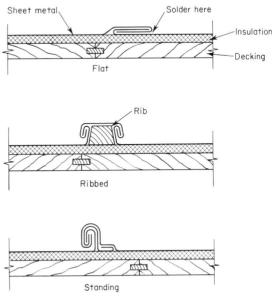

Figure 17 · 18
Sheet-metal roofing seams.

313

Galvanized sheet metal for roofing is produced in a variety of thicknesses, or gauges, which are listed in Table 17·3. It is also made in a number of coating classes, depending on the amount of zinc used per square foot of sheet. The coating classes are numbered as shown in Table 17·4, the number of each class representing the amount of zinc coating consumed in producing sheets which meet the minimum test requirements. Galvanized sheets for roofing are manufactured in lengths from 6 to 10 ft, with each length being available in widths of 24, 30, and 36 in.

Terneplate for roofing is produced in several thicknesses and in three coating weights—namely: 0.29, 0.73, and 1.47 oz of tin-lead coating per sq ft. Plates are normally made 14 × 20 in. or 20 × 28 in., but seamless terneplate roofing is also made in 50-ft lengths, 20 in. wide. Machines are available for turning up both edges of such strips at once to form a pan for a standing rib seam job.

Table 17 · 3
Galvanized roofing sheet gauges.

SHEET GAUGE NO.	GAUGE WEIGHT		MEAN THICKNESS, IN.
	OZ/SQ FT	LB/SQ FT	
10	92.5	5.78	0.138
11	82.5	5.16	0.123
12	72.5	4.53	0.108
13	62.5	3.91	0.093
14	52.5	3.28	0.078
15	47.5	2.97	0.071
16	42.5	2.66	0.063
17	38.5	2.41	0.057
18	34.5	2.16	0.051
19	30.5	1.91	0.045
20	26.5	1.66	0.039
21	24.5	1.53	0.036
22	22.5	1.41	0.033
23	20.5	1.28	0.030
24	18.5	1.16	0.027
25	16.5	1.03	0.024
26	14.5	0.91	0.021
27	13.5	0.84	0.020
28	12.5	0.78	0.018

Table 17 · 4
Weight of zinc coating.

COATING CLASS (POT YIELD)	MIN WEIGHT, OZ/SQ FT
2.75	2.35
2.50	2.10
2.25	1.85
2.00	1.65
1.75	1.40
1.50	1.15
1.25 (commercial)	0.90

Stainless Steel

When chromium is added during the process of manu-facturing steel, the resultant metal—stainless steel—has great resistance to corrosion. Many types of stainless steel are produced, about six of them being commonly employed as building materials. Chromium content ranges from 14 to 20 percent. In addition, most have 6 to 14 percent nickel, and at least one type contains 2 to 3 percent molybdenum. This particular alloy is generally specified for exterior use where corrosion is likely to be a really serious problem.

Because of its high strength, stainless steel for roofing is produced in relatively thin sheets, and because of its hard-ness, all fabrication must be done in the shop. It is also ex-pensive, so its use as roofing is limited usually to special conditions.

Monel Metal

This is an alloy containing about 70 percent nickel, 27 percent copper, and 3 percent iron. It is highly corrosion-resistant and does not tarnish easily. It is also hard, requiring shop fabrication, and expensive.

Copper

Copper has been used for centuries as roofing and is still considered to be one of the most satisfactory and endur-ing materials for metal roofing.

Roofing copper may be soft-rolled or cold-rolled, the former being very easily worked, the latter stronger, harder, but less ductile. Copper roofing sheets are generally produced in four thicknesses or weights—16, 20, 24, and 32 oz per sq ft. Roofing sheets are made 24, 30, and 36 in. wide, in lengths of 8 and 10 ft. Strip copper is also available for roofing in all four thicknesses, 10 to 20 in. wide and 8 or 10 ft long. Rolled copper, in 16-oz weight, from 6 to 20 in. wide, in rolls of 80, 90, or 100 lb, is produced for roofing purposes. Stand-ing and ribbed seams are preferred with copper roofing since it has a relatively large expansion factor.

In most locations an attractive soft blue-green patina forms on copper so that its beauty is enhanced with age. This often results in its being chosen as the roofing material where dignity, warmth, and charm as well as long life are prime considerations.

Lead

Lead is a useful roofing material since it is very pliable and can be drawn and stretched to fit warped surfaces. It weathers to a soft, even gray tone and is little affected by acids. Hard lead, containing antimony with lead, is now produced, and steel and copper sheets are coated with lead to get the lightness and strength of the core material combined with the color of the lead. Ribbed seams are best adapted for lead roofing.

Sheet lead for roofing is usually at least 2½ lb hard lead, which means that it weighs at least 2½ lb per sq ft and contains between 6 and 7½ percent antimony. Sheet dimensions are generally limited to 2×4 ft. Lead work which is to come in contact with fresh concrete should be painted with a heavy coat of asphalt paint on the contact side.

Zinc

Zinc is lighter and stiffer than lead but is affected by acids and has a high coefficient of expansion. Rolled sheet zinc is sometimes used for roofing and flashing, but zinc has a much wider application as a coating for steel roofing sheets.

Aluminum

Aluminum roofing is light, noncorrosive, rigid, and durable but also has a very high coefficient of thermal expansion. It is available in both sheets and coils in a number of thicknesses, listed in Table 17·5. Sheets range in width from 24 to 48 in. and in length from 4 to 12 ft. Coils range in width from 6 to 48 in. A 24-in.-wide coil weighs approximately 750 lb, while a 36-in. coil weighs 1,500 lb.

Table 17·5
Aluminum sheet.

GAUGE NO.	NOMINAL THICKNESS, IN.	WEIGHT, LB/SQ FT
26	0.016	0.226
24	0.020	0.285
22	0.025	0.355
20	0.032	0.455
18	0.040	0.568
16	0.051	0.725
14	0.064	0.910
12	0.081	1.152

Aluminum roofing is produced in natural finish, in polished and oxide finishes, with a painted finish on one or both sides, and in eight different surface patterns.

Mechanical jointing is the most practical method of joining aluminum sheets, although welding can be used with the heavier gauges to produce strong, weathertight joints.

All types of seams are used, but where connections are subject to movement due to thermal expansion or contraction, slip seams should be used. Fig. 17·19 illustrates how one type of slip seam allows for expansion and contraction.

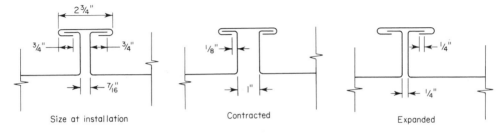

Size at installation Contracted Expanded

Figure 17 · 19
Typical slip joint in aluminum.

Galbestos

Galbestos is a composite roofing made up of a steel-sheet core covered on both sides with a layer of zinc. While the zinc is still hot a layer of asbestos felt is pressed to it and the felt is impregnated with asphalt. Finally a colored waterproof outer coating is applied.

Sheets are manufactured in 18, 20, 22, and 24 gauge and are made up into corrugated panels 30 or 33 in. wide, in lengths up to 12 ft. Joints are made by side- and end-lapping.

ASBESTOS-CEMENT SHEET ROOFING

Common types of asbestos-cement corrugated roofing and decking sheets are illustrated in Fig. 12·5. Decking sheets are intended to be covered with built-up roofing, while others are used as roofing, either over a solid deck or fastened to a wood or steel roof frame.

The board with the regular corrugations 4 in. o.c. is made from 4 to 10 ft long, 3 ft 4¾ in. wide. Board thickness is ¼ in. The other board contains four corrugations, spaced 1 ft 1⅓ in. o.c. Overall width of the board is 3 ft 8 in. and lengths range from 4 to 10 ft. Board thickness is ⁹⁄₃₂ in. This type of sheet is laid with a side lap of 4 in. (one corrugation) and an end lap of 6 in. Sheets weigh approximately 3 lb per sq ft, and 100 sq ft of roofing laid in place weighs approximately 352 lb. Roofing sheets of this type are held in place by nails, screws, and other fastening devices illustrated in (Fig. 12·6). Holes for fasteners have to be predrilled, and sheets are cut by means of an abrasive wheel.

A similar product, known as an asbestos-cement roofing tile, is a corrugated board ³⁄₁₆ in. thick, 4 ft long, and 40 in. wide. It contains five 1¾-in.-deep corrugations per tile, spaced 9 in. o.c. The weight is approximately 25 lb per tile. This tile may be used on roofs with a minimum slope of 3 in 12, with 4-in. side lap and 8-in. end lap.

BUILT-UP ROOFING

Built-up roofing is a term applied to a type of roofing made by building up successive layers of felt paper and asphalt over a solid roof deck of some description.

Figure 17 · 20
Insulating a roof deck.
(Pittsburgh Corning Corporation)

It is generally recognized that there are five basic types of built-up roofing; modifications depend on the type of roof deck involved, the slope of the roof, and the length of time the roofing is expected to perform satisfactorily.

In many cases the first step is the application of a layer of rigid insulation of some kind. For example, in Fig. 17·20, foam glass insulation is being laid in hot asphalt over the roof deck. In other cases the built-up roofing may be laid directly over the deck without insulation.

Roofing type No. 1 consists of asphalted felt paper, asphalt and gravel, or slag and is intended for roof slopes from ½ to 3 in. per foot. With a wood deck, the first step is the application of a single layer of 5-lb dry sheathing paper (Fig. 17·21). Next, two layers of 15-lb asphalt-saturated felt paper is applied dry and nailed with broad-headed roofing nails. These are followed by three layers of 15-lb asphalt-saturated felt paper, each layer being sealed in place with approximately

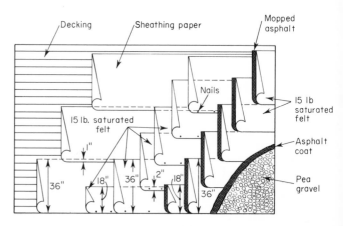

Figure 17 · 21
Four-ply built-up asphalt roof over wood deck.

318

20 lb of hot asphalt per 100 sq ft. Next, a layer of hot asphalt is spread over the surface at the rate of about 65 lb per 100 sq ft. If the slope is ⅛ to 1 in., use 140°F asphalt; if it is 1 to 2 in., use 170°F asphalt, and if it is over 2 in., use 210°F asphalt. Finally a layer of crushed slag or pea gravel is spread over the asphalt at the rate of 300 lb per 100 sq ft for slag or 400 lb per 100 sq ft for gravel. This type of roof should have a useful life of 20 years.

For nonwood decks or over an insulated surface, a similar grade of roofing is applied (Fig. 17·22) by sealing all layers of asphalt-saturated felt paper in hot asphalt.

Figure 17 · 22
Four-ply built-up roof over
rigid insulation.

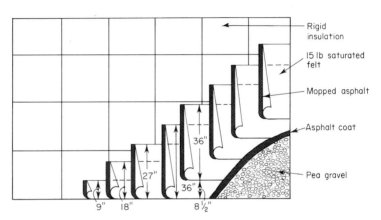

Roofing type No. 2 consists of tarred felt paper, pitch and gravel. It is intended for roofs with a slope of 0 to 1 in. per foot. Over a wood deck, the procedure is the same as with type No. 1 roofing, except that tarred rather than asphalted paper is used. The hot tar used between layers of paper should be applied at the rate of 25 lb per 100 sq ft, and the hot-tar topping at the rate of 80 lb per 100 sq ft. Tar should be heated to not more than 400°F and applied at a temperature of not less than 350°F. Gravel or slag application is the same as for type No. 1 roofing.

Roofing type No. 3 consists of asbestos felt, asphalt felt, and a smooth flood coat of asphalt. It is intended for roofs with a slope of from ½ to 8 in. per ft. Over a wood deck, the dry sheathing paper consists of 9-lb waxed kraft. A single layer of 25-lb asphalt-saturated felt paper is laid over this, held in place with roofing nails. Next, two layers of 15-lb asphalt felt are applied, each layer being sealed in place with a 20-lb-per-100-sq-ft mopping of hot asphalt. Next, two layers of 15-lb asphalt-saturated asbestos paper are applied in the same way. Finally a flood coat consisting of 25 lb of asphalt per 100 sq ft is applied, using the proper grade of asphalt for the roof slope, as specified under type No. 1.

Roofing type No. 4 requires heavy slate-surfaced roofing

319

paper as well as asphalt-saturated felts and may be used on roofs with slopes from 2 to 8 in 12. Over a wood deck, a single layer of 5-lb dry sheathing paper is first applied. Next comes a single layer of 15-lb asphalt-saturated felt, held with roofing nails. Over this are laid two layers of 15-lb asphalt felt and two layers of 120-lb slate-surfaced felt. Each of these is sealed in place with 20 lb per 100 sq ft of 210°F asphalt. This type of roofing is often recommended as a 10-year roof.

Roofing type No. 5 involves what is known as the cold process. The felts are cold-process felts, saturated with cold asphalt emulsion, and the asphalt top coating is applied cold. Layers of felt are sealed together with asphalt adhesive. Roofing of this type is suitable for slopes from ⅛ to 8 in. per foot. Over a wood deck, three layers of cold-process 53-lb felt paper are applied, fastened down with roofing nails and asphalt adhesive at the rate of about 2½ gal per 100 sq ft. This surface is covered with a layer of asphalt-fibrated emulsion applied cold at the rate of 4 gal per 100 sq ft. This type of roofing is also considered to have a useful life of 20 years.

ROLLED ROOFING

Rolled roofing consists of very heavy asphalt-saturated felt paper, with or without finely crushed slate embedded in one surface, put up in rolls. There are four basic types in this kind of roofing: (1) smooth roll, (2) mineral-surfaced roll, (3) pattern-edge roll, and (4) 19-in. selvage.

The smooth roll consists of asphalt-saturated felt ranging in weight from 45 to 65 lb per 100 sq ft covered with a smooth coating of asphalt. The mineral-surfaced roll ranges from 90 to 120 lb per 100 sq ft and has a layer of crushed slate embedded in the asphalt surface coating. Both of these are made 36 in. wide.

The pattern-edge roll is made in two widths, 32 and 36 in., and consists of a 105-lb felt that is mineral-surfaced except for a 4-in. band down the center. The roll is semicut on a pattern along this strip so that a roll produces 16- or 18-in.-wide patterned roofing strips. These are normally lapped 2 in. when being applied to a roof.

The 19-in. selvage roll is made from felt weighing 140 to 150 lb per 100 sq ft in a strip 36 in. wide. A 17-in.-wide band of this strip is mineralized, and the other 19 in. is plain. When applied to a roof, each strip is lapped 19 in. over the one below to present a completely mineralized surface and to provide double coverage.

SPRAYED-ON ASPHALT ROOFING

A new technique for the application of asphalt roofing involves the use of special equipment for applying the material. A special gun with three nozzles and a fiber-cutting chamber is used. Glass fibers are fed into the chamber where they are cut to predetermined lengths and blown out through a center nozzle. Two side nozzles each deliver a spray of asphalt emulsion which coats the glass fibers and carries them to the deck to form a reinforced film of asphalt. The thickness of the film can be increased by repeated sprayings and will be determined by the weather conditions and the slope of the roof.

This type of roofing film is applied over regular base roofing felts and is particularly useful on roofs of irregular shapes. By this method a monolithic film can be applied over the entire surface, regardless of the shape or contours. In Fig. 17·23, a glass-fiber reinforced asphalt film is being applied to a roof deck by special gun.

Figure 17 · 23
Sprayed-on asphalt roofing.
(The Flintkote Company of Canada Limited)

GLASS ROOFING

Two types of glass are commonly used for roofing. One is corrugated glass, which is made in sheets with corrugations which correspond to those in some types of corrugated sheet metal and corrugated asbestos board roofing. The glass is usually ⅜ in. thick, and sheets are made up to a maximum size of 50 × 144 in. Thus glass sheets may be interchanged with the regular roofing sheets to allow the entry of light through the roof. Glass sheets are fastened in place and made weatherproof by elastic caulking compound at side and end laps.

The other type of glass used in roofing is wired glass. This is glass which has embedded in it wire mesh with not larger than ⅞-in. openings. The glass is ¼ in. thick and may have a polished or patterned surface. Sheets are made up to a maximum size of 60 × 132 in. This type of glass is held in metal frames and is most commonly used in skylights, etc.

PLASTIC ROOFING

Plastics are used in three forms for roofing. One is the corrugated plastic sheet, made from glass-fiber-reinforced plastics in color or translucent. Sheets are 34 in. wide and 8, 10, or 12 ft long, with 2½- or 1¼-in. corrugations. Such sheets can be interchanged with corrugated sheet metal, corrugated asbestos board, or galbestos sheets to allow entry of light through the roof. They may also be used alone to provide the roof covering.

Sheets of clear vinyl plastic are also used for roofing, particularly for such structures as greenhouses, conservatories, and factory buildings. Because of their great impact strength, vinyl sheets can be much larger than glass sheets used for the same purpose.

Liquid plastic is also sprayed onto roof decks to form what is known as an envelope roofing. This liquid envelope consists of a pigmented, opaque vinyl plastic which is applied by means of a spray gun to form a continuous film 30 to 40 mils thick. It can be applied over almost any type of roof deck or existing roofing material with the exception of wood shingles. When it is to be used over an existing built-up roof, the surface should first be primed. This liquid-envelope type of roofing is particularly useful for roofs with irregular shapes or very steep slopes or both.

The plastic dries very quickly to form a film which, for a 40-mil thickness, has a tensile strength of about 500 psi and an ultimate elongation of about 200 percent. The vinyl coat is highly resistant to commonly encountered industrial atmospheres containing dirt, grime, and mild acid fumes. It is also highly resistant to deterioration due to extended exposure to sunlight.

Each type of roofing described has certain advantages and disadvantages; in addition, many of them are each connected by tradition with certain characteristics of architecture. Consequently, a wise selection of roof covering is as important as the choice of wall material or facing. When properly chosen, the roofing not only provides the most economical weather protection under the circumstances but contributes considerably to the production of a harmoniously designed building.

GLOSSARY

chromium	A hard, brittle, grayish-white metallic element
coefficient	A number expressing the amount of some change or effect
ductile	Capable of being drawn out thin
fibrated emulsion	An asphalt emulsion containing mineral fiber

flood coat	A heavy, poured-on coating of asphalt
lug	A ridge
molybdenum	A metallic element of the chromium group, used as an alloy
monolithic film	A film containing no joints
nailing concrete	Cellular concrete or concrete made with vermiculite aggregate, into which nails can be driven
patina	A film formed by exposure or treatment with acids
pea gravel	Gravel with a maximum size of ½ in.
rag felt	Heavy paper made largely from rag fibers
ridge roll	A special shape made to fit over the ridge of a roof
selvage	A specially formed edge

REVIEW QUESTIONS

1 Distinguish between the terms roof decking and roofing.
2 Give five reasons why cedar is so widely used for manufacturing shingles.
3 Explain the difference between shingles and shakes.
4 (a) Why is it important to use heavy roofing felt under asbestos-cement shingles, terra-cotta roofing tile, and slate?
   (b) What is the advantage of using copper nails with these roofing materials?
5 (a) Use diagrams to illustrate the three basic types of seam used with sheet-metal roofing.
   (b) Give reasons for using each of the three types of seam.
6 Give two important reasons for using sheet lead as a roofing material.
7 What are the basic differences between built-up and monoform roofing?
8 What is liquid-envelope roofing?

SELECTED SOURCES OF INFORMATION

The American Brass Company, Waterbury, Conn.
American Zinc Institute Inc., New York, N.Y.
Atlas Asbestos Co., Montreal, Que.
Barrett Company Ltd., Montreal, Que.
Building Products of Canada, St. John, New Brunswick
Canadian Johns-Manville Co., Ltd., Toronto, Ont.
Canadian Pittsburgh Industries Ltd., Montreal, Que.
Essex Chemical Corporation, Better Finishes & Coating Division, Clifton, N.J.
The Flintkote Company of Canada Ltd., Toronto, Ont.
Follansbee Steel Corporation, Pittsburgh, Pa.

Lead Industries Association, New York, N.Y.
Ludowici-Celadon Co., Chicago, Ill.
McCready Products Ltd., Edmonton, Alberta
Red Cedar Shingle & Handsplit Shade Bureau,
    Vancouver, B.C.
H. H. Robertson Company, Pittsburgh, Pa.
Sidney Roofing & Paper Co., Victoria, B.C.
Tremco Mfg. Co., Cleveland, O., and Toronto, Ont.
Westeel Products Ltd., Toronto, Ont.

18

ACOUSTICAL
MATERIALS

In this chapter we are concerned primarily with the effects of sound and methods by which sound can be controlled. Sound control is sought in order to improve hearing conditions and to reduce unnecessary noise in buildings.

In order to understand how we can control sound, it is necessary to form a picture of what happens to sound waves and the energy they contain when sound is generated in a closed room.

When sound is produced by a sound source, waves travel outward in all directions radially from the source. These waves all travel at approximately the same speed of 1,120 ft per second, or 763 miles per hour. The variations in speed that do occur result from differences in atmospheric temperature. At 70°F the velocity of sound is approximately 1,126 ft per second, while at 32°F it is approximately 1,086 ft per second.

The frequency of sound waves depends on the number of vibrations per second of the sound source. If the source vibrates 1,000 times per second, the sound wave has a frequency of 1,000 cycles. The series of frequencies with which we are most commonly concerned in acoustical work are 128, 256, 512, 1,024, 2,048, and 4,096 cycles.

The wavelength of a sound wave is the distance the wave travels during one complete vibration of the sound source. The wavelength is equal to the velocity of sound divided by the frequency. Thus a sound with a frequency of 200 cycles will have a wavelength of $1,120 \div 200 = 5.6$ ft.

The intensity—in general terms the strength of a sound field at an observer's ear or at other sound-recording devices —is a measure of the amount of energy contained in the vibrating air particles in a sound wave. The amount of energy depends on the amplitude of vibration of the sound source. The wider the amplitude of vibration, the greater is the intensity. Intensity is measured in *decibels* (db) and a reference sound intensity has been chosen for use with the decibel scale. This intensity has been given a standard value of 10^{-16} watts per sq cm. This amount of energy flow is very small but a sensitive human ear can hear a sound of that intensity, which corresponds to 0 db. Table 18·1 charts the decibel levels of a number of common sounds.

When sound waves strike a surface such as a wall or ceiling, they are reflected and the reflected sound, as well as the

Table 18 · 1
Decibel levels of common sounds.
(Celotex Corp.)

DECIBELS	SOUND	EFFECT
120	Thunder, artillery	
110	Nearby riveter Elevated train Boiler factory	Deafening
100		
90	Loud street noise Noisy factory Truck (unmuffled) Police siren	Very loud
80		
70	Noisy office Average street noise Average radio Average factory	Loud
60		
50	Noisy home Average office Average conversation Quiet radio	Moderate
40		
30	Quiet home Private office Average auditorium Quiet conversation	Faint
20		
10	Rustle of leaves Whisper Soundproof room Threshold of audibility	Very faint
0		

original, is heard by a listener, resulting in an increase in sound intensity. While a sound source is operating, a room becomes filled with reflected sound waves and when the source is stopped, then reflected waves continue to travel back and forth between room surfaces. As a listener picks up these reflected waves, he hears them as the original sound being prolonged and finally becoming inaudible as the reflected waves gradually lose their energy by absorption. This prolongation of sound is called reverberation.

Control of increased intensity and of excessive reverberation are two of the major problems of sound engineering. Along with them are the problems of control of unwanted sound and of transmission of sound from room to room through walls, floors, and ceilings.

A large part of acoustical correction deals with the improvement of hearing conditions and the reduction of unwanted noise in rooms by reducing the energy of reflected sound. This is done mainly by the use of acoustical materials —materials which have a substantially greater ability to absorb sound than such conventional ones as wood, glass, hard plaster, or concrete.

The percentage of the energy absorbed by a material when a sound wave is reflected from it is called the sound-absorption coefficient, or acoustical absorptivity. This absorption coefficient depends on the nature of the material, the frequency of the sound, and the angle at which the sound wave strikes the material. When comparing materials to be used for the improvement of hearing conditions, it is common practice to use the coefficient at the frequency of 512 cycles. In comparing materials for noise-quieting applications, the noise reduction coefficient (N.R.C.), which is the average coefficient for the four frequencies of 256, 512, 1,024, and 2,048 cycles, is generally used.

Most acoustical materials can be classified in three groups: (1) acoustical tiles, (2) assembled units, and (3) sprayed-on acoustical materials.

ACOUSTICAL TILES

A majority of the tiles used for acoustical purposes are made from wood, cane, or asbestos fibers, matted and bonded into sheets of various thicknesses, ranging from 3/16 to 1 1/4 in. The sheets are cut into tiles of several sizes, including 12 × 12 in., 12 × 24 in., 16 × 16 in., 16 × 32 in., 24 × 24 in., and 24 × 48 in. Edges may be square cut, beveled, or tongue-and-grooved.

These tiles are intended primarily for ceiling applications. They can be applied to solid surfaces with adhesives, nailed to furring strips attached to a ceiling frame or the underside of a solid deck, or installed in a suspended ceiling frame.

A great variety of designs, colors, and patterns are avail-

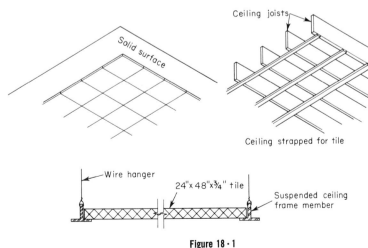

Figure 18 · 1
Acoustical ceiling tile.

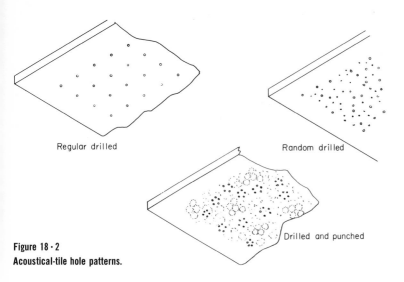

Regular drilled

Random drilled

Drilled and punched

Figure 18 · 2
Acoustical-tile hole patterns.

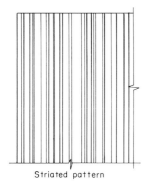

Fissure pattern

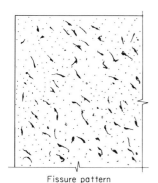

Striated pattern

Figure 18 · 3
Acoustical-tile surface patterns.

able. The acoustic openings in the surface of the tile in themselves provide many different designs. The openings may be holes drilled in uniform or random patterns or a combination of large drilled holes and tiny punched ones. The openings may be slots, striations, or fissures, or the surface of the tile may be sculptured in various patterns. All ceiling tile comes with a factory-painted surface so that it does not require painting after installation. However, fiber tile can be repainted with a nonbridging paint without appreciable loss of acoustical properties.

The noise-reduction coefficient of tiles of this type is about 0.70, with some variations, depending on the particular material, the thickness of the tile, and the kind of pattern used.

Asbestos-fiber tiles $12 \times 12 \times \frac{3}{4}$ in. weigh approximately $1\frac{1}{4}$ lb; wood- or cane-fiber tiles are slightly lighter.

ASSEMBLED UNITS

Assembled units usually consist of some type of sound-absorbing material such as a rock-wool or fiber-glass blanket fastened to an acoustically transparent facing. This facing is generally some type of rigid board, such as hardboard or asbestos board, or a metal sheet. The facings are perforated to allow the penetration of sound waves.

Such acoustical panels can be fastened to a wall over a framework of furring strips or suspended in front of the wall by some mechanical means. By varying the thickness of the sound-absorbing element and the spacing between the panels and the wall, some variation in the overall absorption and the absorption at different frequencies can be obtained.

Sound-absorption coefficients will vary with the thickness of the material, the type of facing, and the size and number of the perforations in the face.

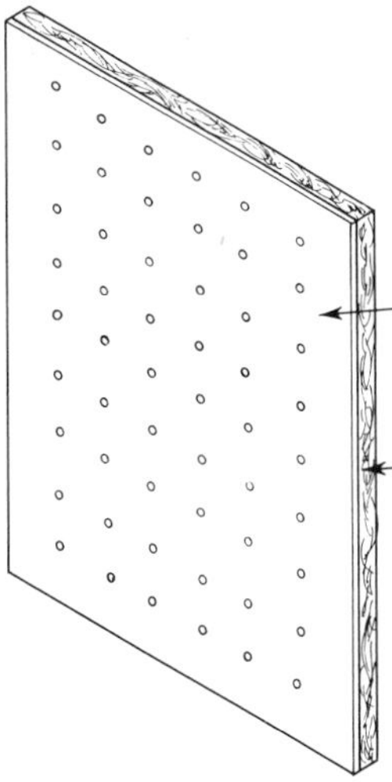

SPRAYED-ON ACOUSTICAL MATERIALS

Two types of material are used for this kind of sound control application. One type consists of plaster made with vermiculite or perlite aggregate and the other of a coating of mineral fiber mixed with an adhesive.

Vermiculite acoustical plaster is generally a premixed product, requiring only the addition of approximately 10 gal of water per bag of mix. The plaster can be applied by hand or by machine spraying and will bond to any clean, firm, water-resistant surface such as base plaster, concrete, or steel. When it is applied by hand, usually two coats are used, a first coat at least ⅜ in. thick and a finish coat at least ⅛ thick. When machine application is used, two, three, or four thin coats are applied so that the total thickness of plaster will be at least ½ in.

According to tests, the noise-reduction coefficient for ½-in.-thick vermiculite acoustical plaster applied by trowel is 0.65, while for trowel-applied plaster 1 in. thick, the coefficient is 0.75. For machine-applied plaster ½ thick the coefficient is 0.55.

Perlite acoustical plaster is usually mixed on the job, using calcined gypsum as the binder. It also can be applied either by hand or by machine. Sound-reduction properties of perlite plaster are approximately the same as those of vermiculite.

The main advantage of using machine spraying as a means of application is that this method presents no difficulties in plastering over irregular surfaces such as those presented in Fig. 18·5.

Perforated hardboard

Fiberglass insulation

Figure 18·4
Assembled acoustical unit.

Figure 18·5
Acoustical treatment on irregular surfaces.
(Columbia Acoustics & Fireproofing Co.)

329

Figure 18·6
Mineral fiber acoustical treatment.
(Columbia Acoustics & Fireproofing Co.)

Acoustical treatment with mineral fiber involves the use of specially prepared mineral wool or asbestos fibers and an adhesive to hold them to the surface.

The fibers are prepared and mixed with an inorganic binding material, which helps to give them body, and packed in bags ready for application. The area to be covered is first primed with a thick coat of adhesive, and the fiber is then sprayed over the surface in one or more coats, depending on the thickness required. For thicknesses of over ½ in. at least two coats are used. Each coat is tamped to consolidate the fibers; the final surface can be sprayed with sealer or color (Fig. 18·6).

Such material is very light; a 1-in. coat weighs 9 to 12 oz per sq ft. The noise-reduction coefficient varies depending on the thickness of the coat and the type of backing. Over solid backing, an unpainted ¾-in. thickness has a coefficient of from 0.60 to 0.70. Over metal-lath backing, the same thickness, unpainted, has a coefficient of 0.80 to 0.90. A 1½-in. thickness, unpainted, over solid backing has a coefficient of 0.90, while the coefficient of the same thickness, painted, is about 0.85.

The transmission of sound from room to room through walls, floors, and ceilings takes place as a result of diaphragmatic vibration. The surface may be set in vibration through impact, such as a footstep, or by the action of sound waves striking it. The first is called impact transmission and the second airborne transmission. In either case sound waves of reduced intensity are generated in the room on the other side by the vibrating surface.

The sound-insulating efficiency of a wall or floor for airborne sound is called its transmission loss and is measured in decibels (Fig. 18·7). The transmission loss of any wall depends on the materials of which it is made and the method of

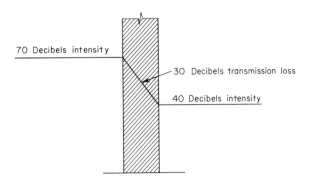

70 Decibels intensity

30 Decibels transmission loss

40 Decibels intensity

Figure 18·7
Reduction in sound intensity level through a wall.

construction. However, the transmission loss of any given wall varies considerably with the frequency of sound.

In order to be reasonably useful as an airborne-sound insulator, a wall should have a sound-transmission loss rating of at least 35 db, and for dividing walls between apartments it is usually recommended that the transmission loss be 45 db.

For solid masonry partitions, the transmission loss depends on the weight of the wall per unit area. For example, if a solid masonry partition which weighs 10 lb per sq ft and has a transmission loss of 26 db has its weight doubled, the transmission loss will be increased by 9 db. Each successive doubling of weight will add another 9 db to the rating. Partitions made from porous concrete block have a superior transmission loss rating if they are plastered on at least one side and preferably on both.

In general, the effectiveness of single- or double-stud walls depends on the rigidity of the material in the wall and the method of construction. Figure 18·8 illustrates some types of partition and the approximate transmission-loss rating, in decibels, of each. Loose fill should not be used as sound insulation in a structurally separated double wall, since it acts as a bridge across the space and reduces the sound-insulation value.

Transmission of sound through floors may be either of the impact or airborne type. Solid floors of concrete or tile effectively reduce airborne transmission, losses being normally in the range of 40 to 60 db for this type of floor. However, impact transmission is a problem with this as well as steel or wood-frame floors, and special construction techniques are necessary to reduce this type of sound transmission.

Suspended ceilings provide high insulation, particularly if resilient hangers are used. A floating floor over the structural floor also provides good impact insulation. It may be a floor supported on springs or it may be laid over a layer of resilient material such as wood or cane fiberboard or some type of rigid foamed insulation.

Wood-frame floors can be improved by providing an insulating cushion between the frame and the finished ceiling

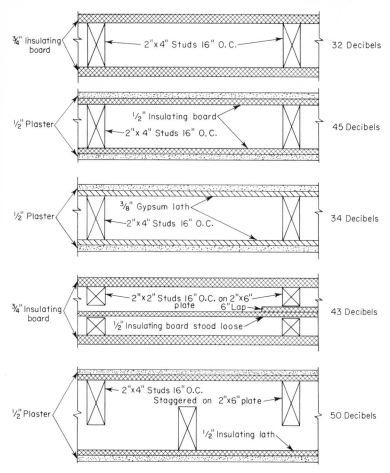

Figure 18 · 8
Approximate transmission losses through various partition constructions.

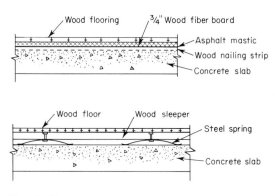

Figure 18 · 9
Floating floors.

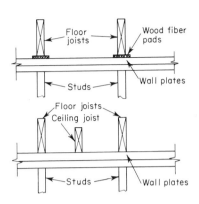

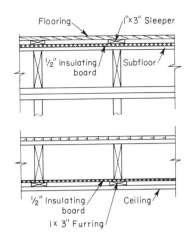

below or by separating the floor and ceiling frames. Figure 18·10 illustrates several possible ways of using insulating materials to improve the impact transmission losses through frame floors.

Figure 18 · 10
Suggested methods for reducing impact transmission through wood-frame floors.

GLOSSARY

amplitude	The extent of a vibrating motion
diaphragmatic vibration	The vibration of a dividing membrane or surface
radially	In concentric circles
striation	A narrow groove or channel

REVIEW QUESTIONS

1 Explain briefly how a sound is generated.
2 Define:
  (a) sound frequency
  (b) wavelength
  (c) sound intensity
3 (a) List four major sound problems with which sound engineering is concerned.
  (b) Explain what is meant by acoustical correction.
4 Explain how acoustical materials control excessive reverberation.
5 (a) How do standard types of paint reduce the sound-absorbing qualities of acoustical tile?
  (b) What is meant by a nonbridging paint?
6 Draw a careful sketch of a typical acoustical assembled unit.
7 What are the advantages of using machine-sprayed mineral fiber for sound control?
8 What is meant by:
  (a) impact transmission?
  (b) airborne transmission?

SELECTED SOURCES OF INFORMATION

Armstrong Cork Company, Lancaster, Pa.
Atlas Asbestos Company, Toronto, Ont.
Canadian Johns-Manville Co., Ltd., Montreal, Que.
The Celatex Corporation, Chicago, Ill.
Columbia Acoustics & Fireproofing Co., Stanhope, N.J.
Hermon, Hosmer Scott, Inc., Cambridge, Mass.
Insulation Board Institute, Chicago, Ill.
International Panel Boards Ltd., Gatineau, Que.
Tectum Corporation, Columbus, O.
Vermiculite Institute, Chicago, Ill.

19

INTERIOR FINISHING MATERIALS

The materials which are used to finish the interior walls and ceilings of buildings are basically the materials which have been described in the various chapters of this book. They include wood, gypsum, clay products, stone, concrete, fiberboards, paper, glass, steel, nonferrous metals, plastics, and paints. A variety of products have been developed from each basic material so that a wide choice of finishes is available in any material.

WOOD FINISHES

Interior finishing materials of wood can be divided into two basic groups: those used to cover walls and ceilings, and those used as trim materials around door and window openings, as baseboard, and as various decorative moldings. Wall and ceiling coverings can be divided into two groups: those made of solid wood and those made of plywood; trim materials are generally of solid wood.

Wall coverings of solid wood may be in the form of boards or in wood sheets. Boards are produced from various species of wood, including pine, fir, redwood, cedar, mahogany, beech, and ash in thicknesses of ¼, ⅜, ½, and 1 in. Widths of boards range from 2 to 12 in. and lengths from 4 to 10 ft. The face of these may be plain, saw-textured, V-grooved, beaded, channeled, or molded, while the edges may be square, tongue-and-groove, tongue-and-groove with bevel, shiplap, or shiplap with bevel. For actual widths, thicknesses, depth of groove, width of bead, width, and depth of chamfer, etc., consult a grading rules book, published by a number of lumber manufacturing companies. This type of material is normally produced plain sawed, with clear or knotty face. It is kiln-dried and may be factory sealed or sealed and prefinished with synthetic lacquer.

The wood sheets are made from a variety of softwoods and hardwoods, kiln-dried, and edge-glued to form sheets which are usually 1 in. thick, 3 ft wide, and 8 ft long, in a

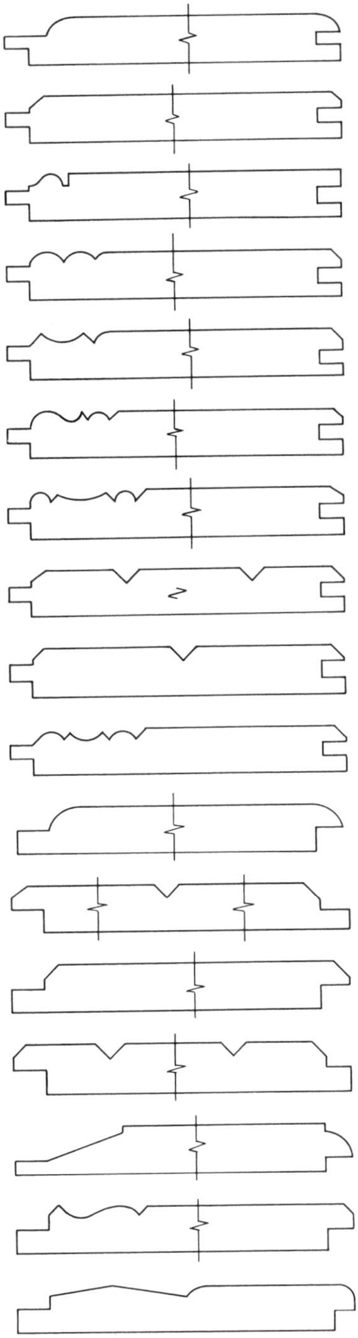

Figure 19·1
Pine paneling patterns.

335

Figure 19·2
Etched plywood surface.

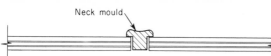
Neck mould

Figure 19·3
Panels separated by neck mold.

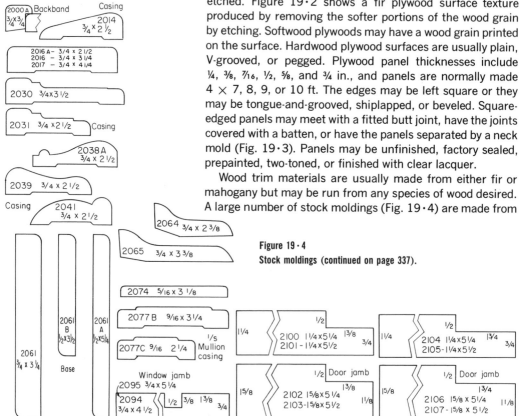

Figure 19·4
Stock moldings (continued on page 337).

variety of face patterns. Surfaces are sanded and the sheet may be factory sealed or sealed and prefinished.

Plywood wall paneling is made from a number of softwoods including fir, pine, and spruce, as well as from various hardwoods such as walnut, birch, beech, ash, oak, mahogany, and teak. Fir plywood paneling in particular is produced in a variety of surface textures—embossed, wire-brushed, and etched. Figure 19·2 shows a fir plywood surface texture produced by removing the softer portions of the wood grain by etching. Softwood plywoods may have a wood grain printed on the surface. Hardwood plywood surfaces are usually plain, V-grooved, or pegged. Plywood panel thicknesses include ¼, ⅜, ⁷⁄₁₆, ½, ⅝, and ¾ in., and panels are normally made 4 × 7, 8, 9, or 10 ft. The edges may be left square or they may be tongue-and-grooved, shiplapped, or beveled. Square-edged panels may meet with a fitted butt joint, have the joints covered with a batten, or have the panels separated by a neck mold (Fig. 19·3). Panels may be unfinished, factory sealed, prepainted, two-toned, or finished with clear lacquer.

Wood trim materials are usually made from either fir or mahogany but may be run from any species of wood desired. A large number of stock moldings (Fig. 19·4) are made from

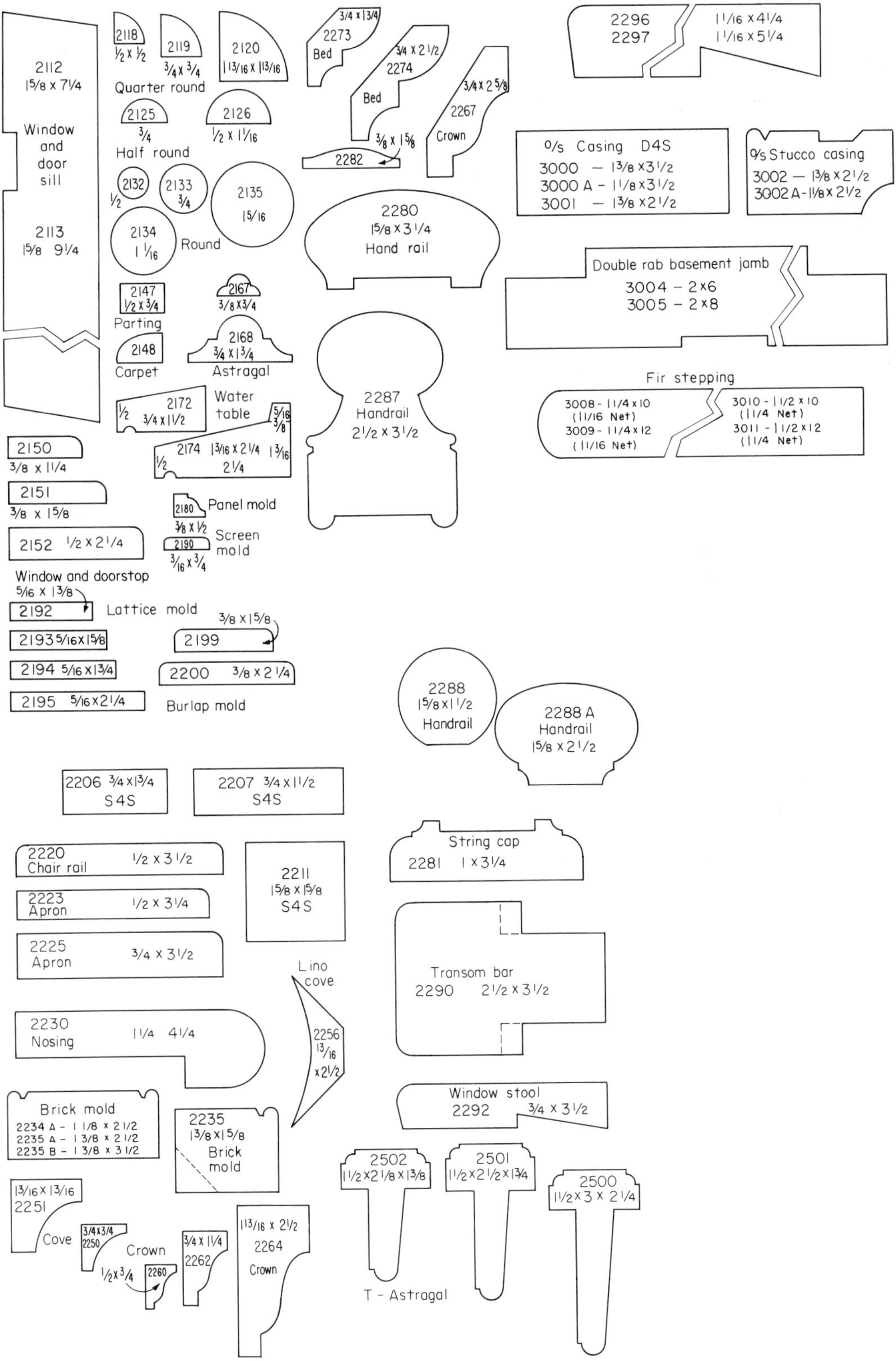

2112
1 5/8 x 7 1/4
Window and door sill
2113
1 5/8 9 1/4
2118
1/2 x 1/2
2119
3/4 x 3/4
2120
1 13/16 x 1 13/16
Quarter round
2125
3/4
2126
1/2 x 1 1/16
Half round
2132
1/2
2133
3/4
2135
15/16
2134
1 1/16
Round
2147
1/2 x 3/4
Parting
2148
Carpet
2167
3/8 x 3/4
2168
3/4 x 1 3/4
Astragal
2172
1/2
3/4 x 1 1/2
Water table
2174
1 3/16 x 2 1/4
2 1/4
5/16
3/8
1 3/16
1/2
2180
Panel mold
3/8 x 1/2
2190
3/16 x 3/4
Screen mold
2150
3/8 x 1 1/4
2151
3/8 x 1 5/8
2152 1/2 x 2 1/4
Window and doorstop
5/16 x 1 3/8
2192
Lattice mold
2193 5/16 x 1 5/8
2194 5/16 x 1 3/4
2195 5/16 x 2 1/4
3/8 x 1 5/8
2199
2200 3/8 x 2 1/4
Burlap mold
2273
3/4 x 1 3/4
Bed
2274
3/4 x 2 1/2
Bed
3/8 x 1 5/8
2282
2267
3/4 x 2 5/8
Crown
2280
1 5/8 x 3 1/4
Hand rail
2287
Handrail
2 1/2 x 3 1/2
2296
2297
1 1/16 x 4 1/4
1 1/16 x 5 1/4
O/S Casing D4S
3000 — 1 3/8 x 3 1/2
3000 A - 1 1/8 x 3 1/2
3001 — 1 3/8 x 2 1/2
O/S Stucco casing
3002 — 1 3/8 x 2 1/2
3002 A - 1 1/8 x 2 1/2
Double rab basement jamb
3004 – 2 x 6
3005 – 2 x 8
Fir stepping
3008 - 1 1/4 x 10
(1 1/16 Net)
3009 - 1 1/4 x 12
(1 1/16 Net)
3010 - 1 1/2 x 10
(1 1/4 Net)
3011 - 1 1/2 x 12
(1 1/4 Net)
2288
1 5/8 x 1 1/2
Handrail
2288 A
Handrail
1 5/8 x 2 1/2
2206 3/4 x 1 3/4
S4S
2207 3/4 x 1 1/2
S4S
2220
Chair rail
1/2 x 3 1/2
2223
Apron
1/2 x 3 1/4
2225
Apron
3/4 x 3 1/2
2211
1 5/8 x 1 5/8
S4S
String cap
2281 1 x 3 1/4
Transom bar
2290 2 1/2 x 3 1/2
Lino cove
2256
13/16
x 2 1/2
2230
Nosing
1 1/4 4 1/4
Brick mold
2234 A - 1 1/8 x 2 1/2
2235 A - 1 3/8 x 2 1/2
2235 B - 1 3/8 x 3 1/2
2235
1 3/8 x 1 5/8
Brick mold
Window stool
2292 3/4 x 3 1/2
2502
1 1/2 x 2 1/8 x 1 3/8
2501
1 1/2 x 2 1/2 x 1 3/4
2500
1 1/2 x 3 x 2 1/4
T - Astragal
13/16 x 13/16
2251
Cove
3/4 x 3/4
2250
Crown
1/2 x 3/4
2260
3/4 x 1 1/4
2262
1 13/16 x 2 1/2
2264
Crown

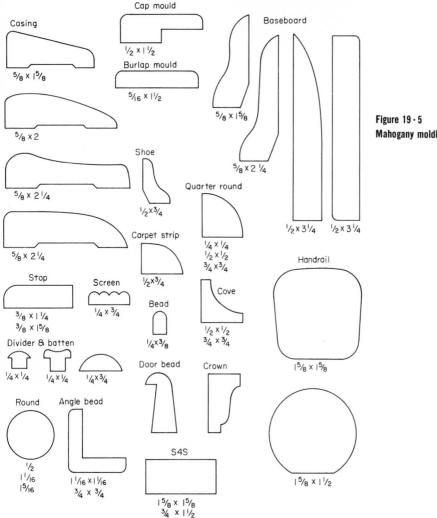

Casing

5/8 x 1 5/8

5/8 x 2

5/8 x 2 1/4

5/8 x 2 1/4

Cap mould

1/2 x 1 1/2

Burlap mould

5/16 x 1 1/2

Shoe

1/2 x 3/4

Carpet strip

1/2 x 3/4

Quarter round

1/4 x 1/4
1/2 x 1/2
3/4 x 3/4

Cove

1/2 x 1/2
3/4 x 3/4

Bead

1/4 x 3/8

Door bead

Crown

Baseboard

5/8 x 1 5/8

5/8 x 2 1/4

1/2 x 3 1/4   1/2 x 3 1/4

Figure 19·5
Mahogany moldings.

Handrail

1 5/8 x 1 5/8

1 5/8 x 1 1/2

Stop

3/8 x 1 1/4
3/8 x 1 5/8

Screen

1/4 x 3/4

Divider & batten

1/4 x 1/4   1/4 x 1/4   1/4 x 3/4

Round

1/2
1 1/16
1 5/16

Angle bead

1 1/16 x 1 1/16
3/4 x 3/4

S4S

1 5/8 x 1 5/8
3/4 x 1 1/2

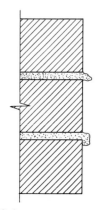

Figure 19·6
Extruded mortar joints.

fir, while a smaller group (Fig. 19·5) are made from mahogany. These standard moldings are usually given a number and can be ordered by number rather than by name. A complete list of stock moldings can be obtained on request from lumber manufacturers or retailers.

GYPSUM FINISHES

One of the best known types of interior finish is produced by plaster in which gypsum is one of the basic ingredients. The various kinds of plaster and their uses are described in Chap. 8. Plaster surfaces can be troweled smooth, stippled, or sand-finished and can be applied over gypsum lath, metal lath, fiberboard plaster base, or directly over a masonry surface. In addition, acoustical plaster, involving the use of lightweight aggregate such as vermiculite or perlite, is used to produce a textured surface and to provide sound insulation. This type of plaster is usually applied by spray.

Gypsum board is also used as an interior finishing material. It is applied in either a single or double layer, using ⅜-in. board for the double or laminated application. Joints and corners are taped and filled with joint filler, after which the surface is sized and painted.

Gypsum board interior paneling is also produced with wood-grain printed surface. Such boards have beveled rather than recessed edges, so that a V groove is produced at joints. Colored nails or gypsum cement is used in applying the board to a wall surface.

Square-edged gypsum board covered with a vinyl plastic fabric is also produced as an interior finish. Joints are usually covered with an aluminum, plastic, or wood batten.

CLAY FINISHES

Clay products of all kinds can be used for interior finishing. They include common brick, face brick, glazed brick, structural tile, glazed tile, ceramic veneer, ceramic wall tile, and ceramic mosaic. In addition, several imitation brick veneer products are made, using lightweight aggregates, cement paste, and artificial color.

Common brick is usually used for interior work to produce a rustic or roughcast effect, often emphasized with extruded mortar joints (Fig. 19·6).

Ceramic wall tile in various sizes and shapes (Fig. 19·7) and usually ⅜ in. thick is used in kitchens, bathrooms, washrooms, laboratories, for a feature wall, or as a dado or wainscot with another material covering the upper part of the wall. Ceramic mosaic—small pieces of plain or colored tile mounted on a paper or cloth backing—is used for similar purposes.

Figure 19·7
Ceramic wall tile shapes and sizes.

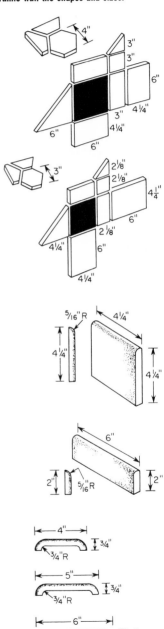

STONE FINISHES

Stone interior finishes can be produced by using solid stone walls and exposing the interior as well as the exterior surface. Any type of building stone may be used for this purpose. The other method is to cover the interior surface with thin stone slabs, from 1 to 2 in. thick. The stone is applied over a backup wall of concrete, concrete block, brick, or tile and is held in place with some type of stone anchor. A number of imitation stone products made from terra-cotta are also used for this purpose.

CONCRETE FINISHES

Concrete is used in various ways in interior work. Plain concrete walls may be used, but they are often given special treatment to make them as smooth as possible. This consists of rubbing down with an abrasive stone and filling the holes and pores with cement grout to leave the walls as smooth and clean as possible. Textured and patterned surfaces are produced by special treatment of the form face.

Precast concrete sandwich panels often have one face finished for interior exposure. The face may be textured, patterned, or colored, or it may consist of exposed aggregate.

Both standard and screen-type concrete blocks are frequently used for inside exposure. Standard blocks may have either a plain or a patterned face. Joint treatments are similar to those used with brick.

Concrete blocks with a glazed face are produced for interior use. The facing may be a ceramic glaze such as is used on brick, a coating of mortar made from pure silica sand and cement paste, or a thin layer of a mixture of marble chips in plastic resin. The ceramic glaze is sprayed on the blocks, while the other two are cast in place and later ground smooth.

Cast stone, another concrete product, is used for interior as well as exterior facing. Pieces are molded in various sizes from 2 × 2 in. to 8 × 16 in., about ¾ in. thick, to represent roughhewn stone; they are set in a mortar backing over a solid backup wall.

HARDBOARD FINISHING PANELS

Tempered hardboard (Chap. 12) is treated in many ways to produce interior facing panels, usually 4 × 7 ft or 4 × 8 ft, ¼ in. thick. One treatment consists of printing a wood-grain pattern on the face and cutting irregularly spaced V grooves along the board to represent random planking. Boards are also produced with an embossed leather grain pattern pressed on the face. Both of these are fastened to the wall with nails.

Another type of treatment consists of covering the hardboard with a plastic film printed in a wide variety of wood, stone, and fabric patterns and then applying a coating of baked-on melamine plastic. Such panels are made with tongue-and-groove edges and can be applied over solid backing with contact adhesives or fastened to studs with special clips, as shown in Fig. 19·8. Boards are also covered with a baked-on enamel coating, applied in 4-in. squares to represent ceramic wall tile.

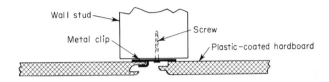

Figure 19·8
Clip fasteners for hardboard panels.

FIBERBOARD PANELS

Fiberboard panels (Chap. 12) may be used as interior finish on ceilings or on walls, particularly above dado level. Wall panels are 4 × 7 ft or 4 × 8 ft, ½ in. thick, with a factory sealed or prepainted surface and square or beveled edges. Boards are fastened in place with finishing nails driven at an angle to the board.

For ceilings, the board may be in the form of tile, in strips 16 × 32 in., 16 × 48 in., or 16 × 96 in. or in 4 × 8 ft panels. Panels may be plain faced or marked off by V grooves in tile pattern.

WALLPAPER

Paper has been used as an interior decorative material for a long time and still finds wide acceptance for many situations. In addition to the conventional designs, wallpaper is produced in a wide range of wood-grain, fabric, stone, brick, and mural patterns. Many papers are furnished with the glue already applied and need only be immersed in water before applying. Several grades are produced, some of which are scrubbable.

Wallpapers are produced in single and double rolls 20 to 36 in. wide containing 36 sq ft per single roll. Selvage edges ¾ to 1 in. wide are removed from each end of a roll before hanging.

GLASS

Glass in several forms is used for inside finishing. Glass blocks are used for decoration as well as for light-diffusing or

Figure 19 · 9
Glass tile as wall finish.
(Columbia Acoustics & Fireproofing Co.)

Section

Figure 19 · 10
Steel wall tile.

light-directing. Structural glass in opaque designs is used for interior partitions, room dividers, screens, etc. Plate-glass mirrors are widely used for interior decoration and to produce special effects. Colored-glass tile or panels are available as a type of wall finish (Fig. 19 · 9).

STEEL

Steel is utilized to produce a number of products adapted to interior finishing. Steel wall tile are made from thin-gauge sheet steel formed as shown in Fig. 19 · 10 to give them rigidity and coated with porcelain enamel in a full range of colors. Common sizes are 4¼- and 6-in. squares and 3 × 6 in. with cap, base, outside and inside corners, feature strips, and other shapes corresponding to field sizes. Special tile adhesives are used to secure tile to smooth surfaces. Wall panels made in similar fashion but in larger sizes are also available.

Stainless steel wall tile are produced in 4¼, 5, 6, and 10-in. squares and in 3 × 6 in. rectangles, in a polished satin finish. Corners, caps, etc., are available to correspond to field sizes.

Galvanized sheet metal casing trim is frequently used in place of wood casing around door and window openings. Common shapes and a typical installation are illustrated in Fig. 19 · 11.

NONFERROUS METALS

Aluminum, copper, and zinc are all used to make wall tile of types and sizes similar to those made from steel. Copper tile are usually supplied with a burnished finish, while aluminum tile may be enameled or anodized. Zinc tile are chrome-plated.

Trim moldings to cover exterior corners of walls or edges of window stool, to be used as a cove base (Fig 19·12) and as window- and door-frame trim, are made from aluminum and chrome.

PLASTICS

Many interior finishing products are manufactured from various types of plastic. Plastic wall tile in 4¼ and 8½-in. squares are made from polystyrene and urea formaldehyde resins in a range of colors. They are applied with special adhesives, and the joints are pointed with a special grout after the tile are in place. Plastic laminate wall panels in wood-grain, stone, and mottled patterns, as well as solid colors, are applied with contact adhesives or as a facing over plywood sheets. Special mouldings are used as panel dividers, edgings, and corner trim. Some typical moldings used for this purpose are shown in Fig. 19·13.

Plastic wall fabrics and films of vinyl are used in much the same way as wallpaper. Molded sheets of plastic reinforced with fiber glass which simulate brick and stone may be used for either interior or exterior. Molded plastic acoustical tile, backed by fiber-glass wool, have been introduced, along with opaque plastic ceiling tile for use with suspended ceiling systems.

PAINTS

Paint is applied to interiors to provide decoration, to cover unsightly surfaces, to prevent the absorption of moisture into the wall, to act as a vapor barrier, and to provide a washable surface.

Three grades of paint, based on appearance rather than quality, are produced in all the paint types: gloss, semigloss, and flat. They differ in the degree of shininess, resulting from the amount of light reflected from the dried surface. The type of paint to be used is determined largely by location. Gloss paints are commonly used in kitchens, bathrooms, washrooms, etc., where the relative humidity is likely to be high.

Paints can be divided into two general groups according to consistency. Some paints will flow out under a brush or roller to produce a flat, smooth surface, while others are stiff enough that when they are applied with a roller the surface produced is rough or stippled. This type of paint is useful for covering uneven surfaces or surfaces with varying density or porosity.

The color range in modern paints is very wide. Over two thousand colors, tints, and shades are available in most good-quality paint. In many cases the colors are produced in

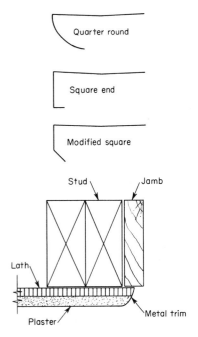

Figure 19·11
Metal casing trim.

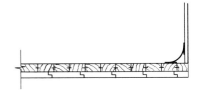

Figure 19·12
Metal cove base.

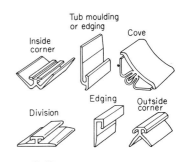

Figure 19·13
Moldings used with plastic-laminate wall panels.

separate containers and one or more are added to a white base paint to create the exact color required.

Paints are applied by brush, roller, spray, or dip, the method of application usually being determined by the size of the object to be painted; the accessibility, smoothness, and location of the area; the type of paint to be used; and the time available for painting.

GLOSSARY

anodize	To coat with a protective film by electrolytic action
dado	The lower part of an interior wall when specially decorated
emboss	To decorate by raising portions of the surface
etch	To decorate by removing portions of the surface
saw-textured	Surface as left by the saw during manufacture
stippled	Rippled plaster surface
textured	Rough-surfaced
wainscot	The lower 3 or 4 ft of an interior wall when finished differently from the remainder of the wall

REVIEW QUESTIONS

1 Compare wall coverings of solid wood to those of plywood from the standpoint of:
(a) size of units
(b) surface characteristics
(c) method of application
2 (a) Make a list of 10 commonly used stock moldings.
(b) Draw a cross-sectional view of each.
(c) Indicate the primary use of each.
3 Describe three methods of producing a textured finish surface, using plaster as the finishing material.
4 Explain how ceramic mosaic is applied to a wall.
5 Give two reasons why tempered rather than standard hardboard is usually used to produce interior facing panels.
6 Why are fiberboard panels recommended for use above dado level?
7 Describe briefly three methods of applying plastic laminate sheets to a wall.
8 Outline the procedure you would recommend for applying a semigloss paint over a gypsum-board wall surface.

SELECTED SOURCES OF INFORMATION

The Arborite Company, Montreal, Que.
Atlas Asbestos Company Ltd., Montreal, Que.
Brick & Tile Manufacturers' Assn., Toronto, Ont.
Canadian Forest Products Ltd., New Westminster, B.C.
Canadian Industries Ltd., Paint & Varnish Division, Montreal, Que.
Canadian Lumbermen's Association, Ottawa, Ont.
The Formica Insulation Company, Cincinnati, O.
International Panel Boards Ltd., Gatineau, Que.
MacMillan, Bloedel & Powell River Ltd., Vancouver, B.C.
National Lumber Manufacturers' Association, Washington, D.C.
Plywood Maufacturers' Association of British Columbia, Vancouver, B.C.
Southern Pine Association, New Orleans, La.
United States Plywood Corporation, New York, N.Y.
Vikon Tile Corporation, Washington, N.J.
Welsh Plywood Corporation, Memphis, Tenn.
Westroc Industries Ltd., Vancouver, B.C.

20

GLUES, SEALERS, GLAZING AND CAULKING COMPOUNDS

All of the materials described in this chapter, with one or two exceptions, have at least two common characteristics—cohesiveness and adhesiveness. Cohesiveness is the ability of particles of a material to cling tightly to one another. Adhesiveness is the ability of a material to fix itself and cling to an entirely different material.

GLUES

The art of making and using glues of various kinds has been known for a very long time. Many of the materials used in ancient times were natural products such as bitumen and tree resins, while others were made by hand by processes which were kept closely guarded secrets. It was not until the eighteenth century that the process of making glues began to develop industrially.

In the nineteenth century chemists and physicists began to take a serious interest in the chemical properties of glues, and it was this interest which sparked the development of the modern glue industry.

One of the early discoveries in the field of modern glues was the adhesive properties of nitrocellulose. This was the first adhesive known which was resistant to water. Today other synthetic adhesives have replaced nitrocellulose to a large extent. About the same time (in the mid-1800s) it was found that rubber could be treated to make an adhesive. Such adhesives, which consist mainly of raw rubber dissolved in gasoline, are still used in the manufacture and repair of rubber products. New and improved methods of making and keeping animal glue, particularly fish glue, were also made during this period. This rediscovery of an old craft resulted in the production of a glue that continued to be of major importance until nearly halfway through the twentieth century.

The discovery of the first synthetic resin made by man—phenolic resin—was announced in 1909. Some 20 years later a phenolic-resin glue had become well known as an adhesive for wood; the plywood industry still relies largely on phenolic adhesives as a bonding agent. In the 1930s another wood adhesive made from urea formaldehyde was developed. It has some advantages over phenolic adhesives (it is quick-setting and produced a colorless glue line), but it is not as waterproof as the phenolics.

The growth of the plastics industry has resulted in the development of many new glues made from synthetic resins. They include resorcinol adhesives, polyvinyl acetate, neoprene phenolic cement, polyurethane adhesives, and epoxy-resin glues. Today many of the old glues, such as animal glue, casein glue, and asphalt adhesives, are still in use along with a wide variety of synthetic glues.

Whereas most of the older type adhesives were intended for gluing wood, paper, leather, rubber, and cloth, some of the new synthetics will also bond to glass, steel, concrete, ceramics, and plastics. As a result, today there are glues for every conceivable purpose, and the glue chosen for a particular job will depend on its properties, the nature of the application, and the cost of the glue.

Animal glue is available in either solid or liquid form. Solid glue is melted and applied hot. It is slow setting and allows time for adjustment to the glue joint. Animal glue has excellent bonding properties with wood, leather, paper, or cloth, developing up to 12,000 psi in shear. It has moderate resistance to heat and good resistance to cold but poor resistance to water. It cures by air-drying at room temperatures.

Blood-albumin glue is a special animal glue made for use particularly with leather and paper. It has only very moderate bonding power with wood. It is usually sold as a dry powder which is mixed with water. It has fair resistance to both heat and cold but poor resistance to water. This type of glue will dry at room temperature or at a low heat of from 150 to 200°F. Its strength is considerably less than that of the animal glue described above.

Casein glue, made from protein materials, is a dry powder to be mixed with water. It has good bonding power for wood-to-wood or paper-to-wood applications and will develop the full strength of the wood in most situations. Casein glue has good dry heat resistance and moderate resistance to cold. It has moderate resistance to water but does not perform well when subjected to high humidity or wetting and drying cycles. It is subject to attack from molds, fungi, and other wood organisms. Casein glue will set at temperatures as low as 35°F but maximum strength is developed at about 70°F with moderate pressure.

Starch and dextrin glues are available in both dry and liquid state, the dry glue being mixed with water. They have good bond with paper or leather and fair bond with wood, but strength does not compare with those of animal or casein glues. They have fair resistance to heat and cold but poor resistance to water. They dry at room temperature.

Asphalt cements are thermoplastic materials made from asphalt emulsions or asphalt cutbacks. They have a good bond to paper and concrete and are used mainly for roofing applications and for laminating layers of wood fiberboard. They have relatively poor resistance to heat but good resistance to cold and good water resistance.

Cellulose cements are thermoplastic in nature and have good bond to wood, paper, leather, or glass, developing up to 1,400 psi in shear with wood. They have moderate resistance to both heat and cold and good resistance to water. A common solvent is ethyl acetate. Cellulose cement cures by air-drying and setting.

Chlorinated-rubber adhesive is usually a liquid; it has good bond for paper and fair bond with wood, metal, or glass. Strength does not compare with animal or casein glues. It has moderate resistance to heat, cold, and water but poor resistance to creep. It cures by drying at room temperature. The usual solvent is a ketone.

Natural-rubber adhesives are usually latex emulsions or dissolved crepe rubber. They have a good bond with rubber or leather and fair bond with wood, ceramics, or glass, developing strengths of about 350 psi in tension with wood. They have fair resistance to heat and cold, good resistance to water, but poor resistance to creep. Room temperature is sufficient for drying.

Nitrile or Buna N rubber adhesive is available in both thermoplastic and thermosetting types. It has good bond with wood, paper, porcelain enamel, and polyester film or sheet. The thermosetting type will develop up to 4,000 psi shear and the thermoplastic type up to 600 psi. It has good resistance to heat and cold and excellent water resistance, while its creep resistance is fairly good. This adhesive cures best under heat.

Neoprene-rubber adhesives are essentially thermoplastic in nature, though they may have some thermosetting characteristics. They have excellent bond with wood, asbestos board, metals, glass, and some plastics, with strengths up to 1,200 psi in shear. They have good resistance to heat and cold and excellent resistance to water. Creep resistance is fairly good. Most of the contact cements used in the application of plastic laminates to walls or flat surfaces are neoprene-rubber products. These adhesives are also used for cementing gypsum board to studs and ceiling joists and for laminating one layer of gypsum board to another.

Urea formaldehyde resin glues are available in powder form, to be mixed with water, and in liquid form, which requires the addition of a hardener. They are thermosetting in nature, with excellent bond to wood, leather, or paper, having a shear strength up to 2,800 psi. They have good resistance to heat and cold and fair resistance to water. Creep resistance is good. These glues often behave unsatisfactorily on wood that is below 6 percent in moisture content. Heat is desirable for curing of some types of urea resin glue while others cure satisfactorily at room temperature. Rapid curing can be achieved by the application of a high-frequency electric current directly to the joint. This technique is known as wood-welding.

Phenolic resin glues are made in both dry and liquid form. They are thermosetting glues with excellent bond to wood and paper. Shear strengths up to 2,800 psi are developed. They have excellent resistance to heat, cold, creep, and water. Some set at room temperature, while others require a hot press. These hot-press glues are commonly used in the manufacture of plywoods. Other similar glues are combinations of phenol-formaldehyde phenol-resorcinol or resorcinol-formaldehyde. All are woodworking glues used in the manufacture of laminated wood structural members.

Melamine resins are thermosetting glues manufactured as a powder with a separate catalyst. They have excellent bond with wood or paper. Resistance to heat, cold, creep, and water all are excellent. Melamine resins are cured under hot press at 300°F. Melamine-formaldehyde resin glues are manufactured as a powder to be mixed with water and may be either hot-setting or intermediate-temperature-setting types.

Resorcinol resins are usually made as a liquid with a separate catalyst. They have good bond with wood or paper, developing shear strengths up to 1,950 psi with wood. They have very good resistance to heat, cold, and creep and are generally used where a waterproof joint is required. Some cure at room temperatures, while others require moderate heat, up to 200°F.

Epoxy resins are thermosetting in nature, manufactured in liquid form with a separate catalyst. The amount of catalyst added determines the type of curing required. They have excellent bond with wood, metal, glass, and masonry and are widely used in the manufacture of laminated curtain-wall panels of various kinds. They are also used in making repairs to broken concrete. They have excellent resistance to both heat and cold, while creep resistance and water resistance vary widely, depending upon how the glue is compounded. With regular catalyst addition, curing is by hot press, up to 390°F, while strong catalyst addition results in a glue which will cure at room temperature.

Polyvinyl-resin adhesives are usually in the form of an emulsion. They have good bond with wood or paper or vinyl plastics and reasonably good bond with metal. Shear strengths up to 1,000 psi are developed with wood. Resistance to cold is good, but heat, creep, and water resistance are only fair. These glues cure at room temperature.

Sodium silicate adhesives are liquids which have excellent bond with paper or glass and reasonably good bond with wood or metal. Resistance to heat, cold, and creep are good, but water resistance is poor. Some cure at room temperature, while others require moderate heat, in the 200°F range.

SEALERS

Sealing compounds are products which are used to seal the surface of various materials against the penetration of water or other liquids or in some cases to prevent the escape of water through the surface. To do this they must have some adhesive qualities and the ability to fill the surface pores and form a continuous skin on the surface to which they are applied. In many applications the adhesion should be permanent, while in others it need only to be temporary.

One common type of sealer is liquid asphalt, either in cutback form or as an asphalt emulsion. This type of sealer has several uses. One is to coat the outer surface of concrete below ground level to prevent the penetration of water to the interior through pores in the concrete. Another similar use is to seal the inside surface of wooden or concrete water tanks. Another use is as a sealer or primer over a concrete slab before asphaltic tile adhesive is applied. Here the sealer prevents liquids from being withdrawn from the flooring or adhesive, allowing it to become dry and hard.

Another well-known sealer is a solution of sodium silicate. It is used to seal the inside surface of concrete liquid containers. The sodium silicate forms a gel-like film on the surface to prevent water penetration.

Various wax compounds are made in the form of emulsions to be sprayed over the surface of newly placed concrete. The wax oxidizes to form a continuous film which prevents the evaporation of water from the concrete. In this case the adhesion is only temporary. As the wax continues to oxidize it becomes hard and brittle and flakes or is worn off the concrete by traffic.

Other waxes are used to make sealers for concrete and terrazzo floors which prevent the penetration of oil and grease into the floor surface.

Liquid silicones are used as sealers over concrete, brick, and tile masonry to prevent the penetration of water into the surface. The absorption of water by masonry walls often leads to staining and efflorescence. The silicone sealers are particularly valuable for such applications because they are colorless and do not affect the appearance of the wall.

Sealers made from various oils and turpentine are used to seal wood surfaces before the application of paint or varnish. They penetrate into and are absorbed by the wood fibers so that the vehicle in paints and varnish will not be similarly absorbed. Similar sealers are used to seal wood which will not be painted against moisture penetration.

Other types of sealer made for wood are synthetic plastic products which form a film over the surface and allow better bonding of synthetic lacquers to wood.

Thin solutions of animal and casein glues are used to coat the surface of plaster and gypsum board under paint. These products are commonly known as wall sizing.

Epoxy-resin formulations are used as sealers over concrete, wood, or old terrazzo surfaces before epoxy-resin terrazzo is applied. The thin liquid adheres to and seals the old surface and provides a good bond for the new application. Similar sealers are used under concrete surface repairs.

GLAZING AND CAULKING COMPOUNDS

These two groups of materials are similar—often identical; the only difference is that when used for sealing glass they are known as glazing compounds.

Asphalt has been used to seal—or caulk—the joints in vessels immersed in water since the earliest recorded history. Later, vegetable fibers impregnated with tar or pitch were also used for the same purpose.

Asphalt caulkings continue to play an important role, but they are only one of a wide variety of materials that are used for this purpose in present day construction. The development of new building methods, such as curtain-wall construction, has increased the necessity for materials which will prevent water passage through joints between panels. This demand, in turn, has resulted in the introduction of many new caulking compounds into the field.

To be useful for caulking, a material must have several specific properties. It must be able to adhere to the surfaces with which it comes in contact. It must remain workable over a considerable range of temperatures. It must be able to form a tough, elastic skin over the surface while the interior of the mass remains flexible. Most important of all, it must be able to stretch or elongate with changes that may occur in the width of the joint.

The ability to elongate differs widely in materials which possess the other characteristics mentioned, and caulking compounds may be classified into two groups, depending on their percentage of elongation after weathering. These groups are: (1) mastic and less elastic types of caulking, and (2) high-molecular-weight elastomerics. The first group includes materials providing 0 to 50 percent usable elongation. In the second group, the usable elongation rate ranges up to over 100 percent after weathering.

One of the most common materials classified as caulking is linseed-oil putty, used almost exclusively for glazing wooden sash. It is made by mixing very finely ground calcium carbonate with raw linseed oil. Putty tends to harden and become brittle with age, but its life can be extended by priming the sash before glazing and by frequent painting. It has no practical elongation value.

Mastic glazing and caulking compounds are composed of a number of materials blended to produce a substance which has a much longer elastic life than putty and which may have an elongation rate of up to 10 percent. They are made up of drying oils, nondrying oils, drier, solvent, mineral stabilizer, and a filler.

The drying oil is usually a vegetable oil such as soya-bean or linseed oil. It provides the cohesion and absorbs oxygen from the air to produce a dry film. The nondrying oil—a hydrocarbon oil—is included to plasticize and to help the material maintain its flexibility with age. A drier is used to accelerate the formation of a surface skin and is usually a metallic salt. Solvents are used to adjust the workability. The mineral stabilizer is often asbestos fiber, which helps the caulking to maintain its position or shape prior to set. A very finely powdered limestone filler gives the caulking body and reduces shrinkage.

The caulking materials described above are oxidizing types and are used in exposed areas where painting over their surface may be desirable. They must be used with materials or in situations that will not exert elongation of more than 10 percent.

Asphalt and polybutene caulking compounds are mastic materials made in a variety of consistencies. They are non-oxidizing and set through the evaporation of the solvent. Both may have fillers and stabilizers combined with them and give good results where a skin is not required, as for example, under flashings, between lapped joints, and in hidden joints between wood and masonry. Caulking made from medium-molecular-weight polybutenes will remain soft indefinitely and produce elongations of about 50 percent.

The high-molecular-weight elastomeric caulking materials include polysulfide polymers; butyl, neoprene, hypolon, and silicone rubbers; vinyl chloride polymers; and butadiene-styrene copolymers. They include both mastic and resilient products. Resilient caulkings are those which are extruded as a plastic strip or as a cellular sponge sheet or strip.

Polysulfide-type elastomer has been used extensively over a longer period of time than most of the others in this group. It is a two-component type of sealant, consisting of a base compound and an accelerator. It cures by polymerization, the rate of curing being increased with increasing temperature and humidity. It is normally applied by caulking gun and has a usable elongation of 100 percent. Aluminum-colored polysulfide-base sealants have been in use for a number of years. Joints that are immersed in water or that have been wet for long periods of time should not be sealed with aluminum-colored sealant because it may be affected by a chemical reaction between the lime and aluminum in the presence of water. A one-part polysulfide mastic is also produced; it does not cure or harden and is used in locations where little elasticity is required.

Silicone mastic caulking is a one-component product which cures on exposure to air. It has excellent adhesion and can be used where high elongation properties are required. This caulking is available in a number of colors.

Butyl, neoprene, and hypolon (chlorosulfonated polyethylene) mastic caulkings are solvent types made with fillers and pigments and are thus available in a range of colors. They compare favorably with polysulfide sealants, though they do have higher rates of shrinkage. All have very high elongation ratings, in the range of 200 percent and better.

Cellular sponge sheets and strips are produced from all the high-molecular-weight materials previously mentioned. The properties of these extruded caulkings are very similar to the mastic caulkings made from the same material. One disadvantage of most of them is that special adhesives are required to join strips, and these are not usually available in the field.

A backup material is an important part of a good watertight joint (Fig. 20·1). The purpose of such a material is to control

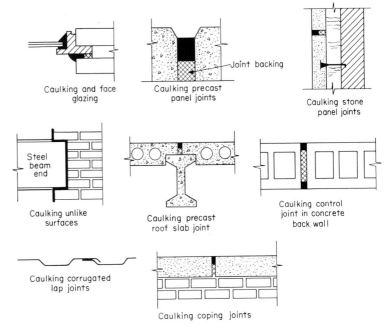

Caulking and face glazing

Caulking precast panel joints — Joint backing

Caulking stone panel joints

Steel beam end

Caulking unlike surfaces

Caulking precast roof slab joint

Caulking control joint in concrete back wall

Caulking corrugated lap joints

Caulking coping joints

Figure 20·1
Typical caulking applications.

the depth of joint, to prevent moisture from attacking the bond between caulking and the sides of the joint, and to serve as a bond breaker. It is important that the sealant not be allowed to bond to the bottom surface of the joint as this greatly restricts the elongation of the material. A backup material prevents such bonding.

Products which have been used successfully as backup material include sponge rubber, nontarred oakum, fiberglass insulation, polyurethane foam, closed-cell polyethylene foam, neoprene or butyl tubes and cords, fiberboard, and corkboard strips. Oil-, tar-, or asphalt-impregnated materials, moisture-absorbing materials, and polystyrene foams should not be used as backup.

Caulking materials are required to seal joints and permit movement under many conditions. Sometimes they are the only means of preventing the entry of water, and often the successful performance of other building components depends on their functioning properly. It is therefore important that careful attention be paid to the selection, application, and maintenance of the materials which are to be used to caulk the joints.

GLOSSARY

albumin	One of a class of proteins derived from various animal and vegetable sources
creep	Longitudinal movement due to external forces
crepe rubber	Crude rubber in crinkled sheets
dextrin	A soluble carbohydrate formed by the decomposition of starch
efflorescence	A powdery surface crust formed as a result of the loss of water of crystallization
elastomer	An elastic rubberlike substance
emulsion	A dispersion of fine particles or globules of a liquid in a liquid
nitrocellulose	Cellulose which has been treated with a nitrate
oakum	Long hemp fibers.
phenolic resin	A synthetic resin made by treating phenol, a distillate of some organic substance, with an aldehyde, a liquid obtained from an alcohol by oxidation
sizing	A fluid material used for filling the pores on the surface of paper, fiber, plaster, etc., before paint is applied
thermoplastic	Having the property of becoming plastic under heat and regaining rigidity under normal temperatures
thermosetting	Having the property of becoming permanently rigid by the application of heat

REVIEW QUESTIONS

1 Define
   (a) cohesiveness
   (b) adhesiveness
2 What is the basic difference between thermosetting and thermoplastic adhesives?
3 List eight types of glue and beside each give the name of one glue that belongs in that category.
4 (a) What is meant by the creep resistance of a glue?
   (b) Name two glues which have high creep resistance

354

and two which have poor or relatively poor creep resistance.

5 (a) Explain what is meant by a contact adhesive.
  (b) Briefly outline the procedure for using such an adhesive.

6 What is wood-welding? Give two examples of the use of this technique in industry.

7 Describe the basic function of sealing compounds and give two examples of the use of these compounds in building construction.

8 What is the difference between glazing and caulking compounds?

9 (a) List four basic qualities required of a caulking compound.
  (b) Explain why caulking compounds have such an important place in building construction.

10 (a) What is a backup material in a joint?
   (b) What properties must a backup material possess?

SELECTED SOURCES OF INFORMATION

Adhesive Products Corporation, New York, N.Y.
Canadian Industries Ltd., Toronto, Ont.
Dural Products, Dorval, Que.
The Flintkote Company of Canada Ltd., Toronto, Ont.
A. C. Horn Company Ltd., Montreal, Que.
I. F. Laucks Inc., Seattle, Wash.
Le Page's Ltd., Toronto, Ont.
Minnesota Mining & Mfg. of Canada Limited, London, Ont.
Miracle Adhesive Corporation, Newark, N.J.
Monsanto Company, St. Louis, Mo.
Northern Adhesives, Inc., Brooklyn, N.Y.
L. Sonneborn Sons, Inc., New York, N.Y.
Tremco Mfg. Co., Toronto, Ont.
United States Plywood Corporation, New York, N.Y.

21

PROTECTIVE AND
DECORATIVE COATINGS

For ages man has been painting his building materials to protect and decorate them. Today painting may be done for one or more of a number of reasons. They include decoration, sanitation, preservation, improved lighting effects, improved heating effects, improved working conditions, safety, and economy.

There is a group of materials which have been developed for such purposes and included in it are paints, varnishes, enamels, shellac, lacquers, stains, fillers, and sealers. Each has special characteristics which has resulted in its being accepted for certain specific types of jobs.

PAINTS

While traditionally paint has been a material with an oil as one of the chief ingredients, many new advances have taken place in the paint industry in recent years. Oil-based paints are being supplemented by alkyd paint, resin-emulsion paint, metallic paint, and luminescent paint.

OIL PAINTS

The fundamental components of an oil-base paint are: (1) body, (2) vehicle, (3) pigment, (4) thinner, and (5) drier.

The body of a paint is that solid, finely ground material which gives a paint the power to hide, as well as color, a surface. In white paints the body is also the pigment. The products most widely used for paint body are white lead, zinc oxide, lithopone, and titanium white.

White lead, basic carbonate of lead or basic sulfate of lead, is the most widely used paint body on the market. It reacts chemically and physically with linseed oil and for this reason will produce a durable paint when used alone with oil. It has good hiding power and, upon aging, leaves a good surface for repainting because of the gradual chalking that takes place. However, white lead is poisonous and white-lead paint should be confined to outdoor applications, where the fumes are less dangerous to the painter. It also has a tendency to darken when exposed to hydrogen sulfide gas in the air.

Zinc oxide has desirable characteristics for paint and used in combination with white lead produces greater hardness and durability, better color retention, greater elasticity, and reduced chalking. It has less tendency to turn yellow than some other paint body materials. If the amount of zinc oxide used in outside paint is too great, there is a marked tendency for the paint to check and crack. Body for outside paint should not contain more than 20 percent zinc oxide. It is also important in the formulation of house paint for the control of mildew. Because of its resistance to yellowing, zinc oxide is finding greater use in the making of inside paints and enamels.

Lithopone is a paint body material made by mixing barium sulfide with zinc sulfate. It is most widely used in making interior paints.

Titanium white (titanium dioxide) is produced in three forms—anatase, rutile, and brookite—all of which have specific uses in paint formulation. Titanium dioxide retains color better than any other paint body and is particularly useful in paint exposed to hydrogen sulfide fumes. Anatase titanium dioxide chalks quite freely and, to a certain extent, this is a desirable characteristic, since it presents a better repainting surface. Rutile titanium dioxide is highly resistant to chalking and is used in exterior paints where the maximum chalking resistance and maximum resistance to discoloration are required.

Extenders are inert materials which are added to the paint body to increase the volume without duly increasing the cost. When mixed with oils, they have very little hiding power, but they are necessary in paints to prevent the active body material from settling to the bottom of the container in a solid mass. Good exterior paint should not contain more than 10 percent extender. Larger amounts will decrease durability and increase chalking. Calcium carbonate (known as whiting), ground silica, aluminum silicate, and barium sulfate are all used as extenders.

The paint vehicle is a nonvolatile fluid in which the solid body material is suspended. The vehicle should consist of from 85 to 90 percent drying oil and the remainder thinner and drier. The drying oils include linseed oil, soya-bean oil, fish oil, dehydrated castor oil, tung oil, perilla oil, and oiticica oil. Sometimes some synthetic resins are added to these to produce a harder film.

Linseed oil is expressed from flax seed and is produced both as raw and boiled oil. Boiled linseed oil is raw oil which has been heat-treated and had certain metallic driers added. Tung oil is obtained from the nuts of the Chinawood tree, perilla oil from the seeds of an oriental plant, perilla ocymoide and oiticica oil from the seeds of a Brazilian tree. Castor oil is obtained from the seeds of the East Indian castor oil plant. All of these are drying oils; that is, they oxidize when exposed to air, forming a hard, resinous mass which coats and protects the surface.

357

The different oils dry at different rates to varying degrees of hardness. Some are more resistant to moisture than others, and the dried films possess varying degrees of elasticity. Therefore the choice of vehicle to be used in a paint will depend on where it is to be used and the length of time to be allowed for drying. For example, raw linseed oil is slower drying but lighter colored than boiled oil. Tung oil produces a stronger film than linseed oil and, when properly processed, is more waterproof than linseed oil.

Pigments are the materials which give the paint its color. In the case of white paint, the body is the pigment. Color pigments are classified into two basic groups, natural pigments and synthetic or manufactured pigments.

Natural pigments are obtained from animal, vegetable, and mineral sources. Most of them are composed of natural mineral oxides such as iron oxide, chrome oxide, cobalt oxide, siennas, ochres, and umbers. Carbon black is also used as pigment. Many of the synthetic pigments are phthalocyanines (coal tar derivatives) similar to those used to make dyes.

The red pigments are red lead, vermilion, and red ochres. Brown pigments are burnt ochre, burnt sienna, and burnt umber. Yellow pigments include chromium oxide, zinc oxide, and cadmium oxide. Blue pigments are cobalt blue, Prussian blue, and ultramarine blue—all natural pigments—and a number of synthetic blue pigments. Green pigments include chrome green, viridian, and emerald green. Black pigments are carbon black and lampblack.

Thinners are volatile solvents, materials which have a natural affinity for the vehicle in the paint. They cause the paint to flow better; they evaporate when the paint is applied. One of the most common thinners for oil-based paints is turpentine, made by distilling gum from a number of pine trees. Some petroleum fractions, such as naphtha and benzene, are also used as thinners.

Driers are organic salts of various metals, such as iron, zinc, cobalt, lead, manganese, and calcium, which are added to the paint to accelerate the oxidation and hardening of the vehicle. Litharge, lead oxide, is a drier commonly used with lead-based paints; zinc sulfate and manganese oxide are used with zinc oxide-based paints.

ALKYD PAINTS

Alkyd paints are so-called because of the synthetic resin—alkyd resin—used in the paint formulation. Alkyd resin is obtained by the combining of an alcohol and an acid. Alkyd paints are produced by combining a drying oil, such as linseed oil or dehydrated castor oil, with glycerine (the alcohol) and phthalic anhydride (the acid). The glycerine neutralizes the phthalic anhydride and the fatty acid in the oil. The ester molecules which form as a result of this neutralization then polymerize to form the paint body.

Styrenated oils are also used sometimes to produce paints that possess fast drying and excellent adhesion characteristics. Such a formulation also has fairly good alkali resistance. In these cases the regular drying oil is either emulsified with the styrene or dissolved in it.

Alkyd paints in general have mild alkali resistance but excellent water resistance. They also have the ability to produce lighter colors and retain color better than paints with natural drying oils. Their speed of curing is at least equal to the curing of oil-based paints. Because of its excellent weathering ability, alkyd paint is particularly useful for porch and deck enamel and paints for other such exposed conditions. With modifications, it is used in making white baking enamel, such as is used on stoves, refrigerators, etc. Non-yellowing white finishes are obtained using soya bean and castor oil in the alkyd, but linseed alkyds give faster drying times and tougher films.

Alkyd resins are also used as modifiers in other types of paints. They usually produce greater permanence and better adhesion properties. They may be mixed with latex paints, up to 20 to 50 percent alkyd. Altogether some 50 types of alkyds are used in paint manufacture.

RESIN-EMULSION PAINTS

Resin emulsion or latex paints are paints in which the vehicle is a synthetic-resin emulsion, usually made from one of four basic resin types: butadiene-styrene, polyvinyl acetate, epoxy resin, or acrylic resin.

The body of these paints is usually titanium dioxide or lithopone, and soya-bean proteins are added to the formulations, using butadiene-styrene and polyvinyl acetate to increase consistency and stability. Preservatives must then be added to prevent the proteins from allowing the formation of microorganisms. Extenders such as China clay may also be used. Pigments are more restricted than for oil paints because the emulsion is alkaline in nature. Pigments usually used include titanium white, lithopone, cadmium yellow, cadmium red, talc, mica, silica, lampblack, and some hydrocarbon colors. The thinner is water, and to it must be added a dispersing agent to keep the pigment and other materials suspended in the emulsion. These emulsion-based paints tend to foam, so a defoaming agent, usually tributyl phosphate, is added. Finally methyl cellulose is added to improve the flow qualities of the paint.

Polyvinyl acetate emulsions produce a much tougher skin than the butadiene-styrene types and so can be used as exterior as well as interior paint. One of its most important applications is in exterior finishes for masonry and stucco.

Neither of these types of paint can be applied to a glossy surface, and, in addition, both must be protected from freezing.

Acrylic- and epoxy-resin-emulsion paints require no oxidation to form a film and remain flexible after drying. They exhibit great resistance to weathering and no tendency to lose their adhesive qualities or color with age. They contain no protein and therefore are not subject to deterioration. However, they are the more costly than other emulsion paints.

METALLIC PAINT

Metallic paint consists of a metallic pigment and a vehicle. The pigment is very fine flakes of aluminum, copper, bronze, zinc, or tin. They are suspended in a vehicle which may be a natural or synthetic varnish, a quick-drying lacquer, special bronzing lacquer, or bituminous-based vehicles, depending on where the paint is to be used.

Spraying is the best method of applying metallic paints as it permits the spreading of a uniform film and encourages even depositing of the metallic flakes. Metallic paints are used for many decorative purposes; aluminum paint in particular makes an excellent primer for exterior paints of other types.

LUMINESCENT PAINT

Luminescent paint is made by adding fluorescent and phosphorescent pigments to any one of a number of drier-free vehicles, including alkyd marine varnish, spirit varnish, or quick-drying lacquers. Color may also be incorporated into luminous paints.

Luminescent paints may be used in residential buildings to produce special effects. They are used in hospitals, schools, factories, hotels, etc., because their unique quality helps provide maximum safety.

VARNISHES

Varnishes constitute a group of more-or-less transparent liquids which are used to provide a protective surface coating in much the same way as paints do. At the same time they allow the original surface to show but add a lustrous and glossy finish to it.

All varnishes have basically the same components as paints—body, vehicle, thinner, and drier. However, varnishes may be divided into three groups, depending on the type of material used to form the body: (1) natural resin varnishes, (2) modified natural-resin varnishes, and (3) synthetic-resin varnishes.

NATURAL-RESIN VARNISHES

The body of this group of varnishes is made from natural resins obtained from certain trees. Some of the resins are exudations from living trees, while others are fossil resins—which usually are superior in quality. Among the resins used are Congo copals, Kauri gum from New Zealand, boea resins from the East Indies, Philippine manila resin, and Pontianak resin from Borneo. Some of these must be heat-treated to produce an oil-soluble gum, while others are naturally soluble in oil. Rosin, a by-product from the distillation of turpentine, is also used to make varnish.

The vehicle used in varnish is one of a number of drying oils, the same oils which are used in the manufacture of oil-based paints. The resins are dissolved into the oil and the mixture heated to temperatures ranging from 500 to 600°F, depending on the amount of gloss required. Varnishes made from a combination of oil and natural resin are known as *oleoresinous* varnishes.

The best thinner for varnishes is turpentine, a distillate of gum from a group of pine trees. It evaporates slowly and gives varnish brushing and flowing qualities that no other solvent can give. It also aids oxidation of the drying oil by absorbing oxygen from the air and passing it on to the oil. Mineral spirits, benzene, and naphtha are also used as thinners.

Driers used in varnishes are essentially the same as those used in paints, namely organic salts of various metals. They speed the drying of varnishes by acting as a catalyst to the oxidation process.

Varnishes are often classified as long-oil, medium-oil, and short-oil varnishes depending on the amount of oil used per 100 lb of solid resin. Long-oil varnish contains from 40 to 100 gal of oil per 100 lb of resin. The result is a varnish which will produce a tougher, more durable, and elastic film but which takes longer to dry and produces only moderate gloss. Marine and spar varnishes belong to this group. Tung oil is the oil most commonly used in making these varnishes, since it is particularly impervious to water.

Medium-oil varnishes contain from 12 to 40 gal of oil per 100 lb of resin. They dry faster and have a harder film than long-oil varnishes but are not as impervious to water. Floor varnishes belong to this group.

Short-oil varnishes contain from 5 to 12 gal of oil per 100 lb of resin. They dry quite rapidly and form a hard, brittle film that will not stand much rough usage. Rubbing and polishing varnishes belong in this group. They can be rubbed and polished to a high gloss or to a satin finish, depending on the finishing procedure.

MODIFIED NATURAL-RESIN VARNISHES

This group of varnishes is made with a natural resin which has been altered by chemical action. Common resin is heat-treated with glycerin to form an ester gum, and this gum is used as the body for the varnish. Generally speaking, this type of varnish is less expensive than oleoresinous varnishes.

SYNTHETIC-RESIN VARNISHES

Synthetic resins are those produced by the plastics industry, including nitrocellulose, phenolics, amino resins, alkyd resins, a number of vinyl resins, polyethylene, polystyrene, silicone, acrylic resins, and epoxy resins. Some of these are thermoplastic, and some are thermosetting. Many varnishes made with plastic resins reach their greatest potential only when baked.

The vehicle for synthetic-resin varnishes is often the same type of drying oil used with oleoresinous varnishes. However, synthetic drying oils have been developed, and in baking varnishes, liquid alkyd resin may be the vehicle.

Because of the great variety of resins used in synthetic varnishes, a wide range of solvents is required. Some are the same as those used in other varnishes. Coal tar derivatives and high petroleum fractions are also used as solvents. Driers are the same as those used for other types of varnish.

ENAMELS

When pigment is added to a varnish, the result is an enamel. Any of the varnish types can be used, and the durability of the enamel depends to a large extent on the quality of the pigment. Since varnishes do not contain the opaque body material which paints do, enamels do not have high covering power; for best results they require an opaque undercoat. Baking enamels, made with synthetic resins, are used on most household appliances, curtain-wall panels of various kinds, aluminum shingles and siding, and various interior and exterior trim materials.

SHELLAC

Shellac is the only liquid protective coating containing a resin of animal origin. The resin is an exudation of the *lac* insect of India and Southeast Asia, deposited on the branches of trees.

The resin accumulations are collected, crushed, cleaned, and dissolved in alcohol to produce *orange shellac,* so called because of its color. By bleaching the resin, pure white shellac is produced.

Various grades of shellac are made by varying the amount of resin dissolved in a gallon of solvent. These grades are known as *cuts;* a 4-lb cut means that the shellac contains 4 lb of lac resin per gallon of alcohol.

The alcohol used is usually special denatured alcohol or proprietary denatured alcohol. The first type consists of a mixture of 100 gal of ethyl alcohol and 5 gal of methyl alcohol. Proprietary denatured alcohol consists of a mixture of 100 gal of special denatured alcohol, 2 gal denatured wood alcohol, 1 gal ethyl acetate, and 1 gal aviation gasoline.

Shellac dries quickly, is easy to apply, and produces a tough, elastic film on wood, metal, glass, cork, and leather. However, it should not be used on work exposed to outside conditions except as a sealer over knots and sap streaks under exterior paint.

Shellac finds considerable use as a seal coat over stains and fillers and is sometimes used as a complete finishing material by itself. This latter treatment, known as French polish, consists of many layers of shellac applied one over the other, using a linseed-oil-soaked applicating cloth.

The main disadvantages of shellac are that it will discolor under strong sunlight, and water containing alkali causes it to soften and whiten. The surface must be dry before shellac is applied and water should never be used to polish shellac.

LACQUERS

The material which we know today as lacquer is a comparatively new product made from synthetic materials to take the place of varnish for clear finishes. Most modern lacquer is based on nitrocellulose used in combination with natural or synthetic resins and plasticizers. These ingredients are dissolved in a mixture of volatile solvents which evaporate, leaving a film to form the protective coating.

While nitrocellulose alone will produce a clear film, it has poor adhesion, poor durability, and poor flexibility. As a result, natural or synthetic resins are added to nitrocellulose to improve adhesion and hardness and to give the lacquer gloss and film thickness. These resins include cellulose acetate, ethyl cellulose, alkyd resins, vinyl resins, epoxy resins, acrylic resins, polystyrenes, and many others.

Plasticizers counteract the tendency of resins to be brittle and allow lacquer to flow out on application. They also contribute to the body of the lacquer and its durability. Most common plasticizers are ester gums, but some nondrying and drying oils—camphor, dibutyl phthlate, and tricresyl phosphate—are also used.

The solvents used are quite complex since no single solvent will dissolve all the lacquer ingredients. In many cases from six to ten solvents are blended to produce a material capable of dissolving all the ingredients present. These solvents are usually grouped according to their boiling point into low, medium, and high boilers. The boiling points of each of these is about 212°F, 260°F, and 350°F, respectively. The proper blending of solvents affects setting time, flow, gloss, and freedom from bubbling in lacquers. The commonly used solvents include ethyl, butyl, isopropyl, and amyl acetate; acetone; and diethylene glycol.

In addition to these ingredients, thinners are mixed with lacquer just prior to application to reduce the consistency for spraying, to control the rate of drying, and to reduce the cost of lacquer. They include a group of alcohols—ethyl, butyl, amyl, and isopropyl—and a number of hydrocarbonic mixtures such as toluol, benzol, and xylol.

When another class of materials—pigments—are added to clear lacquer, the result is lacquer enamel, available in a wide range of colors.

Today a wide variety of clear and colored lacquers are manufactured to meet a great many special purposes:

1   *Clear gloss lacquer.* A clear lacquer that dries to a glossy finish in one to four hours. It may be rubbed and polished with oil or water.
2   *Clear flat lacquer.* It is similar to gloss lacquer but dries without gloss. It is often used to produce satin effects.
3   *Tinting lacquer.* This is a concentrated colored lacquer mixed with clear lacquer to produce lacquer enamel.
4   *Brushing lacquer.* A slow-drying lacquer formulated specially for brush application.
5   *Bronzing lacquer.* This is a clear lacquer into which are mixed metallic pigments to produce metallic effects.
6   *Shading lacquer.* A slightly colored lacquer used to produce wood-color-tone effects on furniture.
7   *Water-white lacquer.* This is an exceptionally clear lacquer that produces a protective coating of greatest transparency over pale finishes.
8   *Dipping lacquer.* This is designed for application by the dip-tank method and is available both clear and in colors.

STAINS

Stains are materials used to apply color to wood surfaces. They are intended to impart color without concealing or obscuring the grain and not to provide a protective coating. They may be used to accentuate the color contrast of a wood grain, to even up color differences, or to imitate expensive wood colors on surfaces which lack desirable color or grain. There are a number of types of wood stain available, based on the kind of solvent used to dissolve the coloring matter—

water-soluble stains, spirit-soluble stains, penetrating oil stains, non-grain-raising stains, and pigment wiping stains.

WATER STAINS

Water stains are synthetic dyes, many of which are coal tar derivatives manufactured in powder form and in various strengths. They are dissolved in hot water at a specified rate in ounces per gallon, depending on the depth of color required.

Water stain is easy to apply by brush, sponge, dipping, or spray; it is nonfading and nonbleeding; and it gives deep, even penetration. However, it has a tendency to raise the grain of wood, thus roughening the surface and necessitating careful sanding. Water stain will air-dry in about 12 hours or may be force-dried in from 2 to 4 hours.

SPIRIT STAINS

Spirit stains are made from dyes which are soluble in alcohol and are manufactured both in powder form and in ready-mixed liquid form.

This type of stain produces the brightest and strongest colors but is most susceptible to fading. It also tends to bleed and to raise the grain of wood. Because they dry rapidly spirit stains are usually applied by spray; because of their high penetration quality, they are often used for refinishing, repair work, and for staining sap streaks. Drying time is usually from 15 minutes to 2 hours.

PENETRATING OIL STAINS

This type of stain is made by dissolving oil-soluble dyes in coal tar solvents such as toluol, benzol, or xylol and further thinning the vehicle with common petroleum solvents. Although they are available in powder form, oil stains are usually produced as a ready-mixed liquid.

Stain is easy to apply by the sponge, spray, or dip method, but the surface must be wiped after application to remove excess stain. Oil stains have a tendency to bleed into finish coats and are not as light-fast as water stains but have no tendency to raise the grain. Drying time varies from 1 to 24 hours.

NON-GRAIN-RAISING STAINS

This type of stain is made using light-fast dyes which are soluble in such substances as glycols, alcohols, and ketones. They are designed to produce all the advantages of the stains previously mentioned with none of their disadvantages.

They have moderate penetration, do not raise the grain of wood, and dry in from 15 minutes to 3 hours. They do not run or bleed and, because of their fast-drying properties, are usually applied by spraying.

PIGMENT WIPING STAINS

Stains of this type are made from translucent mineral pigments ground into a drying oil. They are applied by brushing or swabbing the surface with a cotton cloth and are allowed to set for various lengths of time after application.

They have good light resistance, no tendency to raise the grain, and good color uniformity. However, they lack the staining capacity of many other stains and, because they are not as transparent as some others, tend to obscure the fine grain of the wood.

FILLERS

Fillers are finishing materials which are used on wood surfaces, particularly those with open grain, to fill the pores and provide a perfectly smooth, uniform surface for varnish or lacquer. Filler is also used to impart color to the wood pores and so emphasize the grain.

There are two general types of fillers: paste fillers, which are used on open-grained woods, and liquid fillers, for close-grained woods. Paste wood fillers consist of a base or body, pigment, nonvolatile vehicle, and thinner. The body is generally a translucent, inert material (such as silica, some silicates, and carbonates of calcium and magnesium) which will fill the pores without staining the wood. Color pigment is usually umber, sienna, or similar colors which will give the filler the desired color. Sometimes a small quantity of dye solution may be used. The vehicle is a vegetable oil or special varnish with Japan driers. Thinners are similar to those used in varnishes.

Filler is applied by brush, by spray, or by dipping and must be thinned to the proper consistency for the method of application used. It is then wiped off, across the grain, before it sets on the surface.

Liquid filler is generally a varnish with a small amount of body material added. It is used on medium, close-grained woods in essentially the same way as paste filler but has much less filling capacity.

SEALERS

The primary purpose of a sealer is to seal the surface of the wood and prevent the absorption of succeeding finish coats. It may be applied to bare wood that has been sanded smooth or applied over the stain or filler.

A sealer also tends to seal in the filler, blend the stain, stiffen any raised wood grain and thus make sanding easier, and form a bond between the wood and the finishing coats.

A number of materials are used as sealers, the proper one to use in a specific situation depending on the type of finish to be used.

Shellac is widely used as a sealer, thinned out to a 2- to 4-lb cut, depending on whether varnish or lacquer is to be used. Lacquer finish requires the thinner sealer. It dries rapidly, does not penetrate, and does not soften appreciably under newly applied lacquer or varnish. It does not, however, provide the best adhesion for finish coats and may show crazing tendencies under a thick finishing film.

Lacquer sealer is the type of sealer most commonly used under lacquer finishes. It consists primarily of the same type of resins from which lacquer is made, with plasticizers and solvent and, in addition, solid content in the form of zinc and calcium stearates. These are called sanding agents and increase the ease with which the sealer surface may be sanded when dry.

Varnish sealer is also available for use under varnish or lacquer. It is similar to varnish cut back until the material contains 30 to 35 percent solids. This type of sealer air-dries in about 8 hours or may be force-dried in 1 to 2 hours at 150°F. The surface must be sanded after the sealer is completely dry.

GLOSSARY

alkyd	Any of a group of thermoplastic synthetic resins
anatase	With reference to the length of titanium white crystals
brookite	Containing orthorhombic crystals
chalking	Development of a chalklike surface
crazing	The formation of minute cracks on the surface
ochre	An earthy ore of iron
oiticica	One of a family of South American trees
perilla	A member of an Asiatic mint plant family
rutile	Containing a little iron
sienna	An earthy substance containing oxides of iron
styrene	An unsaturated hydrocarbon
titanium white	A white pigment containing the element titanium
umber	A brown earth containing manganese and iron oxides
viridian	A chromic oxide
volatile solvent	A solvent which vaporizes easily

REVIEW QUESTIONS

1 Explain what is meant by:
  (a) the body of paint
  (b) a paint vehicle
  (c) pigment in a paint
2 Give one advantage and one disadvantage of using paint with white lead as the body.
3 What type of paint is best suited for an area in which the atmosphere contains hydrogen sulfide?
4 Give a concise definition of:
  (a) a drying oil
  (b) an extender
  (c) a drier
5 Outline three advantages of using latex paints.
6 Suggest three specific uses for luminescent paint.
7 List three classes of varnish and give two specific uses for each kind.
8 Compare varnish and lacquer from the standpoint of:
  (a) basic ingredients
  (b) drying time
  (c) method of application
  (d) depth of film produced in one application
9 Outline the sequence of operations for finishing a piece of oak in a walnut color with a varnish surface.

SELECTED SOURCES OF INFORMATION

Borden Chemical Company, West Hill, Ont.
British America Paint Company, Victoria, B.C.
Canadian Industries Ltd., Montreal, Que.
Canadian Pittsburgh Industries, Ltd., Montreal, Que.
CIBA Products Company, Fairlawn, N.J.
General Paint Corporation, Vancouver, B.C.
Le Page's Ltd., Toronto, Ont.
Pittsburgh Paints, Pittsburgh, Pa.
Pratt & Lambert, Inc., Buffalo, N.Y.
Protection Products Manufacturing Co., Kalamazoo, Mich.
Samuel Cabot, Inc., Boston, Mass.
Shellac Information Bureau, New York, N.Y.
The Sherwin-Williams Company of Canada Ltd., Montreal, Que.

INDEX